D1454512

114.0741

BICTON
COLLEGE
of Agriculture

CULTUS EX MENTIS CULTU

Education Services
Centre

BRITAIN'S COUNTRYSIDE HERITAGE

A GUIDE TO THE LANDSCAPE

PUBLISHED IN ASSOCIATION WITH THE NATIONAL TRUST

BRITAIN'S COUNTRYSIDE HERITAGE

A GUIDE TO THE LANDSCAPE

PHIL COLEBOURN AND BOB GIBBONS

BLANDFORD

Blandford
An imprint of Cassell
Villiers House, 41/47 Strand, London WC2N 5JE

Copyright © Phil Colebourn and Bob Gibbons 1990

All rights reserved. No part of this publication may be
reproduced or transmitted in any form or by any means,
electronic or mechanical, including photocopying, recording or
any information storage or retrieval system, without prior
permission in writing from the publishers.

This edition first published 1990

Distributed in the United States by
Sterling Publishing Co. Inc.
387 Park Avenue South, New York, NY 10016-8810

Distributed in Australia by
Capricorn Link (Australia) Pty Ltd
PO Box 665, Lane Cove NSW 2066

British Library Cataloguing in Publication Data
Colebourn, Phil
    Britain's countryside heritage: a National Trust guide
    to reading the landscape
    1. Great Britain. Landscape
    I. Title II. Gibbons, Bob 1949- III. National Trust IV.
    Colebourn, Phil. Britain's natural heritage
    719.0941

ISBN 0-7137-2192-8 (hardback)
ISBN 0-7137-2193-6 (paperback)

Typeset by MS Filmsetting Limited, Frome, Somerset
Printed and bound by Graficromo s.a., Cordoba, Spain

CONTENTS

Introduction

THE SOCIAL AND architectural history of Britain has been written and rewritten many times, in both detailed and general terms, and the last 20 years or so have seen a much greater understanding of how our landscapes have developed. What has been less clear, and much less studied, is the way in which our richest wildlife habitats have developed and been modified by man's influence, and how the plants and animals within them have changed. It is well known that the countryside is becoming less and less natural, and that the area of wild ('semi-natural') country-side such as heaths and ancient woodlands has steadily diminished in recent times. What has often been less obvious is how these remaining 'islands' of habitat reached their present state.

It is generally true that the more ancient a habitat is the richer it is in plants and animals, and we try to show in this book how this has come about. Why is it, for example, that the most ancient woodlands are so much richer than more recently-planted woods, and why do some species *only* occur in ancient woods? Why are some mountains so rich in alpine species, while on others they are completely lacking? Why have there been vast areas of treeless heath-

Seen from Kirk Fell, the old infield of the ancient settlement of Wasdale Head in Cumbria, perhaps founded by Norse settlers around 1,200 years ago, is tightly confined to the relatively level outwash plain of the Lingmell and Mosedale Becks. The fertile infield is still dotted with the huge piles of stones cleared from it in medieval times. The beautiful pattern of stone walls dividing the infield into sheep pastures is a much later feature. On the steep slopes of the fells lies the less productive outfield.

7

land over many parts of southern England since historical times began, despite a climate that is perfect for growing trees?

Ideas about vegetation have fluctuated between the belief that anything not obviously planted must be wholly natural and the belief that all vegetation owes its existence to the all-pervading hand of man. The real truth, of course, is somewhere in between, and it is the fascinating story of the continuing interaction between nature and man, and the products of it, that is really the subject of this book.

Perhaps more immediately exciting is the way in which these changes and interactions can be 'read' from what we can see in the countryside around us now. With but a little guidance and observation, it is possible to work out so much of the hidden *natural* history (in the true sense of the word) that chroniclers and historians ignore. This is most easily done for a single site, such as a wood or meadow, but it can be even more intriguing for a whole parish or an even wider area, as then the ebb and flow of habitats over the centuries may become clearer. Throughout the book, we endeavour to show how this can be done, using visible features on the ground, and the plants and animals in the area, together with old maps and records. So much more needs to be done, before it is too late, since modern agriculture has a greater capacity than that of any previous generation for erasing the traces of the past, and there are fewer and fewer clues in the countryside now to anything but the most recent of activities.

It has become possible to make these sorts of historical and ecological reconstructions through the work of people in many disciplines. Archaeology has advanced enormously as a science in recent years, and much more can be deduced from less evidence as methods improve and a coherent picture emerges. The effects of man on the landscape have been recognized from earlier and earlier in our history, and, as Professor Hoskins has said, 'everything is older than we think'! The picture of life from Neolithic times (or even earlier) onwards that has been built up has given us, often incidentally, a clearer picture of how our natural vegetation has developed in response to, or sometimes in spite of, man's activities.

Historical botanists, through work on plant remains (especially the minute, but recognisable, pollen grains) preserved in peat and the soil have given us a record of the general vegetation of individual areas from the end of the last glaciation (or ice age) onwards, and this forms the background against which so many other deductions and discoveries may be judged. The basis of this work is the fact that, in certain conditions of acid waterlogging (most usually in areas that we would describe as bogs), vegetation does not totally decay, but gradually builds up in a partially decomposed but recognisable state, eventually forming itself into peat. In undisturbed peat, the lowest layers are the oldest, with more recent layers successively deposited on top; not only is the vegetation of the developing bog preserved (including, perhaps, an interlude as woodland), but so is anything falling onto or into it, and this includes a continuous rain of pollen from the surrounding vegetation. Nowadays, this pollen can be identified to species, or groups of species, under the microscope, and this has gradually given a picture of the vegetation surrounding each studied peatland site.

There are problems of course: for example, wind-pollinated plants such as trees and grasses (the causes of hay-fever) produce infinitely more pollen than the general run of insect-pollinated species (about 80 per cent of our flora) and these are therefore over-represented. Similarly, many areas of the country, especially in the south and east, have too few peat deposits to allow a clear picture to be built up. A related problem is that most peat areas have been cut over for peat at some stage in their history, and the evidence from them is thus interrupted. Nevertheless, a broad picture can be constructed, and for the bogs themselves a precise history can often be put together.

Field botanists, too, have contributed, and we are increasingly able to recognise what the presence or absence of a particular species, or group of species, means in historical terms. Hedgerows can be roughly dated (with care) by the number of woody plants in them, thanks to detailed studies all over the country which have established a satisfactory baseline of information to work from. It has been possible as a result, for example, tentatively to identify Saxon hedges from their component plants, and these have been subsequently confirmed from historical records. In a similar way has come the realisation that certain species are so slow-moving in their colonisation abilities that their presence in a habitat indicates considerable antiquity. Lists of such 'indicator' species have been compiled for a number of habitats, and these are described and discussed – together with the necessary *caveats* for their use – in the relevant chapters. Not surprisingly, such species are becoming increasingly rare as their ancient habitats disappear.

A growing possibility for understanding the history of our natural habitats comes from the study of soils, though sadly this may be curtailed as research budgets for soil survey are reduced. The realisation that vegetation types directly influence soil formation, as well as vice versa, is leading to the ability to recognise some aspects of vegetation history from the soil profile. For example, it could be shown that what appeared to be an ancient woodland had records of ploughing encapsulated in its soil profile, and this could even be dated in some circumstances. Such a discovery could then lead back to a better understanding of the vegetation of that wood.

Agricultural historians have contributed to the whole picture by allowing a better understanding of how fields

A superb example of upland common land above Little Langdale, Cumbria. The mixture of rowans and juniper, with anthill-covered turf in the clearings, is typical of lightly-grazed ancient upland grassland on less acid soils.

were worked and managed; the history of individual sites has been charted in great detail in a few cases, and related to the present-day vegetation, such as in the historic Thames Valley meadows near Oxford. Similarly, it has often become possible to date 'ridge-and-furrow' or cultivation terraces (see Chapter 2), thus telling us, sometimes, when a particular pasture was last ploughed. Woodland historians, particularly Oliver Rackham, have contributed an immense amount of knowledge on how woods were managed and how they have changed over the centuries.

Other disciplines have contributed in surprising ways. For example, recent work on anthills has shown that they can be dated according to their size. Coupled with a knowledge of how and why they develop, this has provided another string to the bow of the vegetation historian. You can be very sure, for example, that a pasture dotted with huge anthills has not been ploughed, mown or sprayed for a very long time, and careful measurement of the size of the largest anthills may tell you exactly when.

Inevitably, we concentrate on the plants of ancient habitats, and to a lesser extent on the invertebrates, since these are the species that depend on continuity of habitat. If the habitat changes drastically, they disappear, and their immobility means that they can never return. Nevertheless, one of the most exciting aspects of being a naturalist in Britain is not simply the wealth of plants and animals that can be found, but also the pleasure that can be derived from understanding what the presence of a particular species, or combination of species, means in terms of the way that its surroundings have developed since man first began to influence our natural vegetation. We may complain that Britain is overcrowded and over-used, but it is this intensity of use and study that has led to a greater understanding of what has brought us to our present state (in terms of natural history) than for any comparable area of land anywhere in the world. The following chapters seek to do justice to this fund of knowledge, and to interpret it for each situation.

The National Trust owns a greater proportion of our historic landscapes and natural sites than any other organisation, and we draw heavily on examples from the remarkable range of countryside sites which the Trust protects. For sites listed in the habitat gazetteers, please consult the current National Trust or National Trust for Scotland for further details of of location and access.

1 · *The Ice*

OUR STORY HAS TO start somewhere. There have been plants and animals in 'Britain' for millions of years, yet there are few living traces of most of this history. This is because some 18,000 years ago the slate was wiped almost completely clean, for at least the fourth time, and virtually everything we can see today has developed since then. It is difficult to imagine it now, when looking at the greenery of Britain and feeling the warmth of the summer sun, yet 18,000 years ago was the peak of the last ice age, or glaciation, and at that time an almost continuous ice-sheet extended as far south as South Wales, the Scilly Isles, Cheshire and the Wash.

In places, this ice-sheet was at least 5,500 ft (1,700 m) thick, and in many places even thicker (that is a depth of over a mile), though there is speculation that at least some higher peaks remained free of continuous ice; there is even some thought, though generally now discarded, that these projecting mountains, or nunataks as they are called, supported a sparse population of hardy alpine plants. It is unlikely whether we will now discover the true answer to this, but it is quite clear that the whole of northern Britain,

An almost-aerial view of part of Loch Avon, a high glacial corrie lake in the Cairngorms. The picture shows the inflow from some of the surrounding cliffs, and gives a clear picture of how much eroded material these snow-melt streams bring down. The lake lies in the bottom of a beautiful steep-sided U-shaped glaciated valley.

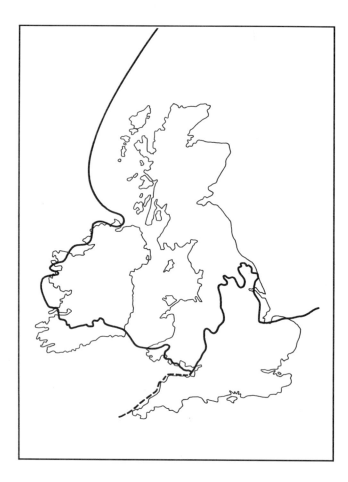

A diagrammatic representation of the extent to which Britain was covered by ice during the last ice age, which reached its peak about 18,000 years ago. The solid line represents the approximate southern limits of the ice, with the dotted line indicating a probable further extension southwards; the north part of the Isles of Scilly was glaciated, but the exact limits are not known.

extreme south, and only an open vegetation of low-growing herbs, grasses and occasional dwarf woody plants. Inevitably the climate in this area was considerably colder than it is now, and the appearance can best be described as arctic, with great similarities to land that is close to the present-day ice-caps in Greenland, Iceland or the far north of Europe. The summers, though short, may have become reasonably warm, and it is clear that grazing animals, such as musk ox, reindeer, woolly rhinoceros and lemmings moved north wherever there was food, retreating again in winter. Naturally, there were predators and scavengers with them: wolves, lynx, arctic fox, brown bear, and even avian predators such as snowy owls are all known to have occurred. Whether Stone Age man (of the Palaeolithic period) was to be found in Britain right through the ice age no-one is really sure, though it is by no means unlikely given the amounts of animal food available and the inherent mobility of a hunter-gatherer life-style.

CHANGING SEA-LEVELS

Besides the fact that the ice covered so much land, and the rest of Britain was suffering from arctic periglacial conditions, there is one other major change that was directly induced by the ice age, which may seem surprising at first, but clear enough on reflection: the water that went into all this enormous extent of ice had to come from somewhere, and it came, of course, mainly from the seas. The effect was to lower the sea-level dramatically, and it is generally reckoned that the sea-level at the time of maximum ice-sheets was at least 330 ft (100 m) below its present-day level. Thus not only was 'Britain' a totally different shape, but it was joined both to present-day Ireland in the west, and the continent of Europe in the south-east and east and probably further west too. A vast area of land, with tundra vegetation at first, once therefore existed, and is now under the North Sea or Irish Sea. Our link to the continent of Europe, which was no mere isthmus but a broad low-lying area of land probably several hundred miles wide, is known affectionately as Doggerland. As we shall see later, these land-bridges, and their ultimate demise as the British Isles were formed, have played an important part in the development of our present-day natural history, and it may be that their existence allowed the early Britons to enter the country in favourable seasons, or periods of temporary climatic amelioration, and leave it again when they chose. We may never know, since the chances of finding identifiable remains 18,000 years later from a tiny mobile population who left few traces at the time seem remote in the extreme.

There was one other effect, which is of interest but much

with the exception, perhaps, of a few small areas, was covered by deep ice, with separate tongues of ice reaching down into north Norfolk, Shropshire and Gwent, as the map shows. This represents the maximum extent of an ice age that affected the whole world, during which huge ice-sheets were formed over much of the northern hemisphere. This was the so-called Devensian ice age, the latest of several, with their peak cold periods separated by about 100,000 years, to affect the world. The time we are in now, thousands of years after the ice last retreated, is optimistically called the post-glacial period, which is probably true in terms of the span of human lives but is equally likely to be an inter-glacial period as far as geological time goes!

Lying to the south of the ice-sheet was a vast area of open tundra-like landscape, with no trees, except perhaps in the less significance, and that is the way in which the rivers flowed. Inevitably, with an ice-sheet to the north (which both prevented flow northwards and provided the main source of summer water) and a main connection to the continent, the drainage pattern was quite different from that which we have now. The river Severn, for example, used to flow north but the dam caused by the ice-sheet produced a great lake, Lake Lapworth, which eventually overflowed southwards to begin the course of the present-day river Severn.

Similarly, the course of the Thames was changed by a previous ice age which moved it from a course through Colchester and Hertford to nearer its present-day route, and many other rivers or whole drainage patterns were altered at this time. Some, of course, became the routes by which the sea later re-invaded the land, such as the Solent between the mainland and the Isle of Wight, once a major river but now a strait a mile or more wide.

The sea-level did not rise smoothly, for it depended on the rate of melting of the ice-sheets, which in turn depended on the climate. Since the seas of the world are interconnected, the levels of sea around our coasts were equally affected by the North American ice-sheets as by our own; such overall changes in sea-level, in distinction to local apparent changes caused by land masses rising and falling, are known as eustatic changes. Although the ice retreated quite quickly, apart from occasional breaks and re-advances, from about 16,000 years ago, the sea did not rise concomitantly, since the ice of the North American ice-cap was barely changing and its huge bulk was keeping the sea-levels down. It is generally reckoned that Ireland finally became an island about 10,000 years ago, the straits of Dover were breached about 9,600 years ago, and Britain eventually became an island (or, more accurately, a group of islands) about 8,600 years ago, when the last links between Norfolk and Holland were breached.

CHANGING LAND-LEVELS

The speed at which the sea-level has risen in relation to the land is complicated by the fact that the enormous weight of ice pushed the land over which it lay downwards into the crust of the earth, and as the burden has been removed so the land has been gradually rising again. Because there was infinitely more ice over northern Britain than the south, this was pushed down more and is consequently rising more. Although the whole country has risen since the ice age, Scotland has risen much more, and Britain is now, in effect, pivoted around a line between the Wash and More-cambe Bay, with Scotland still rising by about 5 cm (2 in) every 100 years and the south-east of England sinking

rather faster. At times the land in Scotland has actually risen faster than the sea has risen, taking the eroded coastline well above the sea, to leave visible 'raised beaches' in its wake. It has been difficult for anyone to work out the exact change in coastline, especially in the south, because any rise in relative sea-level tends to destroy the evidence of anything that went before, by eroding it away, but overall the picture is reasonably clear. At the same time as the ice retreated and sea-levels rose, so the famous warm Gulf Stream, which had been diverted southwards towards Portugal and North Africa, gradually moved northwards eventually to bathe north and west Britain in its warm, damp embrace, contributing to the changes in climate, and related changes in flora and fauna, that were taking place then.

THE RETREAT OF THE ICE

We do not know exactly what the ice-free parts of Britain looked like at the height of the ice age, when glaciers reached the midlands of England, but we have a fair idea, and many of the species that occurred then *are* known for certain. In the coldest areas, generally nearest the ice or on high ground, the land was probably almost bare but for a sparse vegetation of lichens and mosses, with a few scattered hardy grasses and herbs. A little further from the ice, though, a wide range of plants seems to have been able to thrive, though as far as can be told almost all of the area of 'England' was free of genuine trees, except for a few junipers, birches and possibly stunted pines in the extreme south-west. It is known that tundra-like conditions, at the height of the ice-advance, extended as far south as Bordeaux in France, so it can be imagined how much colder Britain was.

Although there may not have been permanent ice in southern England, conditions were undoubtedly very harsh: the ground was frozen below the surface for all of the year (permafrost), with only the surface melting in warmer areas. This softening and melting of a surface almost bare of vegetation naturally gave rise to a very mobile surface layer which slipped away readily on slopes, and heaved and churned elsewhere. Each summer, great quantities of snow and ice formed meltwater, probably swollen by rainfall, causing tremendous erosion and movement of debris and silt around the countryside. Bare surfaces are always more readily eroded than vegetated ones, and the effects of freezing and thawing exacerbated and extended this effect dramatically.

This situation is described, appropriately enough, as periglacial conditions (literally 'around the ice') and it can still be seen taking place many hundreds of miles further

Comparative Table of Events					
DATE (in years before present day)	NAME OF PERIOD	CLIMATE AND VEGETATION	AGES OF MAN	NATURAL EVENTS	HISTORIC EVENTS
18,000	FULL ICE-AGE	Arctic climate. Sparse tundra vegetation in southern England.		Ice-cap at maximum extent. Britain part of Europe. Sea-level about 330 ft (100 m) below present level.	
12,000	LATE GLACIAL	Climate warming then cooling. Advance of open woodland, then retreat again.	Upper Palaeolithic: small mobile population.	Britain more or less ice-free for 1,000 years, then ice re-advances locally.	First pottery used in Far East. Earliest cultivated plants, in S.E. Asia.
10,000	LOCH LOMOND READVANCE PRE-BOREAL PERIOD	Climate similar to present day.		Ireland becomes an island. Straits of Dover breached. Britain becomes an island.	Jericho recognisable as a walled town.
8,000	BOREAL PERIOD	Mixed forests dominate southern and lowland areas. Peat formation increases. 'Climatic optimum'. Timber line much higher than now.	Mesolithic period.		
6,000	ATLANTIC PERIOD		Neolithic period		First use of bronze in Thailand. First cities developed, Middle East.
4,000	SUB-BOREAL PERIOD	Sudden elm decline. Pattern of gradual clearance of woodland, and increase in heaths, grassland and arable areas.	Bronze Age		First accurate calendar devised, Egypt.
2,000	SUB-ATLANTIC PERIOD		Iron Age		Roman invasion of Britain. Birth of Christ.
			Roman/ Romano-British. Anglo-Saxon. Norman,		
0 (present day		Climate about 2°C cooler than 'climatic optimum'.			Norman invasion of Britain.

north, within the arctic circle. It accounts for much seemingly-puzzling erosion of southern England, where deep chalk valleys have no streams at their base, and small rivers have huge gravel terraces on their floodplains. It is believed that the permafrost tundra conditions prevented water from sinking into the chalk, as it does now, so the meltwater and rainwater flowed over the surface, easily eroding the soft chalk as it melted its surface, leaving us with a legacy of mysterious deep dry valleys like the Devil's Kneading Trough in Kent, or the Devil's Dyke near Brighton.

For the plants that could stand the cold, and remain rooted despite all the soil movement, conditions were good, since there was little competition and a constant supply of nutrients brought from below or carried in by water. Characteristic species of this situation during the ice age included herbs such as mountain avens, purple saxifrage and alpine meadow-rue, with very dwarf woody plants such as the tiny dwarf birch, a dwarf version of juniper, and several prostrate arctic willows. All these species occur now in northern and highland Britain, but there are also records of plants that no longer occur in Britain, such as arctic poppy, the snowy cinquefoil, or an arctic buttercup (*Ranunculus hyperboreus*), later to become victims of a warming climate and increasing tree cover. The mixture of plants was a strange one to modern eyes, however, for in addition to these obvious arctic or alpine species, there were also many weeds such as docks, mugwort and plantains, coastal species such as sea buckthorn or thrift, and also species that seem today to prefer warmer conditions, such as the hoary rock-rose (*Helianthemum canum*) or the shrubby cinquefoil (*Potentilla fruticosa*). These species rear their heads again in the story when we look later at what has survived from this periglacial mixture of plants.

From its peak at 18,000 years ago, the ice began to retreat steadily as the climate warmed, and the story from now on is more or less one of the movement of successive waves of increasingly warmth-demanding plants northwards, in the wake of the ice. It has to be remembered that, because the ice was so thick, it needed a tremendous amount of heat to melt it, and the climate was frequently warmer than the extent of ice might lead one to expect, so that many quite warmth-demanding species could colonise as the ice melted. Ice-sheets are exceptionally erosive, and as they spread southwards they naturally accumulated a heavy burden of eroded rock material and silt. At the tip of the ice-sheet, where the southward movement was just balanced by the rate of melting, this load was deposited in large piles known as moraines, which may be very clearly defined where an ice-sheet was static for a while, as in north Cheshire, or more spread out where the end was less clearcut. When the ice began to retreat more continuously, the silt and rock 'flour' incorporated in the ice was simply dumped on the exposed rock surface as a more or less continuous covering of unformed soil known as glacial till. This covers large areas of Scotland and northern England from East Anglia northwards, though the southernmost extensions of till date from earlier more extensive ice-sheets than the latest one. In other places, the ice retreated to reveal clusters of hummocks of till known as drumlins, formed under the ice, or streaks of more gravelly material known as eskers, deposited by rivers flowing below or within the ice-sheet.

Mountain avens (Dryas octopetala) *on limestone pavement, the Burren, Eire. The mountain avens is one of the most characteristic of glacial plants, and it has only survived in Britain in a few cold limestone areas, though where conditions are right it may be very abundant.*

A glacial landscape in the Cairngorms. The high corrie cliffs, still snow-covered in June, the cold corrie lake, the frost-shattered rocks and the ridges of morainic (deposited glacial debris) material are all evidence of a past and present arctic climate. The foreground flowers are marsh marigolds.

In any event, what was exposed was a bare landscape partially or wholly covered with till, combined with gravel and larger rocks brought from elsewhere (glacial 'erratics' as they are endearingly named). Although this mixture had no soil structure whatsoever, it was well supplied with nutrients and, in most cases, high in lime or calcium. The periglacial plant communities were well able to make use of it, and colonisation followed quickly. Today, if you go to the high Himalayas, or even the more lowly Cairngorms in Scotland, you find that there is a continuous 'rain' of material brought in from the lowlands, consisting of dust, pollen, seeds, plant fragments, spiderlings, small insects and much other debris. Most of that falling onto the ice simply dies, to be deposited centuries later as part of the glacial till (though small interdependent communities of invertebrates do survive in ice-sheets, relying on the constant influx of food). When the ice retreats, however, this rain of propagules and debris falls directly onto the ground, and some, at least, have a chance of surviving. Although we cannot now know precisely, we can judge by a knowledge of this, and by what happened elsewhere when glaciers have retreated in historical times, that the bared ground was probably colonised very quickly by lichens, mosses, grasses, sedges, some herbs, and very dwarf willows, together with a small community of invertebrates. Interestingly enough, studies of well-preserved deposits dating from the early stages of the ice retreat have shown that there was a considerable population of beetles present, and many of the species were warmth-demanding species fitting incongruously with the arctic vegetation at the time. This is probably explained by the fact, outlined above, that the climate was always ahead of the ice retreat, because the ice took so long to melt, and that it was really quite warm (at least in summer) close to the ice at this time. Unfortunately, it is a rather rare event for the insects of the time to have been both preserved and subsequently discovered, and we do not know as much as we would like to.

As the belt of arctic tundra moved northwards with the receding ice, it was followed by a more developed vegetation, moving in from the extreme south of England or land to the south of that, that has been graphically described as 'park-tundra'. Junipers became more upright and tree-like, while aspen, birches, willows, rowan and sea buckthorn presaged the coming dominance of trees. It was still an open landscape, though, with trees only scattered or forming open woodlands where shelter and soil permitted, and dwarf heath with crowberry and heathers spread into some of the gaps. Associated with this park tundra, there was a rich flora, including many familiar species such as bellflowers, knapweed, willowherb, rock-roses, devil's-bit scabious, sheep's bit, thrift and docks, together with now limited species like the beautiful Jacob's ladder, the fir clubmoss and the tiny arctic plant *Koenigia islandica* only quite recently discovered in present-day Britain, but widespread in late glacial times and still frequent in the arctic today. The remains of plants, including their pollen, found in any one site cannot convey a full picture of the situation, but it is of interest to know what was growing together in one place. Some deposits in the Colne Valley in Hertfordshire, dated to about 12–13,000 years ago, have been shown to contain evidence of a mixture of plants including mugwort, plantains and docks (all plants of disturbed open habitats), some pollen from willows, birches (including the dwarf birch) and pine, together with shrubby plants like sea buckthorn and the strange little joint-pines (*Ephedra*), no longer found in Britain. They probably did not all occur quite together, but they were close enough in space and time to have provided remains for one level of these beds.

THE ICE RETURNS

By about 12,500 years ago, Britain was virtually ice-free (though still of a quite different shape to now, and still firmly attached to Europe) and waves of juniper, then birch, then pine, and even oaks had moved well to the north. Even the north of Scotland had well-developed plant communities by this time, with heathy moorland and a rich flora in open areas. The ice age was not yet over, though: some 11,000 years ago the climate began to cool again and ice-sheets formed in Scotland, the Lake District, north Wales, and the highest parts of the Pennines. The developing temperate woodland was forced to retreat again, not directly by ice but simply by a climate that was too cold to allow it to persist. This period reached its zenith about 10,800 years ago, and in Britain it is known as the 'Loch Lomond re-advance'. Tundra conditions re-established over much of the country, except the extreme south, and this period is frequently referred to by botanists as the Young *Dryas* time, indicating the abundance of mountain avens (*Dryas octopetala*) pollen in remains from then, and the presumed abundance of this beautiful plant in the plant communities of the time.

BRITAIN AFTER THE ICE

By 10,000 years ago Britain could be said to be out of the ice age (for the time being, at least) and this date is taken as the start of the post-glacial period that we are now in. The same pattern of colonisation followed in the wake of the 'Loch Lomond re-advance' with juniper leading the way as the first dominant tree. In Cumbria, for example, as shown by deposits from Scaleby Moss, the peak period for juniper fell at just about 10,000–9,500 years ago, dominating a vegetation of grassy open heathland, with willows and many herbaceous plants with the familiar meadowsweet especially abundant. Water was very prevalent at this period, and there were numerous lakes, ponds and streams, many of which later dried out, or became bogs, fens or marshes, and ultimately dry land. Plants such as water milfoil thrived in this wet environment.

This juniper zone moved northwards, and into its southern regions came the first real trees – the birches. Their light seeds blew in and colonised the warming environment with its improved soil structure, and their remains indicate that birches dominated the scene, at varying times, over the whole country. They can travel far and fast, and grow quickly on most soils, so there were few barriers to their spread, given reasonable weather; and they ousted the juniper heath from the south. By about 9,000 years ago, towards the end of the period known as the pre-Boreal, the climate was generally similar to that of today, and the vegetation was not so very different from what we would have now if man had not intervened. Birches had reached north Scotland, perhaps 1,000 years later than they had reached northern England, and they were followed by Scots pine which had moved up through England to appear in the highlands by about 8,000 years ago, gradually becoming dominant over much of Scotland by about 5,000 years ago, where it was never really replaced by any other tree.

The period from 9,000 to 5,000 years ago, the so-called Boreal and Atlantic climatic periods, was a warm time, warmer than today, and known collectively as the 'climatic optimum', since the climate has not been better before or since within the post-glacial period. This time is also known as the 'forest maximum', since by about 7,000 years ago virtually the whole country was covered in forest, with deciduous mixed forest over most of England, Wales and southern Scotland, and pines, birches or junipers in the higher and more northerly areas. The story of this great natural forest (the 'wildwood') and its demise at the hands of man merits a whole chapter, and it is covered in detail in Chapter 3. We are concerned here more with the dwindling remnants of arctic Britain, and what happened to them.

REMNANTS OF A VANISHED AGE

Apart from the relatively few species of plant that survived in southern England through the ice age, all our native plants have colonised the country since then. Not many plants are able successfully to cross seas (though a few undoubtedly do), and so it is reasonable to assume that most of our present-day native flora colonised into Britain across the land-bridges with the continent, so that most movement was from the east or south-east towards the north and west. Ireland not only parted from mainland Britain rather earlier (about 10,000 years ago) but it is also much further away from the main colonisation route, so it failed to acquire many of the naturally re-invading species (though it acquired a few of its own from the south-west). Conversely, it might be expected that eastern England should have the richest flora today, but, while there is an element of truth in this, things are too complicated by geology, climate and history to say this with certainty.

It is easy enough to see how our woodland flowers arrived and spread, with an unbroken extent of woodland to move through. Yet, almost all the early colonisers, perhaps for as long as several thousand years, were plants of open habitats demanding light, lime and frequently readily-available nutrients for their survival: plants like mountain avens, purple saxifrage, hoary rock-rose, Jacob's ladder, or alpine meadow-rue: what has happened to them? The answer, of course, is not simple. One is tempted to think of the flora of post-ice-age Britain as a uniform tundra flora, but of course, it was almost as varied then as now, with each plant species finding its niche according to its requirements of soil, water, warmth, nutrients and so on. As circumstances changed, with woodland and then, in many

areas, agricultural land covering the countryside, so the flora changed, in a very dramatic way.

Some plants have gone completely and these are mostly plants that simply cannot stand warmth; we no longer have arctic poppies, arctic buttercup, woolly cinquefoil, the joint-pines and many others that were frequent in the periglacial flora, but have succumbed to the increased warmth, and the invasion of woodlands. Another group, those that needed bare disturbed conditions, free from competition for at least part of the year, have developed to become familiar weeds of arable land, gardens and waste places where now the ground is kept bare by artificial means such as ploughing or digging. Docks, sorrels, chickweed, willowherbs, stinging nettles, plantains and many other common weeds are known to have had a considerable presence in the periglacial flora thriving in the bare nutrient-rich soil. Their most difficult time must have been during the forest maximum, when bare areas were probably almost confined to the river valleys and coasts, but the arrival of man as a farmer was their saviour, and they have never looked back. Admittedly, modern seed-cleaning and herbicide methods have caused the recent demise of many specialist cornfield weeds, and their heyday is over, but most weeds are highly adaptable and will always be with us.

THE GLACIAL RELICS

Perhaps the most interesting story, though, comes from the plants that appear to have survived in exactly the same place, right through all the post-glacial changes. There are a few places in Britain where we can get a glimpse, and in some cases a very revealing glimpse, of what the immediate post-glacial flora looked like, and what species were in it. For a long time, the presence of motley collections of rare plants in these places, some coming from south Europe, some from the arctic, and some from the east, seemed quite inexplicable, but our recent knowledge of what plants grew in the newly-bared soil of Britain has cast a new light on such places, revealing them as relics (albeit rather modified ones) of our glacial past. There are three places in the British Isles that seem to reveal most about this history, and it is worth visiting them each in turn; they are Upper Teesdale, the Burren in western Ireland, and the Ben Lawers mountain range in Perthshire.

THE HIGH FELLS OF UPPER TEESDALE

Upper Teesdale, high in the northern Pennines, has been known for centuries as an area for an exceptional number of rare plants, and more recently it has become an area of

intensive research partly focused by the threat to some of the plants by the construction of a reservoir. It has been estimated that about 120 rare or reasonably rare plants occur in Teesdale – an impressive enough figure in itself, but made more so by the fact that some barely occur anywhere else, while others that are nationally rare occur in Teesdale in exceptional abundance. The 'cream' of the Teesdale rarities includes the stunningly blue spring gentian, the very rare Teesdale violet, a tiny blue milkwort, sometimes called the Teesdale milkwort, the upright sandwort, hoary rock-rose, mountain avens, the bright blue mountain forget-me-not, alpine bartsia, alpine bistort and alpine meadow-rue, as well as many others. It is obvious enough from the names that many are arctic or alpine plants, which gives one clue to their survival: the cold climate of Upper Teesdale.

Other plants, though, are clearly there for quite different reasons: horseshoe vetch occurs in one place in Teesdale, over 1,500 ft (400 m) up, *at its most northerly world locality* as well as its highest in the British Isles; two familiar coastal plants, the thrift and the buck's-horn plantain, occur there in damp open flushed areas, and the Teesdale locality for the

Purple saxifrage (Saxifraga oppositifolia) *on Pen-y-ghent, Yorkshire. The purple saxifrage is a characteristic periglacial plant in the arctic today, and it is one of our hardiest alpine plants. On British mountains, it comes into flower from March onwards, even at high altitudes, long before anything else is in flower, often appearing as soon as the snow melts.*

alpine foxtail grass, high on the slopes of Cross Fell, is almost the most southerly site for it in the world. This extraordinary mixture of plants, with different world distributions, has come to be known as the 'Teesdale assemblage', and for many years their existence together here was, not surprisingly, a complete puzzle.

The wealth of knowledge now amassed has shown, though, that virtually all of these rarer plants were present in Britain just after, or even during the ice age, and there is increasing evidence for the occurrence of many of them in Teesdale itself in the late glacial period. The once widely-held theory that the plants survived *in situ* through the ice age, clustered on ice-free peaks known as nunataks, is now

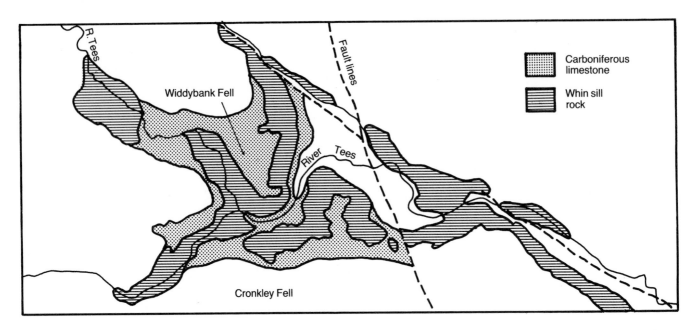

Sketch map of the geology of Upper Teesdale showing how the Whin Sill has intruded into the Carboniferous limestones, producing the 'sugar limestone' on Cronkley and Widdybank Fells, wherever the two come into contact.

almost totally discarded, since the areas where they occur are known to have been glaciated; and it now seems certain that we are looking at the remnants of the early colonisers that moved in during the centuries or millennia after the ice cleared.

So, this only leaves the question of why they remained here, in the heart of the high Pennines, but not elsewhere in the country. The simple answer to this is that a small part of Upper Teesdale escaped the twin death-knells (for glacial plants) of a closed woodland canopy and blanket bog formation, which reached its zenith in the warm wet climate 6–7,000 years ago; but in reality it is rather more complicated than this. The centre of the Teesdale area of rarities is the twin hills of Cronkley and Widdybank Fells, both about 1,700 ft (520 m) high, separated by the deep rocky gorge of the Tees. Most of the greatest rarities occur on one or other of these hills, and apart from their altitude and location they share a common characteristic that is one of the keys to the puzzle. Across the top of each fell runs a band of strange aptly-named 'sugar limestone' which is so loose and friable that the presence of sheep, paths or even rabbits causes the turf to erode and the grains of rock to appear, bare and white. Its geological name is the rather more prosaic 'saccharoidal marble', but at least this gives a better clue to its formation. Strictly speaking, it is not a

limestone at all, but a limestone that has been changed into a form of marble by the intense heat and pressure caused when volcanic lava intruded into and through the existing rock. This lava gradually cooled and solidified into the great Whin Sill, a major landscape feature of northern England, but its effect here was to turn Carboniferous limestone into loose sugary marble, and at the same time the mineral-rich fluids that accompanied the lava left the 'sugar limestone' with a legacy of heavy metals, like lead, spread through it.

The pollen evidence shows that once, at the forest maximum, there was woodland throughout this area, up to a much higher level than now, but it seems almost certain that the cover over the sugar limestone was always very open, perhaps consisting of scattered hazel bushes, never forming a closed canopy due to the difficult nature of the soil. Our glacial relics survived, in reduced numbers, through this period (though many were probably lost, too) to expand again when man, and a changing climate, cleared the woodlands away. The quick-draining lime-rich rock also prevented peat from forming, as it has on the hills all around, which helped the rarities to persist.

The sugar limestone is probably the central strand in the survival of periglacial plants in Teesdale, but it is not the only one, for only an exceptional combination of circumstances could allow so many rarities to survive. The cool climate of the dale (likened by some to that of southern Iceland) has slowed the growth of stronger plants, keeping more areas open, while the steep rocky cliffs and screes must have always remained partly open. The river Tees itself cuts through glacial till and scattered drumlins, producing steep eroding banks, and gravelly river terraces, both of which have probably always remained open, giving refuge to alpine bartsia, shrubby cinquefoil and other

rarities, most of which occurred in the immediate post-glacial period. The great Whin Sill itself, the cause of the sugar limestone, forms magnificent cliffs where the river Tees cuts through it, at Falcon Clints, and at the dramatic waterfalls of High and Low Force. These have stayed at least partly open since the ice age, apart from the shade of a few rowans or whitebeams, and they have provided another haven for plants from the effects of shading; it is here that parsley fern and some rare versions of the male fern grow, in addition to serrated wintergreen and some uncommon (but exceptionally difficult to identify precisely) yellow-flowered hawkweeds. Although the Whin Sill is moderately rich in lime, it is too unyielding and not really limey enough to suit many glacial plants, so it is a minor strand in the tapestry.

All over these Upper Teesdale fells, wherever there are changes in the porosity of the rock, there are springs or, if the water spreads out more widely through the soil without gathering into a rill, flushes. Many of these are lime-rich,

A general view of upper Teesdale at Langdon Beck, showing some of the features that have made this area so rich botanically, and so important for the survival of arctic-alpine plants. The fells in the background support the sugar-limestone communities, and the dark cliffs provide additional refuges; the hill on the left is a glacial 'drumlin' (a heap of eroded rock flour) which erodes continuously where the river keeps removing parts of it; and the steep uneven hay meadows and pastures (such as in the right foreground) have remained unimproved agriculturally, a haven for many upland grassland plants.

and the ground is often stony, and they support a wonderful mixture of plants, most of which can probably be traced back to the early post-ice-age colonisers. These wet areas may have stayed even more open than the dry limestone areas, since not many woody plants thrive in wet, stony, heavy-metal-ridden flushes at this altitude, and the lime and the slope combined to prevent peat from forming. Now,

21

Teesdale violet (Viola rupestris) growing on sugar limestone in upper Teesdale. This violet is one of the numerous glacial relicts to be found on the sugar limestone soil of upper Teesdale. The granular character of the 'sugar' can be seen in the photograph, and it can be appreciated why it has always remained partly free from woodland, since it is not an easy soil for plants to grow in.

Alpine bartsia (Bartsia alpina). One of the many alpine or arctic plants that have persisted in Teesdale since just after ice-age times. The alpine bartsia has survived in steep damp pastures and on eroded drumlins in Teesdale, and only occurs in a few other places in Britain.

the better flushes are full of the pink bird's-eye primrose, the white spikes of Scottish asphodel (probably commoner here than anywhere in Scotland!), numerous alpine or arctic sedges, and, rarest of all, the tiny white bog sandwort. This diminutive plant grows nowhere else in Britain (and there is very little of it in Teesdale) and it obviously needs the most open and uncompetitive conditions to survive. Lower down the fells, similar but rather less stony and more productive flushes occur, and they are the habitat for other rarities

such as the deep blue-purple spikes of alpine bartsia, the waxy white flowers of grass of Parnassus, yellow globe-flowers, early marsh orchids and many others. These flushes overlap with more 'normal' habitats, so the special plants are mixed up with more common plants of damp pasture for this altitude, but again it is likely that some plants have persisted in these flushes for thousands of years.

One final addition to this assemblage of habitats that mimics the periglacial circumstances is the high hills that encircle the better-known fells around Cow Green. Mickle Fell, Cross Fell, Dun Fell and their neighbours are the highest hills in the Pennines, and the climate on their tops is genuinely arctic even today. All the evidence available indicates that the tops of the higher fells, which reach almost 3,000 ft (900 m), were never forested and some habitats were never covered with peat either. The limestone cliffs of Mickle Fell, the stony flushes of Cross Fell (the same story as lower in the Dale) are rich in glacial relics, often now at the extreme south of their range, such as the

Aran islands, the Burren. The extraordinary physical nature of the Burren in western Ireland can be clearly seen here, and it is hardly surprising that a peculiar range of plants have survived here. This photograph shows the extensive Carboniferous limestone pavements on Inishmore island, just off the mainland coast.

intensely blue alpine forget-me-nots and the exceedingly rare alpine cat's-tail grass.

The Teesdale flora is not as rich as it was, for we have lost the beautiful blue Jacob's ladder (a known periglacial plant, now growing wild only in the Craven area of north Yorkshire and in the Peak District) and a very rare alpine fern, amongst others, within historical times, and probably others from before records began, but what is left probably gives us a clearer idea of the vegetation of post-ice-age Britain than anywhere else on the mainland. It is not a 'time-capsule' but it could reasonably be described as a living museum – an area that has undoubtedly seen many changes over the millennia but which still, with a bit of interpretation, reveals an enormous amount about what has been happening to our native flora.

THE BURREN

In the west of Ireland, about as far as one can be climatically and geographically from Upper Teesdale, there is another, and equally remarkable, living museum. It is not a place that appears in many tourist brochures, but for botanists it is a mecca, one of the most important and fascinating areas in Europe. Its interest lies not only in the presence of many rare plants, often in exceptional abundance, but, again, in what this particular collection of plants shows us. The area is known as the Burren, and it is a strange wild area lying across the borders of Clare and Galway in the mid-west of

Ireland. It consists almost entirely of Carboniferous limestone (again!), which forms hills up to about 1,000 ft (300 m), many of which appear from a distance to be made up solely of bare slabs of white or grey rock, with hardly a plant to be seen. In other parts, the soil is a little deeper and fields have been cultivated, and there are even a few woods, but the over-riding impression is of bare limestone hills, with pavement-like blocks. In contrast to Teesdale, the winters are very mild with only rare frosts, though just occasionally these are more severe; it is a strangely equable climate, with winters equivalent to those of Rome or southern France, and summers equivalent to sub-arctic Finland in temperature!

The plants in the Burren are exceptional. They are sometimes described as being a mixture of arctic, alpine and mediterranean plants, and this is not far from the truth. There is nowhere else in the world where you can see the Irish orchid *Neotinea maculata* (a plant with a mainly Mediterranean distribution, despite its name) growing intermingled with mountain avens which, as we have seen, was one of the first colonisers of the glacial landscape and is now virtually confined to the arctic or to high mountains. These are the extremes, but the presence of spring gentian (another predominantly alpine plant, only found elsewhere in the British Isles in Upper Teesdale), maidenhair fern (a southern and western species, commonest in warm damp areas), pyramidal bugle (normally a northern or mountain species, yet always found close to sea-level in the Burren!), and the shrubby cinquefoil (with a widely separated distribution, occurring in a handful of sites in Britain, and otherwise no closer than the Pyrenees or south-east Sweden) and several others lend weight to the conclusion that the Burren, botanically, is a strange and remarkable place.

One of the nicest features of the Burren, for both botanist and casual visitor alike, is the way in which so many of the plants grow in such wild profusion, and flower so strongly. The beautiful white flowers of mountain avens, followed by their clematis-like fruits, are literally everywhere, even at sea-level, in May (and, unusually, again in August, though less abundantly) with a profusion unequalled in north-west Europe; the shrubby cinquefoil, while hardly abundant, is probably more frequent here than anywhere else in western Europe. Spring gentian grows in an abundance that makes you puzzle over its total absence from the remainder of Ireland, and the rest of the British Isles bar Teesdale. It occurs in every mountain range of mainland Europe, but not in any Welsh or Scottish mountain, nor on the seemingly-suitable limestones of the Mendips or the Malham area of North Yorkshire, yet it is here, growing all over the place, in the Burren. The tiny (and, it has to be admitted, rather dull) Irish orchid occurs no nearer than southern France or one place in northern Spain (except that it has been quite recently found, sparingly, in the Isle of Man), yet it is widely spread and occasionally common through the Burren and adjacent areas.

There is much more of interest in the Burren, but enough has been said to show how unusual a place it is. The story of how its assemblage of plants came together, though, is still obscure and many questions still remain unanswered. Historical research, mainly using remains preserved in peat (see page 27) has elucidated the broad sweep of its history, but left many details unexplained. The Burren was certainly covered by ice at the height of the ice age, but was clear by 12–13,000 years ago, leaving a bare rocky landscape with virtually no soil, especially as little in the way of glacial till was deposited as the ice receded. The composition of the early stages of vegetation is not fully clear, but it is reasonably certain that there was a very sparse cover, typical of a tundra vegetation, but probably made even more thinly-spread by the complete lack of soil and the extensive areas of bare rock. Mountain avens and dwarf willow were the commonest plants, as judged by pollen and other remains, but juniper, creeping willow, burnet rose, fairy flax and rock-roses all occurred about 11,000 years ago, so there was clearly a mixed, mainly open community with many plants typical of limestone areas today. About 10,000 years ago (the traditional end of the ice age) woodland began to develop, though it was probably very stunted except in particularly favoured localities. Juniper came first, dominating the pollen record, to be followed by birches and the larger willows. After this, following a similar pattern to sites elsewhere, came Scots pine and hazel, probably often growing together, though this is rarely seen today. Aspen probably came in quite commonly early on (it is still something of a pioneer tree today, growing on the edge of more stable habitats) but its pollen is difficult to record. The more stable, climax trees of oak and elm soon followed, but it seems that open pine forest probably dominated the Burren for thousands of years, possibly right up to historic times, well after the birth of Christ. If this is so, then at least some of the dense hazel 'woods' of the Burren, and indeed the bare pavement areas, are of quite recent secondary origin.

What we do not know, and can never accurately know, is the exact coverage and density of this pine forest. Its very existence is fraught with questions. Why did pine dominate a limestone landscape when trees like ash, elm, hazel and lime tend to do so elsewhere, with pine confined to sandier soils? Why did pine persist for so long here as the dominant, when it had long since been ousted from most of England, Wales and Ireland as the dominant forest tree? Finally, why did it eventually disappear 1,500 years ago? The usual explanation for such events involves the devastations of man, but there is abundant evidence from numerous monuments and remains that man had been present for thousands of years before, which makes this idea less likely, though not impossible. The same applies to yew, which was quite a significant tree in the woodlands for 3,000 years up until 2,000 years ago, when it became rare, and has remained so ever since.

None of this explains why the rarities survive here, and whether they really date from the time just after the ice age. Mountain avens was abundant just after the ice went (as it was almost everywhere) but it disappears completely from the record 9,000 years or so ago. Shrubby cinquefoil has been found in recent remains, but there is no trace of it in the late glacial or immediate post-glacial record, though it does occur almost everywhere else just after the ice age. Spring gentian does not appear in the pollen record either, nor does the Irish orchid or some of the other rarities, though these are rather less surprising absentees, since they are difficult plants to find in peat, and some were probably just too uncommon to show up in the record.

We know that Ireland was cut off 9–10,000 years ago, so, with plants like these that have no agricultural value nor particular association with man, we can safely assume that the great majority entered Ireland naturally before this, and either survived the ice age in the unglaciated south-west of the country, living in severe arctic conditions, or migrated back by some route or other early in the post-glacial period. It is unlikely that they could all have leaped the sea, the forests and the peat bogs to reach the Burren in later times, and it is much more likely that they have survived in open pine forest, in hazel scrub, around bare rock, and perhaps even in man-made clearings, since the ice age, and have all simply failed to show up in the pollen and peat record.

Incidentally, in this context, some of the differences in flowers between the Burren and Upper Teesdale, or other mainland 'refuges', may be due as much to plants occurring that reached Ireland *directly* from Europe when the western seaboard of Europe was almost continuous, rather than via Britain, in contrast to the general idea that everything in Ireland had to get there through England and Wales. This helps to explain the presence of the Mediterranean species, Irish orchid, in western Ireland but virtually nowhere else, as well as plants like the strawberry tree (*Arbutus unedo*), the large-flowered butterwort, and many other plants that only occur wild in south-west Ireland.

BEN LAWERS MOUNTAIN RANGE

It is obvious enough that the plants living around the ice-sheet, and following its retreat, must be able to stand severe frosts, and it is to be expected therefore that they would be able to grow on mountains, where conditions most closely resemble those post-glacial tundra conditions, with heavy frosts and open conditions with little competition. Why is it, then, that our mountains are not covered with a wealth of flowers dating from the halcyon days for arctic-alpine

Mountain lichens at 3,500 feet (1,050 m) on Ben Lawers. At very high altitudes, the vigour and range of flowering plants is greatly limited, but lichens can do well even in the harshest of conditions. Even the white skin surrounding the central black-speckled lichen is itself a lichen.

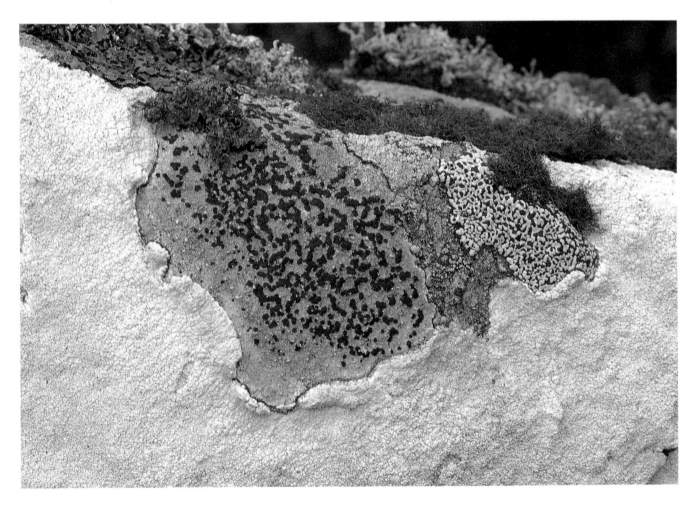

plants, 12,000 or so years ago? The pollen record shows numerous such plants as having occurred in Britain just after the ice (and no doubt there were many more of which there is no evidence) yet they are now either completely absent from Britain, or merely confined to one or two mountains; the question inevitably arises as to why more did not survive on our abundant bare windswept mountain tops, especially in Scotland. The answer, as usual, is not simple.

First there is that unaccountable element, chance, that ensures that plants and animals have simply never arrived where we might have expected them to, or have become extinct by some chance event. This only accounts for part of the story, however, since we know of species that were definitely common in mountain areas, say, 10,000 years ago, but which no longer occur there anywhere. The other factors that have affected our mountain flora most, and sadly diminished it beyond repair compared to its richness thousands of years ago, are the surprisingly-extensive former cover of woodlands over mountains, the spread of blanketing peat over the uplands, excessive grazing by domestic animals in later times, and the slow, insidious, but largely natural, change from the very lime-rich conditions of post-glacial Britain to much more acid conditions, as the glacial till is eroded down to the bare, usually acidic bedrock, and all the soluble nutrients are gradually leached outwards and downwards from the soil, leaving the more acid habitat unfavourable to many of these glacial survivors. It has been rather like putting a series of overlays with holes in over the countryside, with each overlay obliterating everything under it except where the holes are. Succeeding 'overlays' have obliterated some of the survivors from the preceding one, and it is only in a few sites (which we will visit shortly) that the 'hole' has stayed in the same place with each 'overlay', and this is where our best mountain flora has survived.

By 6–8,000 years ago, forests were very extensive over virtually all of the country, and, because the climate was better then, the treeline reached higher than the natural treeline now. There was woodland up to 2,500–3,000 ft (760–900 m), or even higher in places, so within this it was only in open areas that sun-loving herbaceous plants could survive, and many lower, or more southerly, mountains lost virtually all of their existing flora at this time, acquiring an upland woodland flora in the process. The composition of the woodland (whether it was pine, elm, or oak dominated) is not really important since few of these glacial plants survive in the shade of anything.

From about 7,000 years ago onwards, the uplands of Britain began to suffer from a gradual accumulation of blanketing peat, that is the barely-decomposed remnants of the plants that grew there, accumulating under acid waterlogged conditions. There is many a peat bog, high in the highlands, that has pine or birch stumps preserved within it, relics of the woodland that this peat replaced. In many cases, it extended higher than the former treeline and may often have engulfed places that had been partly free of trees, thus removing another section of the alpine flora, since few plants of lime-rich, well-drained conditions can survive on waterlogged acid peat.

Just why peat became so dominant, even ousting established woodlands, is not entirely clear. It has been generally assumed that the wetter climate of the 'Atlantic' period at this time led naturally to increasing bog and peat formation, yet this is now being questioned, as areas with a similar climate elsewhere in the world have continuous woodland cover. Pollen and other records have also shown that the start of peat formation does not always coincide with the start of the wet period, and it is increasingly being noticed that this starting point is also often associated with the remains of many weedy plants. Not infrequently, there is evidence of fire at this period from the charcoal remains, and it is beginning to look as though Mesolithic man may have had more effect than is generally credited, perhaps deliberately clearing woodland to assist grazing. The effect of clearing woodland in wet, cold conditions is naturally to increase the trend towards waterlogging and acidification, and peat formation would naturally follow. However, peat formation is always less where the rocks are rich in calcium, and is often prevented altogether if the rocks are free-draining or very crumbly as well (as they are in Teesdale).

It is probably becoming clearer by now which sorts of mountains are most likely to have a reasonable 'relict' alpine flora: they are likely to be high, to have reached above the tree and peat lines, and to be at least partly composed of base-rich, preferably crumbly rock, with as many cliffs as possible. Such mountains do indeed exist, and the best ones do have the flora that we might expect, rich in colourful herbaceous arctic and alpine flowers. There are many mountains in the British Isles that have some of these plants, which have, perhaps, survived in a gully, on a cliff, or in a patch of different rock. For sheer richness and variety of plants, however, the Breadalbane range in Perthshire, with its most famous mountain, Ben Lawers, is hard to surpass.

Most of the mountains of this range are made up of a rock called mica schist, which is high in lime and weathers

---

Peat cutting in north Sutherland. In all the wetter upland areas of Britain, peat development has proceeded more or less unchecked for thousands of years, making conditions unsuitable for most plants that lived in Britain after the ice age, though leaving a legacy of fuel for present generations.

THE CAIRNGORM MOUNTAINS

The best area in which to experience 'arctic Britain', and to understand most clearly what post-glacial Britain must have been like, is undoubtedly the Cairngorms in the eastern highlands of Scotland.

The Cairngorms are the remnants of a huge granite plateau, forming the largest area of land over 3,000 ft (900 m) in Britain, a mecca for skiers in winter but frequently wintry even in summer. They have our closest approach to glaciers in Britain, in the form of permanent or almost-permanent snow patches in the high north-facing glacial corries, and several peaks, like Ben Macdui, are well over 4,000 ft (1,200 m). Summers are short in the high Cairngorms, with frosts likely in any month of the year, and summer snowfalls always a possibility.

The plant and animal life reflects this arctic climate. Coming up the slopes from the Spey valley, the Scots pines (see p. 119) gradually become smaller and more stunted by 1,500 ft (450 m), though in one place they struggle on to just over 2,000 ft (600 m), the highest pinewoods in Britain, giving way first to high-altitude heather moors then to extensive montane heaths, lacking any heather but dominated mainly by bearberry, trailing azalea (our closest approach to a native rhododendron), and mountain crowberry. Scattered amongst these dwarf shrubs are quantities of the few alpines that can grow on peat: cloudberry, dwarf cornel, dwarf birch and chickweed wintergreen. Higher still, above about 3,000 ft (900 m), the vegetation breaks up, and the plateau is mainly covered by an open 'fell-field' vegetation with just a few flowering plants, like three-leaved rush, stiff sedge, and moss campion, while the remainder is either covered by mosses and lichens or is bare gritty granite. Where the snow patches lie until early summer, there is more vegetation, but in some of the high north-facing corries of Braeriach or Ben Macdui the snow may lie all the year round.

Dotterel, snow bunting and ptarmigan all breed on the high plateau, mountain hares are common, and a herd of reindeer has thrived on the sparse vegetation since its introduction (or re-introduction, perhaps) over 30 years ago – a good sign of arctic conditions!

The landscape of the high Cairngorms is a glacial, shattered one; even in early June there are snow patches everywhere; vast corrie cliffs brood menacingly over their eroded screes below, tumbling down towards a clear icy corrie lake at the base; there are deep, scoured U-shaped glaciated valleys, like those containing the beautiful lakes of Loch Avon or Loch Einich; icy waterfalls from the melting snows thunder hundreds of feet down granite cliffs bearing their eroded rock flour with them, and everywhere has the feel of active frost erosion, even though the ice-sheet itself has long gone.

Granite 'fell-field' vegetation on the high Cairngorm plateau at about 4,000 feet (1,200 m). The open nature of the vegetation at this height can be readily appreciated, with large areas of the granitic rocky soil completely bare of plants. This was photographed in early June, giving a good picture of how arctic the high Cairngorms are, even in early summer.

REFUGES FOR THE ICE-AGE SURVIVORS

Once you realise that lime-rich, permanently open habitats are so important to our glacial relict plants, as the closest approximations to the former 'tundra' conditions, you soon start to recognise them, even though you may not know which are glacial relicts and which are not. The important factor is that the site has remained open more or less continuously through the period of maximum forest, 6–8,000 years ago, so they must be *naturally* open sites. The most likely sites are: limestone cliffs and gorges, limestone pavement, mountainous areas with readily-eroded, lime-rich rock like sugar limestone, mica schist or serpentine; sand dunes, if ancient, or the remnants of ancient systems; and gravelly river terraces that remain open as rivers flood and change course annually.

Some suggested places to visit to contemplate our glacial flora include the following.

Arnside Knott, Cumbria. A fascinating limestone hill, south of the Lake District, with many rare plants. (National Trust.)

The Avon Gorge, Avon. Notable for its quantities of rare plants on Carboniferous limestone cliffs. Partly owned by the NT.

Cader Idris, Gwynedd. Mountainous area with a rich flora. Partly owned by National Trust and National Nature Reserve.

Cheddar Gorge, Somerset. More spectacular than the Avon Gorge, sharing some plants, but with a number of different ones, notably the beautiful Cheddar pink. Partly owned by the National Trust.

The South Gower Coast, Glamorgan. Spectacular Carboniferous limestone cliffs, with many rare plants, like goldilocks aster, hoary rock-rose, and yellow whitlow grass, growing in open uncompetitive conditions in a mild climate; Oxwich dunes, to the east, are a fine example of varied dunes, too, with a rich flora and fauna. Large sections owned by the National Trust.

The Craven Area, North Yorkshire. Collectively, this is one of the most beautiful and species-rich areas of the country. Much of it is Carboniferous limestone, giving rise to magnificent cliffs and coves, such as at Malham, Gordale, and Pen-y-ghent, as well as limestone pavements *par excellence* and many grasslands, wetlands and woodlands of interest. It is the home of masses of glacial relicts like Jacob's ladder, alpine bartsia, bitter milkwort, bird's-eye primrose, and many others. Many areas owned by the National Trust in this region.

Upper Teesdale, mainly County Durham. The National Nature Reserve clustered around Cronkley and Widdybank Fells is of extraordinary importance for its vast assemblage of post-glacial plants growing together, in many habitats, but particularly associated with the strange 'sugar' limestone. These include spring gentian, Teesdale violet, upright sandwort, alpine bartsia, Scottish asphodel, alpine forget-me-not, and many many others.

Ben Lawers, and neighbouring mountains, Perthshire (Tayside). This area of the Breadalbane mountain range has the finest of our mountain floras, with well over half of the British mountain plants. Its richness derives from the lime-rich, crumbly mica schist rock, and above about 1,500 ft (450 m) almost every cliff and outcrop is a rich natural rock garden. This is the best area of Britain for seeing 'alpines', all of which are glacial relicts. (National Trust for Scotland reserve.)

Carboniferous limestone cliffs on the south Gower peninsula. The towering cliffs all along this coast have probably always remained free from woodland cover, and they have provided a refuge for some of the more warmth-demanding plants of open conditions. The plant in the foreground is a prostrate coastal form of common blackthorn. The National Trust owns all the land visible in the picture.

easily, giving rise to numerous rather unstable cliffs. It is soft enough to allow soil formation to take place quickly, and new lime-rich surfaces are constantly being exposed. As a direct result, almost every cliff and crag above about 1,500 ft (450 m), is a real natural rock garden, and the best are simply spectacular. Over 60 per cent of the montane flora of the British Isles occurs in the Ben Lawers area, and it is the richest single mountain site in the country. Amongst the numerous plants to be seen there, the blue flowers of snow gentian (only found here in Britain), alpine forget-me-not (only here and in Teesdale) and some rare alpine speedwells stand out, but this is only the tip of the 'iceberg' and there are examples of saxifrages, sandworts, cinquefoils, fleabanes, alpine bartsia, numerous rare sedges and grasses, and so many others that it is no surprise that it has been a lodestone for botanists for centuries. This is the real mountain flora, deriving almost exclusively from the immediate post-glacial survivors, of exceptional interest and beauty. Other mountains with similar recipes for survival of arctic or alpine plants include those around Glen Clova and Glencoe, on Beinn Dearg in the western highlands, and most places where mica schist, limestone or serpentine rocks outcrop at the surface. The flora and fauna of much of the rest of our uplands is a sad result of over-exploitation by man over many thousands of years, which has successively and collectively helped us to lose much of our arctic-alpine flora, *and* the woodlands and their flora and fauna that succeeded it. Huge areas are covered by peaty moorland and poor grassland, now threatened with the (in most respects) worse fate of row after row of alien conifers – a poor substitute for what we have lost.

Durness limestone cliffs at Inchnadamph, north-west Scotland. In the far north of Britain, limestone cliffs and screes such as these have provided a continuous refuge for some plants from the problems of peat development and tree cover.

The present-day distribution of thrift (Armeria maritima) in the British Isles compared with its past known distribution in previous periods, mainly those associated with the ice ages. A closed circle denotes present distribution, and all other symbols distribution in glacial times. The contrast between the modern coastal and mountain distribution with the previous wider range is noticeable, as the plant has steadily had to contract its range to survive only in those sites with conditions most like those just after the ice age.

SOME LOWLAND REFUGES

We have seen how remnants of our 'glacial' flora have survived in the places where we would most expect it, in the harsher climates of the north and west, but what happened in the soft fertile lowlands of England and Wales? It barely seems possible for plants of open lime-rich conditions to have survived almost total dense woodland cover for thousands of years, followed by intensive and all-pervading cultivation (see Chapter 2), yet they have in a few places.

The coast is constantly changing, partly because of the changing sea-levels since the ice age, giving rise to new open habitats all the time, and a few of our glacial plants that could survive salt and tolerate heat have persisted there, like thrift, sea plantain and scurvy grass. The history of the coast is looked at in more detail in Chapter 7, but it is interesting to note that all these plants have also survived in Britain in mountains; the link is not climate or salinity, but the presence of open tundra-like conditions, in two very different situations.

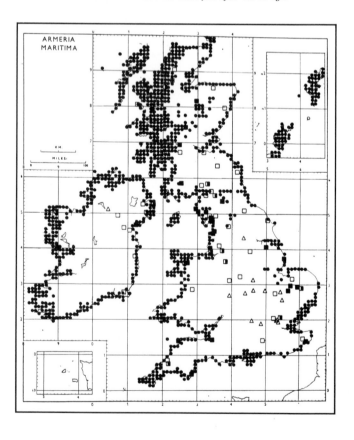

Bristol rock-cress (Arabis stricta). *This plant is confined to the Carboniferous limestone cliffs of the Avon gorge, which has one of the finest lowland assemblages of ice-age survivors, and other rare plants, in the country.*

There are also a few places where there are ancient inland gorges, and where these are in limestone rock (usually Carboniferous limestone, since it is hard enough to form gorges, often where huge caves have collapsed) then the flora is likely to be quite exceptional. The best two, as well as several lesser ones, are in the Mendip Hills on the Somerset/Avon border, at Cheddar and near Bristol. At Cheddar, the huge famous gorge has steep cliffs that abound with rare plants: the Cheddar pink (now greatly reduced in this sole British locality by the depredations of gardeners and collectors), Welsh poppy, mossy saxifrage (perhaps now extinct since the summer droughts of 1976 and 1984), lesser meadow-rue, alpine penny-cress and spring sandwort, amongst many others. These are the glacial relicts that need lime and open habitats, but can stand considerable heat and occasional drought in addition, leaving a rather different mixture of plants to be seen by the botanist of today.

A few miles to the north lies the Avon Gorge, cut by the River Avon through the Carboniferous limestone on the south edge of Bristol, and more famous for Brunel's suspension bridge than its rare flora, though it is difficult to say which is more interesting. The flora of the gorge is remarkable for its variety and abundance, as well as the number of rare plants there; despite the loss to roads, bridges, climbers, botanists and others, you can still find Bristol rock cress (in its only British site), the tiny rock pepperwort (very rare elsewhere), spring cinquefoil (generally uncommon), the beautiful blue western form of spiked speedwell (rare), round-headed garlic (confined to the gorge in mainland Britain), the aptly-named bloody crane's-bill, and so many others. Out of these, the Bristol rock cress, bloody crane's-bill and spring cinquefoil are known late-glacial tundra plants, and most of the others probably are, so we are seeing yet another range of relict ice age species in this warm southern gorge. As we will see in Chapter 4, other periglacial plants have survived by adapting to chalk and limestone grassland, becoming widespread for a time during the last 1,000 years or so, but dwindling again as the grassland is cultivated. These sites, however, both in the mountains and the lowlands, are just remnants, and dwindling ones at that, of a vanished ice age flora. The remainder of our countryside has followed a quite different course, as we shall see.

2 · Fields and Farmscapes

MOUNTAIN BRITAIN, as we have seen, is a wilderness beyond the reach of farming, where the winter climate reminds us how close the ice age really is. Here the communities of mountain plants form a vegetation cover which owes its character entirely to natural factors; the complex interplay of rocks and soils, watercourses and accidents of climate or aspect.

Below the mountain wilderness lies the man-influenced countryside, where, although the plants themselves may be just as wild, they dance to a tune composed by man, growing only where we have created suitable conditions, by deliberate management or neglect. Of course there are really many different countrysides; in the *upland zone*, north and west of the famous 'Tees-Exe' line, the hard old rocks and humid oceanic climate give us the craggy moors and pastures of much of Wales, Cornwall, Lakeland and the Dales. In the mainly south-eastern *lowland zone* we find the sweeping folds of downland Dorset, Hampshire or Sussex; black dyke-dissected Fenland; limestone country with its grassy scarps and stone buildings; the close-knit bosky landscapes of Devon or the Weald; or the prosaic fieldscapes

The countryside pattern. Wherever you are, in England, Wales or lowland Scotland, you are likely to see a pattern of fields, forming a fascinating mosaic of features of different ages; Roman, Saxon, medieval or enclosure period. Finding wildlife habitats is very much a process of understanding the pattern, and the age and management history of different features in the countryside.

33

of Bedfordshire or Nottinghamshire. Why do these land-scapes differ so much, not just in their vegetation but in the complex patterns of fields, villages, woods and boundaries? Many people will tell you that this magical mosaic, the envy of half the world, was 'made' by farmers, meaning it was laid out since, say, 1800 or thereabouts to suit modern farming. This attitude is often used to justify the destruction of some ancient feature, such as an old wood or trackway or some other obstacle to 'progress'.

Of course, farming has been one of the greatest agents of landscape change, and there are, indeed, some areas of planned countryside. It is also perfectly true that there is very little truly natural vegetation left in the lowlands, where man continually upsets nature's applecart by ploughing, draining or clearing land. Nevertheless, much of our countryside is vastly older and much less planned than most of us realise, an ancient and complex amalgam of human and natural factors.

Farming never eliminates nature; any let-up with the ditch-clearing, herbiciding or cultivation is instantly ex-ploited by re-colonising plants and animals. Indeed, one group of plants is completely dependent on farming (two groups if you count cultivated cereals) and that is the 'weeds' or 'ruderals', the pioneers adapted to a short life-cycle in disturbed ground. They include corn marigold, fluellen, cornflower, heart's-ease and the beautiful corn cockle; all can survive long dormancy and rapidly bloom after a soil upheaval in forty or fifty years' time.

An abandoned field soon starts the long tumble-down to scrub and woodland. Grazing stock will turn fallow land to grassland, rich in prostrate plants which hug the ground and escape nibbling animals. Grasslands, hedges and woods all collect new species as time goes on. Iron age chalk-grasslands are thought to be richer in species than fourteenth-century sites. A Tudor hedge has more shrubs and flowers than a nineteenth-century hedge; a Saxon boundary hedge is richer still.

So time is always on nature's side, and though the ancient vegetation of the uncultivated parts of the country-side is not wholly natural, it is certainly not man-made. We call this vegetation *semi-natural*, and it is the main subject of the following chapters. Any lowland parish is likely to contain hedgerows or boundary walls with their 'edge' habitats, permanent pasture or meadow; commons, greens, heaths or moors, ancient woodland, streams and bank habitats, ponds or meres, or coastal habitats, and it is here that semi-natural vegetation can be found. The origins of all these features lie deep in history; they are not just the result of two hundred years of farming, but they *are* vulnerable to future farming techniques (see Chapter 8).

The harder we look at the countryside, the more com-plicated, and the older, it seems to become. When we look closely we can see, by a subtlety of hedge alignment here, a species or two of the woodland flora there, or elsewhere a scatter of medieval or Roman pottery in the plough soil, how ancient much of the countryside really is. In fact in at least half of England, and parts of Wales and Scotland, there are very few features *younger* than 150–200 years; and an abundance of features 1,000 years old or more. A wood-land 300 years old only just counts as 'old' at all! Even in the 'planned' countryside of the Midlands, a deeper look will soon show Saxon, Roman, Iron-Age or medieval features almost everywhere beneath the grid-like pattern of ruler-straight hedges planted in the nineteenth century.

The patterns in the countryside have a historical sig-nificance and a richness in wildlife which we could never hope to re-create. To begin to understand where these natural and man-made treasures can be found, we must go back 8,000 years or so, to the earliest days of farming in Britain.

PREHISTORIC FARMING PATTERNS

Stone-Age people had roamed Britain long before the last ice age brought arctic gales howling across the barren wastes. It is just possible that a few managed to eke out a miserable existence in the tundra right through the ice age itself, but these people left few traces and we will probably never know for sure.

As the climate improved, and plants and animals spread north, man too began to exploit the landscape. The early settlers were nomadic fishermen and hunters, who gath-ered berries and roots in a land where great forests of pine and birch were slowly being replaced by more mixed woodlands. Their stone axes have often been dredged up from their camp sites, once perched between the sea and the forest but long ago drowned by the rising waters of the channel.

From about 8,000 years ago, in the Mesolithic or Middle Stone Age period, there is some evidence that Mesolithic men were already beginning to have a recognisable effect on the expanding primeval forest. Careful analysis of pollen from places where peat was being laid down on Dartmoor, the southern Pennines and the north Yorkshire moors shows that people were attacking the forest with their

Corn marigolds are typical cornfield weeds, requiring regular soil disturbance. Prehistoric farms would have abounded in such weeds; today they are destroyed by herbicides, but occasionally, as here, they explode from the earth when an old pasture is ploughed to make arable. There is a wheat crop in there somewhere!

chipped stone axes, making clearings not where we might have expected, at the lowland edge, but at the treeline in the uplands.

The remains of so many Mesolithic camps have been found along the ancient treeline (which was higher then than it is now) that the evidence strongly suggests the clearance was more than a casual activity; its purpose may have been to create grassy glades, where grazing deer could be killed more easily. The trees may have been ring-barked, left to die and then felled and burned, an easier task than burning them standing; as Rackham says, our native broadleaved woods burn 'like wet asbestos'!

An abundance of hazel pollen shows the hazel re-grew from the hacked stumps, just as it still does in countless coppices today (p. 85). It would have given the deer a leafy treat and provided a feast of nuts for the humans; important in an age before cereal cultivation.

Bodmin Moor, Cornwall. Monuments of the late Neolithic and early Bronze Age are common in Cornwall – Bodmin alone has nine stone circles, including The Hurlers, shown here. Despite fragmentary attempts at farming in medieval times, most of this acid grassland and moorland has not been cultivated since the Bronze Age, although some places such as Rough Tor (National Trust) were recolonised in the Iron Age and again in the Middle Ages.

This evidence strongly suggests that in these places the Mesolithic way of life involved *transhumance*, a seasonal migration from the coastal plain in winter, up into the high clearances in summer, a pattern which you can still see in Switzerland and Norway today. Individually, the clearings were small, but altogether over 2,000 years they had a considerable effect; after the fires the soluble plant nutrients were washed down the slopes and away by the streams, the brown forest soil structure was destroyed, and the water-logged, infertile remains began to develop peat and turn into blanket bog. In southern England, where rainfall is lower, the result of this leaching in places with sandy soils was the development of heathlands in the New Forest, Surrey and Dorset. Certainly, the heathland at Iping Common, West Sussex, is thought to date from those far-off days.

Around 6,000 years ago, a fundamental change from hunting or gathering food to growing it began to affect the landscape of Britain. This culture change signals the beginning of the Neolithic, or 'New Stone Age', a period marked by the earliest pottery known in Britain, flint arrowheads and new kinds of stone axe. The pottery is of special interest, because some sherds (fragments of pottery) show clear impressions of cereal seeds, picked up when the clay was still plastic. Soon the people of Britain were keeping domesticated cattle and sheep, and cultivating several cereals, including emmer and einkhorn wheat,

hulled barley and naked six-row barley. Storage pits and saddle querns for grinding are also known from this time.

The Neolithic culture has been studied in some detail in the Wessex chalklands and the uplands of the north-west, and we have a good picture of a still semi-nomadic people, moving about England, clearing woodland to make temporary villages and fields, such as those at Storr's Moss, Lancashire. When the soil was exhausted, the plots were abandoned and new clearances made. Some of the derelict fields were taken over again by woodland, but where there was a high density of grazing animals the woods could not regenerate, and the sites were gradually colonised by plants of grasslands which were able to withstand the grazing. In this way the landscape became much more open. By about 5,500 years ago the pollen record across much of north Europe shows a dramatic decline in the pollen of elms, caused either by feeding elm leaves to domesticated cattle, or else by the clearance of elms, which tend to grow on fertile sites, for farming. Within a few hundred years the pollen of other forest trees, oak, lime and ash for example, also began to decline, and we believe this shows the development of more organised farming on a wide scale. Archaeologists have found that in the same period there was an increase in charcoal in soil samples, suggesting tree clearance, and the species of land snails changed towards those favouring open habitats today. Even stronger evidence comes from the growing abundance of pollen from cereals, and from farmland weeds like ribwort plantain. We know very little about where these new farming ideas came from but they spread rapidly and within a thousand years or so large parts of Britain, from the channel to the Shetlands, had been cleared for farmland and pasture.

The Neolithic people left permanent reminders of their presence 4–5,000 years ago in the great 'causewayed camps' like Knapp Hill atop the chalk scarp towering over the Vale of Pewsey; these were concentrically-ringed earthworks, pierced by many entrances and almost certainly ceremonial or social centres. Other monuments such as the 'henges' (the word is related to 'haya', 'haga' or 'hedge') like Avebury Circle in Wiltshire, Arbour Low in the Peak District, or Mayburgh near Penrith, and the many long barrows, hint at a much more settled way of life.

Most fascinating of all for the landscape historian is the earliest evidence of ploughing: a pattern of criss-cross scratches in the ancient soil surface buried when the South Street Long Barrow of Avebury was constructed, and dated by radio-carbon means at around 3000 BC. Marks such as these, made by a primitive hand-dragged plough called an 'ard', are known from later Bronze-Age and even Roman sites, such as Walker in Northumberland, and Fritham in Hampshire, so this kind of plough must have continued in use long after better technology was available.

Whatever the pattern of life in Wiltshire, further north in Cumbria pollen deposits at Barfield Tarn and Great Langdale reveal that there the old nomadic ways lingered, in a seasonal migration from coastal crop-growing areas to the upland summer pastures, cleared from the upper fringes of the great Lakeland forest up to around 2000 BC.

PREHISTORIC FIELDS

So far we have gained a few fragmentary and indirect glimpses of prehistoric farming; subtle changes in the pollen rain trapped in peat bogs, some charcoal and a few seeds or snail shells. What about some actual fields? Most of the earliest English ancient fields are poorly preserved, as they have been re-ploughed many times over the centuries. Intact Stone-Age fields are rare indeed; there are a few later Neolithic field boundaries, but England has nothing to

A great network of tiny prehistoric fields in the upland limestone around Grassington shows that 3,000 years ago or more, when the climate was warmer, arable farming flourished here. At the top, the straight-walled nineteenth-century fields follow the lines of twelfth-century strip lynchets; here the intensive medieval ploughing has destroyed the prehistoric fields.

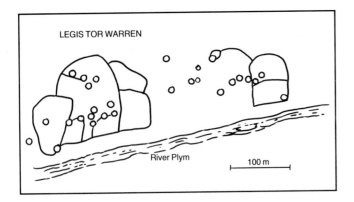

Groups of tiny enclosures are known on Dartmoor and elsewhere. They could be primitive fields, but more probably are stock pens built close to the summer huts used by Bronze-Age transhumance graziers. The National Trust protects several thousand acres of southwest Dartmoor, containing hundreds of these ancient enclosures, almost all of which can be seen plotted on the 'Outdoor Leisure' Map 28.

Ancient fields at Amalveor and Embla, in Towednack parish, Cornwall. The broad, curved boundaries are the outfields, pushed out from the farms as great cattle enclosures, leaving narrow lanes and funnels of unenclosed land – along which the parish boundary runs. Within these Bronze-Age outfields, smaller fields were later walled off near the farmsteads and managed as infield.

compare with the complete set of Neolithic stone-walled fields found buried in a County Mayo peat bog.

Even so, spreads of prehistoric fields can still be traced on the shallower slopes of Dartmoor, the chalk of Wiltshire, Dorset and north-west Hampshire, and the limestone soils of Oxfordshire, Derbyshire and Yorkshire. Fine examples abound north of Dorchester in a belt from Maiden Newton across the Cerne Valley to Milton Abbas, and in Yorkshire in the Grassington and Malham areas. These ancient fields, the earliest surviving physical farmscapes, have two particularly obvious features. They are rather small, and were probably cultivated by hand, with the ard, and they are more or less rectangular. Archaeologists have discovered that many were first marked out by ditches or piles of stones; a few on Dartmoor had upright stone slabs. Centuries of ploughing and stone-clearance dragged soil and rocks to the field-edges, forming huge boundary banks. On steep slopes the continual ploughing gradually undercut the bank of the upper field edge and loosened soil crept downhill to build up the lower edge, forming a series of terraces bounded by 'lynchet' banks. Lynchets occur at the lateral edges too, though it is less clear how this happened.

These small square lynchet-banked fields have survived

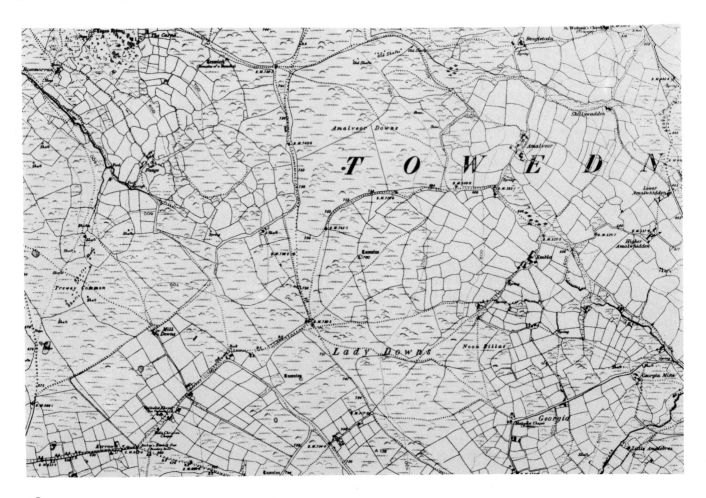

best on the steep chalk and limestone slopes because the light cohesive soils easily formed banks, but these sites soon lost their natural fertility and were abandoned to sheep grazing, creating the springy, scented flower-rich turf of the chalk and limestone grasslands, which still covers the bones of the old fields today, as the steep slopes have never again been ploughed up since those far-off days.

We cannot be sure whether these were really the first true fields; in Yorkshire, on Dartmoor and at Garrow Tor in Cornwall there are quite different fields, small, roughly circular plots, bounded by stone walls and often dotted with the clearance cairns of stones carried off the field surface. These could be older, or they could just be a localised type, a response to the stony environment.

In other parts of England, these ancestral fields have disappeared, perhaps ploughed out by later farmers, but even here the penetrating eye of the aerial camera may reveal traces of vast systems of fields laid out by prehistoric farmers between three and five thousand years ago. They can show up either as *shadows* when the sun is low, revealing low banks or depressions in present-day grassland; or as *parchmarks* in drought-stressed grasslands. Old banks or walls under ploughland can betray their existence through *cropmarks* in cereal or root crops. Cereal stem height-growth depends a great deal on the available soil moisture; underground walls inhibit stem growth, whilst buried ditches with a deep rich soil actually increase stem height. From the air, oblique sunlight shows up the height differences as a remarkably clear impression of the long-buried features.

Iron-Age fields on the Dorset chalk, at Smacam Down near Cerne. These fields are planned, rectangular and bounded by steep lynchet banks formed by soil creep and built up by stone clearance. On the nearer slope there is an ash/hazel coppice, which may also have existed in the Iron Age. (Compare this 1986 photograph with that on page 64 of Taylor's Fields in the English Landscape – *notice the destruction of a wood in the valley bottom and on the far slopes. It is in ways like this that our countryside heritage is gradually eroded.)*

One surprising discovery from air-photo work is that many ancient fields were not formed piecemeal, but were planned out in great tracts of hundreds of hectares, systematically subdivided. By the very nature of farming and ploughing, prehistoric fields are often difficult to date. We do know that these rectangular patchworks were made over a long time, as a number of excavated lynchets have yielded datable artefacts, like the Bronze-Age hoards from Lulworth in Dorset, or Amalveor in West Cornwall. A Bronze-Age burial was placed in an even older field corner at Winterbourne Abbas in Dorset, and at Ogbourne Maizey in Wiltshire a settlement dated to 1200 BC clearly overlies an earlier lynchet.

Many prehistoric fields went in and out of cultivation; at Fyfield Down in Wiltshire a field ploughed in the Bronze Age was in pasture for 300 years between 200 BC and AD 100. Pasture was widespread, and the countryside became more open as great sheep and cattle ranches were created, for example round Quarley and Sidbury in Hampshire, where continuous banks several miles long parcel up the chalk-

Cropmarks in arable, Willington, Bedfordshire. Air photographs can provide an enormous amount of information, without excavation, of features invisible or uninterpretable at ground level. The photograph was taken in the dry summer of 1976, and the dark thin lines are buried ditches, irregular enclosures of prehistoric date (right centre), and probably recent field drains.

Bronze-Age 'reave' field systems are common on Dartmoor; this one is on Mountsland Common in Ilsington parish. Notice how on one axis the reaves run parallel for long distances, but on the other the divisions are irregular. These fields were probably abandoned during the early Iron Age, and reverted to moorland under a grazing regime of some kind.

lands into huge blocks. Prehistoric cattle ranches occur at Martin Down in Hampshire, where a great Bronze-Age track curves diagonally across disused earlier fields, and at Amalveor where a whole series of Bronze-Age curved banks enclose what must have been cattle farms, and can still be seen intact today. Later fields either subdivide these ranches, or use the Bronze-Age walls and tracks as their edges.

By the middle Bronze Age, around 1500 BC, most field systems are definitely related to recognisable hamlets or farmsteads, seen in air photos as clusters of small irregular paddocks within the rectilinear field systems. In these inner paddocks, cattle, sheep and pigs were kept, as at Shearplace Hill, near Cerne Abbas in Dorset. One of the fullest studies of Bronze-Age farming has been going on at Shaugh Moor, on the southern edge of Dartmoor near the Lee Moor china clay works. Here, stone and timber houses form the focus of an enclosed settlement, probably based on stock farming. In fact much of Dartmoor is parcelled into cattle ranches by ancient stone walls called 'reaves'. Archaeologists studying Saddlesborough Reave have even turned up the hoofmarks

of Bronze-Age cattle nearby! The scant evidence of cereals or occupation debris suggest that these moorland sites may have been summer cattle pastures, and the people would have migrated to the lower settlement in the winter. These ancient pastoralists were also expert miners, however, extracting the ores of tin and copper from the rich mineral veins outcropping in the pasture. In Cornwall, on Bodmin Moor, a great enclosure containing hut circles surrounds the weathered granite of the Cheesewring, looking out over Rillaton Barrow and the mysterious old stone circle of the Hurlers, to the great tin-dyke. Similar hut circles occur at Rough Tor, and in fact the moors abound in Bronze-Age and Iron-Age relics, most of which do not need discovering as they are marked on the 1:25,000 'Outdoor Leisure' and 'Pathfinder' Ordnance maps!

Clearly, the landscape of many parts of Britain in prehistoric times was already a farmscape of arable fields and pastures; abandoned farmland on infertile soils like the Eocene sands of the Thames and Hampshire Basins, or the Triassic sandstones of the West Midlands, had already begun to yield to the advancing heathlands, which survive today in the New Forest, Purbeck, the Surrey heaths, or Sutton Park. Agriculture had already devastated much of the uplands too. Soil exposure by woodland clearance and farming led to the gradual stripping of slopes and uplands of their rich topsoils; a process of downwash which left thin mineral soils, leached of nutrients, on the slopes, and deep deposits of fertile clay *colluvium* at the foot of slopes and in valleys. Soon the uplands were colonised by peat-forming mosses and heather, and their blanket bog spread inexorably down the slopes into the former forest zone.

On the heavier soils or other places where farming was difficult the landscape was still quite well wooded, especially in deep valleys or the clays of the Weald, the Midlands and East Anglia. Even in farming areas, some woodland was kept and was being managed by coppicing, cutting poles regrown on previously cut stumps – many of the poles themselves have actually been preserved in Bronze-Age trackways later buried under the advancing peat in the Somerset levels. Nevertheless, we actually know much less about the clayland farmscape than about the chalky or acid light soil areas where most prehistoric remains are found. If there were fields in these areas, they have not generally survived Roman or Iron-Age farming intensification.

Towards the end of the Bronze Age, about 1000 BC, the climate began to worsen, and by around 750 BC the mean annual temperature had dropped by 2°C. This may not sound dramatic, but it is more than the difference today between the annual mean of 10.6°C (51°F) in Southampton, and the mean of 9.1°C (48°F) in Keswick, 300 miles (480 km) to the north and with almost double the rainfall. The really significant effect is in the shortening of the crop-growing season: in Southampton it is about 190 days per year, but in Keswick it is less than 155 days, a growing season more than *five weeks shorter*. Such a contraction in the farming season would have devastated prehistoric agriculture, and fields high on Dartmoor, which had been arable at intervals for thousands of years, were abandoned, and attention turned towards the heavier, more fertile and still forested lower slopes.

To make matters worse, population was increasing, and the resulting pressure on the deteriorating stock of farmland is revealed by the appearance of multiple-ditched enclosure settlements, defensible places characteristic of the period around 1000 BC–600 BC.

IRON-AGE FARMSCAPES

By about 400 BC, a pattern of stable territories, based on the spectacular hill-forts, had emerged across southern Britain from Sussex to the Welsh borders. These were the work of

Hill-forts were a feature of the Iron Age, defensible enclosures rather than settlements. This one is Hod Hill, in Dorset, bought by the National Trust in 1984, and well known for its ancient flower-rich chalk grassland turf, which contrasts dramatically with the surrounding arable fields.

the Iron-Age people, and can be seen both on hilltops and coastal promontories like Hengistbury Head in Dorset, and Rumps Point, St Minver, in Cornwall.

In the chalklands, the coming of the iron culture probably made little difference to what was already an intensively-farmed landscape, with farmsteads spaced evenly about a mile apart. Often they were perched on gentle valley-side spurs, close to the springline, yet within easy reach both of the wide open downland pastures above, where flocks of sheep grazed, and of the security of the hillfort. Around the farmsteads stretched the great patchworks of squarish arable fields. Even where their lynchet banks have since been destroyed enough can be seen as soilmarks from the air to show that in many places the Iron-Age farmscape covered the land completely: a carefully-tended and (as Peter Reynolds and his team at the Butser Ancient Farm in Hampshire have shown) an extraordinarily efficient food-producing machine. Below the farmsteads, on the valley sides, lay the steep 'hanger' woods of ash, hazel and wych elm; carefully managed, for each settlement

Iron-Age fields near the coast of Cornwall at Zennor, Land's End peninsula. The irregular stone-walled boundaries are characteristic. The old fields extend well beyond the present farmland, onto the rough clifftop grazing. Many of these farms were abandoned until re-used in medieval times, when land was very scarce. Much of this area, known as West Penwith, has been protected from further agricultural improvement by being notified by the Ministry of Agriculture as an Environmentally Sensitive Area, one of twelve where conservation grants can be given.

would have needed about twenty acres of coppiced woods. On the valley floor the deep loess (i.e. wind-blown material) soils derived from downwash were also used for cereals, and probably for hay to feed the stock in winter.

In the far west of Cornwall other patterns emerge. At Zennor can still be seen extensive spreads of tiny irregular fields bounded by stone hedges built on bases of huge boulders cleared from the fields; at Castallack there is an Iron-Age cattle ranch; and a special feature of Cornwall are the numerous 'rounds', walled enclosures of an acre or so for defence by family groups.

The use of iron-tipped clearance ploughs allowed many of the heavy soils of the Midlands to come under the plough for the first time, but though settlements are numerous their field systems have not survived later farming.

In Scotland, Iron-Age culture did not arrive until around 200 BC, and forts were built on coastal promontories in Strathmore and Fife. Later, hill-forts can be traced in the Ochill Hills and the foothills east of the highland line. In the Highlands themselves the culture was still predominantly Neolithic, though there was a Bronze culture in occupation on the east coast from about 1600 BC.

Later, lake-dwellings or 'crannogs' were built in south and east Scotland, and we now think these artificial islands were designed not just for defence but to avoid building on what little good farmland there was.

The Iron Age was a remarkable period when agriculture

BUTSER ANCIENT FARM

High on a flank of the great chalk rampart of Butser Hill, rising to 900 ft (275 m) above South Hampshire, a unique experiment in prehistoric farming has been going on since 1972. The Butser Ancient Farm Research Project aims not so much to re-create the Iron-Age life-style, but to test archaeological theories about the techniques which Iron-Age farmers might have used. The results so far have confirmed some theories and shattered others, and cast new light on the chalkland landscape of the times.

The site was carefully chosen, in an area with Iron-Age remains but no signs of ancient ploughing. The 4 inches (10 cm) of soil over bare chalk were covered in chalk grassland, full of wild flowers, an indication that chemicals which might upset the experiments were probably absent.

Five small fields were laid out, and carefully ploughed using a replica 'crook-ard' (a primitive plough modelled on an illustration from Donnerupland in Denmark). The interesting result was a very good tilth for sowing, but no sign of the criss-cross ploughmarks found for example beneath the South Street Long Barrow at Avebury. Further research showed that such marks were much more likely to have come from a different sort of plough, an iron-tipped 'rip-ard' designed to dig in and break up fallow or uncleared land for farming. In fact similar implements are still used in a remote part of northern Spain, even today, and are thought likely to produce the kind of interrupted deep grooves seen on the Avebury subsoil.

Another experiment showed that the crook-ard made superficial furrows in the loose soil, and that seed losses were very low if individual spikelets were sown in the grooves and then covered with soil by a hand-drawn blade. The resulting crop-rows were easy to weed with a mattock-hoe, and suggest that Iron-Age farmers would not have broadcast seed, since most would be eaten by birds.

Iron-Age farmers grew a wide range of cereals and other crops, including wheats (emmer wheat, *Triticum dicoccum*, spelt, *T. spelta*, club wheat, *T. compactum*, and old bread wheat, *T. aestivum*), barleys (two-row, *Hordeum distichum*, and six-row, *H. hexastichum*), flax, rye, oats and beans, and perhaps fat-hen, which we now think of as a weed.

At Butser, the yields obtained from these varieties have been astonishingly high. Sowing individual spikelets as described, very little seed is used, about 56 lb to the acre, or about half the most cautious modern drill rate. Measured per acre yields are quite low, and very much at the mercy of the weather. Measured as seed harvested compared to seed sown, however, they are amazingly good: even the lowest rate, 7 : 1 in a disastrous year, was much better than typical seventeenth- or eighteenth-century yields, which ranged (in documentary reports) to as low as 2 : 1. The best yields were simply extraordinary: emmer wheat produced 59 : 1 and spelt 40 seeds per seed sown in their best years; and this on thin chalk soil with no added fertiliser!

Of course, without modern chemicals, weeding two or three times was essential, and even then the crop before harvest was nothing like our familiar golden-brown monotones, but a riot of yellow charlock, purple thistles and scarlet poppies. Others too, like the beautiful blue of cornflower, the golden yellow corn marigolds, magenta corncockle, and ground-hugging pansies and fluellen, could be seen. Nowadays these are so rare that they were specially grown at Butser to give a realistic Iron-Age competitive environment for the cereals!

Experiments suggest that cereal heads and the valuable straw were harvested separately. The Iron-Age farmers seem to have many lessons for us today: their yields were high, nothing was wasted, no chemicals were needed, and the varieties of wheat they used seem to have been highly resistant to fungal rusts and mildews.

The Butser experiments suggest that the Iron-Age chalkland farmscape was intensively managed, and land was at a premium. It would be surprising if the chalklands alone were farmed; even then they may have been marginal land. This would mean there must have been Iron-Age fields in the clay vales, now destroyed. Coppiced woods must have been kept going as well, however; wood was the main construction material, and a great deal would have been needed.

The experimental 'Iron-Age Farm' at Butser, near Petersfield, Hampshire. In the distance runs the great wooded chalk scarp marking the western edge of the Weald. The farm itself has a few small experimental fields, confined by the old woods of yew and whitebeam on the flanks of the chalk buttress on which it lies.

An Iron-Age landscape survives at Egbury, on the north Hampshire chalk, where the 1870 6-inch map shows a pattern of regular squarish fields, confined by thick hedges. In the field, these hedges (which mainly exist today) are found to overlie the lynchets of the Iron-Age farmscape.

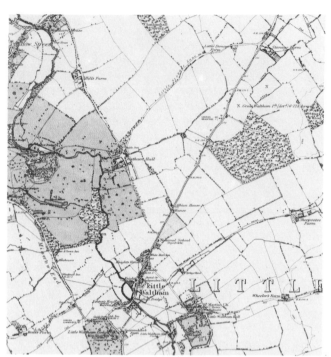

Roman fields are extremely hard to find, but at Little Waltham, Essex, a surviving Roman road clearly cuts across a pattern of earlier fields which may well date from early in the Romano-British period. The road also separates the Saxon settlements of Great and Little Waltham.

became very intensive and most of the easier soils in Britain were probably open farmland. Its potential for growing food, which is still being explored at Butser (see p. 43) is still only beginning to emerge, yet this may have been the main reason why the Romans finally decided, in AD 43, to annex Britain to their empire.

THE ROMAN COUNTRYSIDE

The Romans brought a military organisation, and the potential of a vast export market for cereals and wool, to British agriculture. No doubt the British peasants still toiled in the fields; though perhaps their elders adopted the fashionable Roman ways, and moved into the towns or built outlying villas. One technological change, though, was important. The Romans imported a wider range of iron tools and especially the heavy plough, with its vertical knife or *coulter* to cut the sod, followed by the *share*, to cut beneath it, and the *mouldboard* to turn it over. Now a field could be ploughed in one go, rather than using the old Iron-

Age rip-ard for site clearance, followed by the ard to make a seed groove. Agriculture expanded even further onto the clays, and there is scarcely a single part of England which does not abound with Roman settlements (Cornwall is an exception). The visible relics of actual Roman fields are, as usual, mainly found on light soils, those on the clays having long since been lost to later ploughing, especially in the Midlands where the open-field system developed in Saxon times. There is some evidence that Iron-Age square fields were ploughed together, forming long rectangular fields, about four or five times as long as wide. In most pre-existing farms, however, the Romans were probably happy not to interfere, whilst some examples of small irregular paddocks round Roman villas are known.

The most distinctive new farmscapes of Roman times are in eastern England. In south Essex, Drury and Rodwell have found an area of squarish fields which was clearly planned on a massive scale; yet many of its field boundaries are cut across by Roman roads, so this pattern must date from at least 1,900 years ago.

There is a similar pattern at Holme-next-the-Sea, Norfolk, where the fields, laid out in blocks of around 200 acres

(80 hectares), are bounded by Roman roads, an Iron-Age track, and the saltmarsh of the Wash. Parish boundaries follow several of these old features – a sure sign of great antiquity. It was during the Iron-Age and Roman periods that the silt-rich floor of the Wash was emerging from the sea, and naturally the land-hungry farmers of the time were not slow to enclose the washlands with sea-banks and reclaim them for farming. In Lincolnshire, Norfolk and north-east Cambridgeshire whole patterns of Roman fields, with their settlements and trackways, can be seen from the air, though there is little evidence here of planning; merely great spreads of irregular fields now almost lost to later ploughing.

At its height, the Romano-British period was one of great prosperity and stability in the south, though firm control was never established over much of Scotland. In England the countryside was thickly dotted with well-to-do villas and farms, bound together by a sophisticated transport and administrative network. In Lincolnshire, much research has been devoted to the Car Dyke, a system of Roman drainage canals lying roughly along the Iron-Age coastline, betrayed by the many Iron-Age saltworks. Four miles (6.5 km) to the east lies a second ditch, the 'Midfendic', marked by younger, Roman, saltworks; and it looks as though the silt fens between the two drains, including the well-known Roman site at Hacconby, were won from the sea in about the second century AD.

Despite intensive farming, many forests and wetlands still remained uncleared and undrained. Much of the woodland was managed as coppice, and the wetlands were exploited for reed, sedge and peat. Nevertheless, in the absence of herbicides or mineral fertilisers, the whole Romano-British countryside with its forests, fens and ancient grasslands would have been unimaginably richer in flowers, insects, birds and mammals than anything we have left in the lowlands today.

THE DARK AGE COUNTRYSIDE

The social upheavals in Europe which threatened the over-extended Roman Empire led to the recall of the legions in AD 410, the year in which Rome itself was over-run. In Britain, however, the rot had set in long before; there were rebellions in 268 and 383, and devastating raids by the marauding alliance of Picts, Scots, Franks and Saxons.

Saxon mercenaries, originally invited by Vortigern to defend England, began to come to Britain to settle for good. The Saxon colonisation was slow, convoluted and nowhere complete – military conquest of six million Britons by a few hundred Saxons was never a serious possibility. Instead, the mixed bands of Jutes, Saxons and Angles settled, from the fifth century on, amongst a demoralised British population, shattered not by war but by economic depression; the disease was chronic, rather than acute. The loss of the Roman export markets for wool, cereals and metals devastated the British economy. No longer did the endless pack trains plod down the Roman highways to the channel ports. Arable fields fell into disuse and scrub and woodland developed in a pattern which is still with us today; in parts of Hampshire, Dorset and Wiltshire perhaps a quarter or a third of all surviving ancient woods have their roots in these abandoned Roman fields and are still bounded by the great Iron-Age or Bronze-Age flint lynchets which preceded the Romans by 1,000 years or more.

Villas and farms were choked with dust and weeds, and the Roman cities fell into disrepair. Some, like Silchester, vanished completely, others including Chester, York and London declined but survived. Roman Watling Street through Northamptonshire remained in use, and formed a boundary for later Saxon estates and parishes. Akeman Street in west Oxfordshire shows a different history; some stretches disappeared under later farms, other short lengths were woven into the fabric of lanes linking the tiny Saxon hamlets.

The Britons called all the invading Germanic tribes Saxons (Scottish: *sassenach*) but they tended to call themselves Angles, and gave their name to 'Englaland'. Settlement was piecemeal, and political domination slow in coming. In fact it took the Saxons almost two centuries to reach the Severn estuary and the Mersey. Their relatives the Jutes never spread far from South Hampshire and the New Forest was known as 'Ytene' until long after the Norman conquest. The Chilterns, Cranborne Chase and the Cotswolds remained British strongholds until late in the sixth century, and Purbeck people still wrote in Latin and thought of themselves as Roman in the eighth century! Cornwall seems to have become another repository of the Roman way of life and was not finally absorbed until 924 under Athelstan.

Farther north, the countryside came under the influence of the Danes, who established a Norse overlordship over the Anglian kingdoms of Mercia and Northumbria from 965. The West Saxon King Alfred stabilised the frontier and stemmed the southward spread of Danish influence, but soon after the suppression of the Viking kingdom of York in 954 the newly-united kingdom of England again came under the sovereignty of King Swein and his son Cnut.

Thus there are several threads to the creation of the Dark-Age countryside; the decline of the British ideas, the Saxon tribal conflicts, and the spread of new ideas on farming and estate management; and through all these changes the peasants still toiled in the fields and tended their sheep and cattle.

In the early Dark Ages, population does seem to have

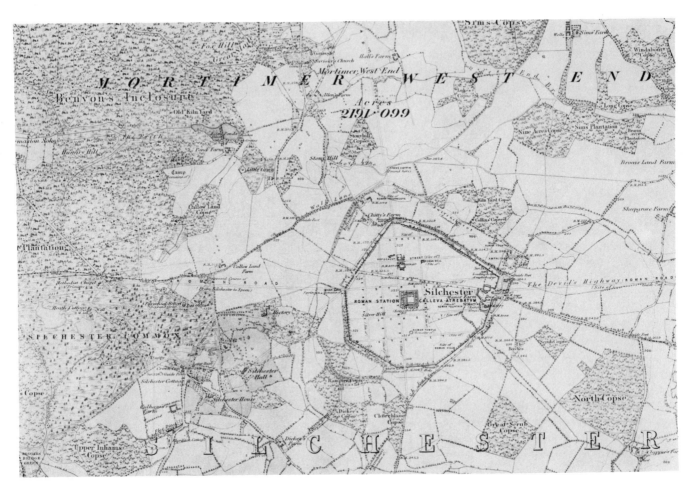

Silchester, near Reading. The remarkable Roman town, the slightly earlier north, south and west entrenchments and the great heathland of Silchester Common are all ancient landscape elements. After the Dark Ages, a different pattern emerged in Saxon and medieval times; the new network of lanes, tracks and Dark-Age woods ignores the lines of most of the Roman roads.

declined, probably due to plagues rather than the bloodshed and destruction we read about in history books; the bones of plague-carrying black rats have been found in late-Roman buildings. The loss of the Roman export cereal markets was complete; no Roman coins were minted or imported after 410 and there was little pressure on the land. Though the decline was slower in the north, the picture we form is of a return to mixed subsistence farming, and a reversion to woodland and scrub or pasture in the south-eastern 'granary' belt.

The early Saxon settlements were small groups of thatch and timber huts, forming tiny hamlets with a few fields adapted from the mosaic of Romano-British enclosures. There is more and more evidence that the Saxons re-used Roman sites; a fascinating study by Warwick Rodwell portrays Saxon settlers at Rivenhall in Essex, converting the old aisled barn of an abandoned villa into a new home; and similar stories emerge at Totternhoe in Bedfordshire, and Barton Court in Oxfordshire.

In some places the new hamlets took their name from a nearby Roman road, and were called Stretton or Stratton, the 'farmstead near the street' (Old English *straēt*). Stratton St Margaret, Swindon, Little Stretton and its deserted neighbour Stretton Magna, near Leicester, are examples.

Each of these early hamlets was probably occupied by an extended family group working the land together, representing a type of settlement common all over western Europe; in Germany it would be called a *drübbel*. Most English examples have been swept away by later land re-organisation, but a few survive in the uplands, in the Pennines, and on Dartmoor. They are particularly interesting places because they reveal much about early Saxon farming; not the often-repeated myths about invading Saxons sweeping aside ancient patterns and imposing their system of communal 'open-field' farming, but the reality of a scatter of dispersed farm settlements. Such farmsteads must have been very like the Welsh *trefs* set up as people

Land Copse, Ashmansworth, north Hampshire, is an ancient secondary oak/ash/hazel wood overlying a pattern of Iron-Age or Roman fields, bounded by lynchets. Besides defining these ancient Dark-Age secondary woods, lynchets underlie many of the ancient wood-relic hedges in the area, and are an important determinant of landscape pattern.

cleared the dense lowland forests. Though dispersed they were loosely organised into territories called a *cantref* – literally '100 trefydd'. In Cornwall, similar scattered farms were called *trevs*, and they can still be seen on the map, and more importantly on the ground, today. The earliest have names suggesting Iron-Age fortification links such as *Dinas*, *Castel* or *Caer*; later examples begin with *Lan* (an enclosure or wood clearing), *Ty-*, *Lis*, and then *Tre*, *Bos* or *Bod*.

It is these places which give us the best idea of early Saxon farm management. Clearly most people worked on the primitive *infield-outfield* system, with an intensively-cultivated, annually-cropped infield, where all the available manure was spread; and the outfield beyond, rougher ground usually grazed but parts of which were cultivated occasionally, then left to recover. At Hound Tor, high in the eastern flank of Dartmoor, a mid-Saxon settlement of four longhouses shows this system remarkably well. Each long-house sheltered humans and, at the lower end, stock, and each is accompanied by a corn dryer, a small cottage and a few paddocks. Around them, in the valley between Hound Tor and Hay Tor, lies the grassy once-cultivated infield, marked out with stone walls and banks and separated by ditches, still known today as 'corn-ditches', from the rough

granite-strewn outfield of the moor beyond. Hound Tor was abandoned in the fourteenth century, but an infield-outfield system was worked at Exford in Somerset until the late nineteenth century. At Ribblehead, 1,000 ft (300 m) above sea-level on windswept Ingleborough, a similar ninth-century farm huddles beneath a low limestone cliff. Some of its infield is still traceable, other parts have disappeared into the ankle-jolting clitter of rubble and solid clints jutting from the sheep-short limestone grassland; it is a remarkably evocative relic of this early form of farming.

This pattern also fits what we know of the *clachans* of the Scottish (and Welsh) moors, and even today many an isolated farm in Yorkshire or Cumbria still shows a well-fertilised green infield area, and a steep brackeny outfield

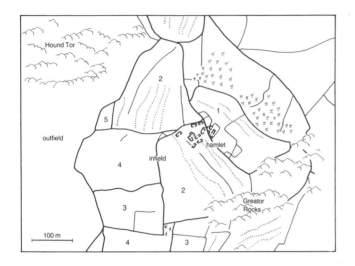

A plan of the medieval settlement at Hound Tor, Dartmoor. As the settlement grew, further fields with their ditched and banked boundaries were added. The farmstead was a group of long-houses each sheltering a family and its stock. Similar sites in National Trust ownership include Trowlesworthy Warren, Dartmoor, and Rough Tor on Bodmin Moor, at both of which there are medieval fields with ridge-and-furrow on top of Bronze-Age features.

Hound Tor, high on the east side of Dartmoor. The least rocky pasture is the infield of the medieval or Saxon farmstead, whose ruins can be made out just top left of the centre of the photograph. Farms like this were early recolonisations of the long-abandoned moorland, where the rough brackeny grazing still formed the outfield.

The old infield, Wasdale Head, Cumbria, still dotted with the clearance cairns, perhaps created by Norse settlers about 1,200 years ago. The fertile infield occupies the river floodplain; beyond on the hillsides lies the outfield. Infield and outfield are now divided into sheep pastures by irregular stone walls. The National Trust owns parts of Wasdale, including Wastwater itself, and has a major role in conserving such historic landscapes.

beyond – though both are now used for grazing. At one Yorkshire site, Wheldrake, June Sheppard has shown how a massive field-bank, the 'turf-dyke', still demarcates the ancient infield, and although parts of the old outfield were later taken into arable use, the turf-dyke survives scarcely interrupted, as a monument to an earlier style of farming. At Wasdale Head in the Lake District, the ancient infield is now dissected by medieval stone walls, but still dotted with cairns of stones cleared from the field by Norse settlers.

The pattern of Dark-Age settlement varies enormously across England, shaped by the form of the ground and the spread of Saxon or Danish political influences. Apart from the re-used Roman farms, the earliest settlements were on the easiest soils, though these were often poor. On the east Dorset heaths around Poole Harbour there are still remote farms with irregular old fields, bounded by thick hedges full of different trees and shrubs (see p. 160), almost certainly a Saxon fieldscape. Similar patterns can be seen in the New Forest and represent the first re-colonisation of light soils abandoned to heathland in the Bronze Age.

Place names can help plot the progress of the Saxon settlement, and the uses to which they put the land. Names with *ingas* in their earliest spellings are often settlements of early date – Eling, Wymering or Hayling, all in Hampshire, are examples; whilst the suffix *ey*, as in Northney, Pevensey or Witney, may show a location on an island, even if the surrounding fen or marsh has long gone. Three elements at least, *ley, hurst* and *field*, are usually held to show Saxon clearance of woodland to make a farm; they are concentrated in areas where there was still a great deal of woodland long into medieval times, such as Shropshire, Derbyshire, Worcestershire and Essex. In the north, the Anglians colonised the Yorkshire Dales and the eastern margin of Cumbria in the seventh century; their progress through the Aire Gap is charted by the *ing* and *ham* farm or settlement names: Whicham, Heversham, Beetham, Tatham and Bentham. The alternative *ton* appears in Skelton, and Dalston in Cumbria, both of which are still enclosed by their ancient fields, and in Skipton and Grassington. There are also *ley* names, demonstrating that the clearance of the lower dale slopes was still going on, especially on the Millstone Grit.

The Angles were not left to themselves for long, though, as by the late ninth century the Danes were also settling in the area; their settlements carry the endings *by* and *thorp*, as well as *thwaite*, their word for a meadow clearing in woodland. Often the Danes created a hamlet in close contact with an Anglian nucleus, and the names were combined in medieval times, as in Burnsall-with-thorp. Scandinavian settlers continued to spread into the Dales and Cumbria through the tenth century, and Old Norse or Old Danish may have been the common tongue as late as the Norman conquest. One of the most evocative features of north England is the abundance of names left by these old Norsemen, who penetrated to the heart of the dale (*dalr*) with its rushing beck (*bekkr*), and beyond to the open fells (*fjoll*), establishing their summer pastures or shielings, still recognisable by their *erg* names (as in Hesleden High Bergh), and spring pasture names ending in *sett* or *side*, as in Burtersett or Selside. Their pattern of upland grazing and valley-floor arable or hay meadow has endured for more than 1,000 years; and their isolated hamlets have also kept their distance from the more integrated Anglo-Danish villages on the lower valley floor.

ESTATES, BOUNDARIES AND CHARTERS

Farm and estate boundaries have long histories, partly because, once built, their banks were difficult to move, but also because parcels of land have been taken over intact at intervals by new owners. In the Dark Ages, while the peasants struggled to survive on the land, the land was being seized, lost or traded by the incoming Saxon or Danish overlords. Since much was seized from its previous British owners, many Saxon estate boundaries are identical with the boundaries of Romano-British estates. Though Saxon kings often retained the biggest or best estates, they all made enormous grants of land to endow the early monastic churches or minsters after their seventh-century conversion to Christianity. Later these created daughter churches, paid for by the lord of each smaller estate or hamlet.

Finberg has shown how in the Cotswolds the large medieval parish of Withington is actually an intact Roman estate granted in the seventh century to the Bishops of Worcester, in whose ownership it remained for almost 1,000 years! This continuity of boundaries is a fascinating aspect of the countryside and is often a great help when looking at the history of a piece of land. Ancient boundaries are often marked by great banks or ditches, and once built they were rarely moved, as they often separated not just owners but whole communities and even counties or 'hundreds'. Even in parts of England where field and farm patterns have changed more than once there are often a few of these ancient 'signposts' to the structure of the ancient landscape.

Some of the most useful boundaries are those recorded in the Saxon land charters drawn up to delineate ownerships of land more than 1,000 years ago. About 2,000 of these old documents either exist or were copied out before they crumbled away in medieval times. The early ones were brief affairs, but ninth- and tenth-century charters (from a time when the land was under more pressure) often give lengthy descriptions of boundaries, with references to barrows, streams, hedges, old trees of all kinds, and even the furrows between plough-lands.

Careful following-up of a charter is great detective work, but Hoskins warns it can take a year or two to deal satisfactorily with one charter. Even so it is fascinating to push through tangles of scrub or coppice along an ancient bank in pursuit of a boundary set out by some long-forgotten Saxon scribe. Charters can give much more information about the landscape than do place names, but they do not exist everywhere; there are just six for Rutland and eight for Leicestershire (none with bounds), but a great many in the West Midlands, particularly the remarkable collection of the see of Worcester. In Hampshire there are 180, of which more than 60 give boundaries, in the Codex Wintoniensis, whereas adjoining Dorset has very few as the cartularies (charter-books) of Milton and Abbotsbury have been lost. Luck is therefore important: it is much easier to trace boundaries based on streams or barrows than those relying on long vanished trees. Using the charter to discover the actual extent of an estate on the ground requires many field trips, alternating with consulting the 6-in map. Often clues lie in the way the ground drains, changes in level or ancient field names (often recorded in the Diocesan Registry).

These charters reveal a great deal about Saxon life. Not all estates were of equal status. Typically the richest were owned by the king, or an abbey church, they tended to lie on the best land and were often the earliest recorded, with a topographical name – 'river', 'hill' and so on. These head or 'caput' estates often had minster churches and later became the centres of the judicial 'hundreds' into which the 'shires' were divided between 800 and 900. Even the shires may have had territorial beginnings: Dorset and Wiltshire are thought to be small kingdoms of branches of the West Saxon dynasty.

Smaller estates can often be identified with medieval parishes or manors, and this helps to explain why even today parish boundaries often converge on some feature which had to be shared by several estates; a ridge-top woodland or an ancient pond like the mere called Ringmere, north of Thetford, in the waterless Breck heaths. No fewer than five parishes converge here, each having its share of the water and the common grazing. Quite different are the long thin parishes, running up from the chalk streams of Wessex onto the high downland, but the purpose was the same: to share out the haymeadow, arable, pasture and woodland fairly. In the Avon valley above Amesbury we can see how many early narrow estates, each with its tiny farmstead, were amalgamated into later 'strip' parishes. The beautiful 1870 6-in Ordnance maps show how parishes were allocated to the hundreds, and also how many parishes had detached portions. These too were the result of sharing out woodland, seasonal pasture or meadow, or a multiple-use area like a fen as in the Somerset levels or the East Anglian fens.

Parish boundaries are sometimes extremely old. A walk along the seventh-century Wansdyke, built to keep apart the sparring Mercian and Wessex kingdoms in the Vale of Pewsey, shows how the ancient bank strides across the chalklands, ignoring parishes altogether, yet leaving small parts of some parishes 'trapped' on the 'wrong' side. Surely this means the parishes were laid out long before the bank, or it would have been an obvious 'edge' to the parishes? In fact the parishes probably originated in Roman estates; Bishops Cannings parish does follow the Roman road for some way. This fossilisation of ancient boundaries and patterns of use helps us to interpret the history of ancient woods or grasslands even today. Although a few parishes were altered or combined in Victorian times, parish boundaries of great age are the rule rather than the exception in southern Britain at least.

OPEN FIELDS AND THE MEDIEVAL COUNTRYSIDE

The early Dark-Age countryside was peppered with small hamlets and farmsteads with their infield-outfield system, which worked very well as there was plenty of land for expansion when more arable was needed. Perhaps a third of England was still wooded with ancient forest and post-Roman woods.

By the eighth and ninth centuries, the population of England was rising again, and several deep-seated changes began to spread through the countryside. In the claylands, woodland began to be cleared from heavy soils which had never felt the bite of the plough, in the Weald for example. In chalk country the high-slope settlements of Romano-British times were gradually deserted, and new hamlets began to appear on the edges of the river valley flood plains. Perhaps this was because the population shifted from the exhausted thin slope soils to the deep valley loams, but a more pressing

The oldest boundaries in a landscape often stand out quite clearly. The thick hedge running from near right away towards the sea is the ancient parish boundary between Tyneham and Kimmeridge in Purbeck. Notice how other hedges butt up, but do not cross it; this is quite likely to be the boundary between two Iron-Age or Roman estates. Such ancient boundaries are often rich in wildlife.

reason could have been the continuing drop in the water table and the drying-up of hillside springs. Saxon documents show that the Hampshire Itchen rose in the tenth century some $5\frac{1}{2}$ miles (9 km) above its present-day source.

The settlement shift was remarkably complete; Barry Cunliffe's excavations at Chalton in Hampshire revealed a

LOOKING AT HEDGEROWS

Hedgerows and walls are ways of separating grazing animals from crops or each other, and have been used for this purpose for thousands of years; there is archaeological evidence for Roman hedges, and many of the thick boulder-filled Cornish hedgebanks were made, partly to clear the ground, as long ago as the Bronze Age.

Hedges tend to be taken for granted, but in fact they can tell you an enormous amount about the history of a tract of countryside. You need to bear in mind:

1) *Origin of hedges.* Many hedges were planted, at various times, but others grew up naturally where tree and shrub seeds fell on unploughed ground at lynchets or headlands. A third group are relict hedges, linear strips of woodland left when fields were cleared from forest.

2) *Character of the hedge.* Is it straight? Truly straight hedges, or walls, are invariably eighteenth- or nineteenth-century. Older hedges weave about, wind, turn corners or run in arcs.

How thick is it? Victorian hedges may be pathetic affairs only a foot or two thick, on a tiny steep bank: very old wood-relict hedges may be 20 or 40 ft (6–12 m) thick. Medieval or Tudor hedges lie somewhere in between.

Are there any trees? Hedgerow trees were an important source of timber and wood, and are abundant in medieval and Tudor hedges, usually surviving as coppice and pollards. Georgian hedges had regularly spaced oak or ash, but the fashion had declined by Victorian times.

Is it growing on a bank? Some wood-relict hedges still grow on the old wood-bank; others on broad ancient lynchets. Hedges at changes in ground level, at the edge of a flood-plain for example, are usually very old. Enclosure hedges often cut right across natural banks or slopes, or across ancient field-systems, and tend to be set in narrow steep-sided foundation banks. Banks occur where medieval or Saxon lanes have become sunk into the ground; hedges on these edges are very often ancient.

3) *Hedgerow composition and hedge-dating.* In 1974 Max Hooper suggested that ancient hedgerows were much richer in tree and shrub species than recent hedges. Hooper's rule of thumb is that a hedge acquires species at about one per century, so a Saxon hedge is likely to have eight to ten woody species per 30-yard length, a Tudor one five or six, whilst a Victorian hedge may have only its original hawthorn, or perhaps one or two others.

Hooper's rule is not an exact one: northern hedges will be poorer for their age because fewer species grow there; acid soils have fewer species than chalky ones, and so on. The rule will, however, distinguish a medieval hedge in a generally late enclosure landscape, and is helpful for tracing the progressive enclosure of a parish, with Saxon hedges near the village or along lanes, for example, medieval or Tudor ones enclosing former open-field, and Victorian hedges across open downland or heath.

The species you will most likely find and count are:

ash	hawthorn
aspen	lime
beech	maple
blackthorn	oak
buckthorn	roses (trailing
crab apple	or dog)
cherry	rowan
Cornish elm	spindle
dogwood	sycamore
English elm	sallow
East Anglian elms	privet
elder	woodland hawthorn
guelder rose	whitebeam
gorse	wayfaring tree
hazel	wych elm
holly	wild service tree
hornbeam	yew

Ivy and bramble are usually ignored.

Hedgerow species can be very indicative even on their own: lime, wild service and

A Dorset hedgerow. The deep bank along this lane suggests that the route is a deeply-sunken old trackway, though now metalled. In the bank grow red campion, bluebells and cow parsley; and the leaves of field maple, a tree often found coppiced in old boundaries, can be seen at the top.

midland hawthorn are invariably relics of long-vanished woods; maple and hazel, and in some areas spindle, are also slow to colonise and often show an ancient hedge.

4) *Hedgerow wild flowers.* Hedges which originate as woodland often still have a rich flora of bluebells, anemones, primroses, yellow archangel and dog's mercury. Victorian hedges usually have a very poor flora, but hedges of Georgian or Tudor age will have quite a few hedgerow specialists, such as Jack-by-the-hedge, hedge parsley, hogweed, arum, hedge woundwort, stitchwort or red campion. Hedges are 'edge-habitats' which give partial shade but plenty of light for flowering, so they are frequented by many insects, including particularly butterflies like the gatekeeper, orange tip and brimstone.

A great deal of concern is devoted to the loss of hedgerows for agricultural developments. The trend of the 1960s and 1970s to larger fields has now slowed down, and in most places the hedges lost tend to have been the youngest, hawthorn hedges of Victorian times; rather fewer of the ancient thick hedges which often skirt lanes and estate boundaries have gone, but there is no room for complacency.

USING OLD MAPS

For historical work on old woods, or heaths, downs and other old features, there are many old maps which will be useful.

1) *Early estate maps:* from about 1600 onwards. These are detailed, and usually accurate, but limited in coverage. Available in County Record Offices or estate archives.

2) *Proprietary County Maps:* Early small-scale ones, like Speed, are unhelpful, but from about 1750 more accurate 1-inch or ½-inch maps were made by Rocque, Milne, Chapman and André, Taylor and others. Useful, but many woods missed and boundaries not always clear. Record Offices or reprints by Harry Margary.

3) *Ordnance Survey 1-inch maps 1st edition:* wide coverage, surveyed around 1800, but small copses far from roads often omitted. If in doubt you can check details on the original field drawings (in British Museum or copies in Record Offices) at 2 or 3 inches to the mile.

These 1st edition 1-inch sheets are very good for distinguishing unenclosed forests, downs and commons from enclosed farmland. (They have also been used as the basis of the Nature Conservancy Council's desk Inventory of Ancient Woods [in preparation] which assumes that if a wood was old enough to be surveyed as woodland in 1800, it probably existed before 1700. This is not an infallible rule!)

Reprints of two editions of these are available: early sheets as originally published; from Harry Margary; and later printings, altered with railways etc, from rather worn plates, by David and Charles.

4) *Ordnance Survey 6-inch 1st edition,* surveyed between 1850 and 1890; these are without question the best topographical and administrative maps ever made in England, recording enclosure patterns, contours (on some sheets), hedgerows and their trees, and the fine detail of all the ancient parish and hundred boundaries – an indispensable link with the ancient countryside. In Record Offices.

5) *Tithe Surveys and Enclosure Award Maps:* various dates, 1780–1840, and various scales. The 'Award' lists owners and users of land.

6) *Ordnance Survey 6-inch 'County' series,* about 1908: useful for time-series work, and formed the basic survey for the pre-war 2½-inch maps. Still a helpful field guide.

7) *Scottish map series:* these are different. The beautiful semi-pictorial maps at about 2 miles to the inch by General Roy pre-date English Ordnance maps, about 1747–1755.

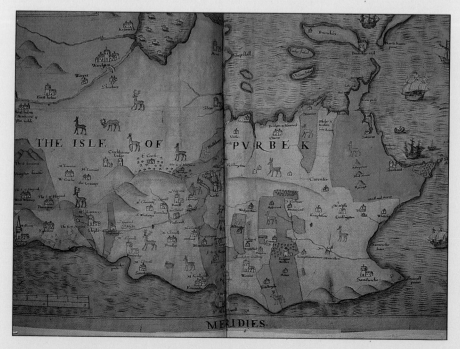

An old estate map by R. Tresswell, dating from 1585, showing the bounds of the Isle of Purbeck and the locations of the various manors, such as Studland, Langton Wallis and Povingdon, which made up the Corfe Castle Estate. The estate was owned by the Bankes family of Kingston Lacy from 1635 until 1982.

*Open-field farming still survives in a modified form at Laxton,
Nottinghamshire. The main area of unhedged fields, cultivated in strips, lies
beyond the village; notice too the long narrow 'tofts' behind the houses, and
the other hedged strips with their curved boundaries. All around can be seen
the squarish fields of parliamentary enclosure.*

whole Roman farmscape of villas, farms, fields and the trackways between them. Now it is almost all gone, obliterated by the late Saxon and medieval pattern focused on the valleys.

The most dramatic changes of all, however, overtook a vast area of countryside in central England and created the new landscape of villages or *townships*, with their wide-open, unhedged fields for which Saxon England is best known. The scattered hamlets were replaced by single 'nucleated' settlements where all the farms and cottages were grouped together, a change which was only possible because land tenure was re-organised at the same time.

Under the newly-created 'open-field' system, the countryside had few hedges or trees, except in the permanent 'closes' near the village or in the surviving woodland. The open fields were divided up into hundreds of strips. Each strip contained between two and five plough-ridges, the bones of which still form the 'ridge-and-furrow' corrugations of midland England. Many parallel strips, all about 220 yards or a 'furrow long', were parcelled up into large bundles known as 'furlongs'.

Each peasant holding consisted of about 40–80 individual strips dispersed throughout the township's furlongs, and totalled a *virgate* or *yardland* (*bovate* in northern England) of about 30–40 acres (12–16 hectares). In this way the good and bad soils were shared out between farmers. There was another reason for dispersal, however; farming in open fields had to be a communal affair, in which even the estate lord shared, because adjoining strips had to be managed similarly each year – corn and cattle make bad neighbours unless divided by a fence. Every year the village 'Court leet' met to decide which crops to plant in which furlongs, and to regulate the grazing on the stubble after harvest, the fallow land and the common uncultivated waste, if any. Initially, the rotation of crops may have followed a two-year cycle: one year cultivation, then one year grazed fallow. Later, more complex three or more

course rotations developed, and the well-known 'three-field' organisation of many groups of furlongs developed. The actual unit of rotation, though, was probably the furlong, these being ultimately temporarily (or even permanently) hedged when necessary.

Within each strip, the actual unit of cultivation was the plough-ridge or *land*, averaging about 7 yards across by 220 yards long. Ploughing one ridge, about one-third of an acre in extent, was a day's work for an ox-team, and the great curving ridges which were gradually built up over the centuries are a characteristic of the Midlands even today, and one of the easiest ways of spotting areas where open-field farming took place (see p. 54).

The open-field system came to dominate much of central England, especially the area of the Mercian kingdom, perhaps because of the great pressure on land created by the Danish invasion. Its ridges can still be seen all over Leicestershire, Northamptonshire, Oxfordshire, Warwickshire and Bedfordshire. It spread north through the Peak District, wherever valley floors were wide enough, to Lancashire and Northumberland and in a modified form to Scotland. It also spread south to Dorset, Wiltshire and even a small area of Cornwall. Nevertheless, wherever the lie of

Winter sun and a dusting of snow picks out the sinuous ridges of early medieval ridge-and-furrow at Tissington, Derbyshire. Notice the complex relationships of the walls and hedges to the boundaries of the 'furlongs', or bundles of plough-ridges. Early boundaries conform to furlong edges, later ones tend to ignore them. The ridges are preserved under permanent, sometimes ancient, pasture.

the land restricted re-organisation the old infield-outfield lingered; in the uplands of Cumbria, North Yorkshire, the narrower dales of the Peak District and on the thin chalk soils of Wessex.

There has been a lot of discussion over the age of ridge-and-furrow. Some furlongs are referred to in Saxon charters, in Warwickshire, for instance, and there is also physical evidence for example from ridge-and-furrow overlain by eleventh-century castle earthworks at Hen Domen in Glamorgan. It is certain that much of it was in existence by early medieval times; there is normally an exact correspondence between present-day ridge-patterns and the plans in medieval 'town-books' or 'field-books'.

The boundaries of some furlongs can also indicate dates

of origin. Many are clearly Saxon, for example David Hall shows how the open fields of Raunds and Ringstead in Northamptonshire contain an interruption in their pattern which suggests that a small area between them once had a separate open-field system, and research has revealed a small Saxon township, West Cotton and Mallows Cotton, deserted perhaps in the Black Death. Similarly the ancient Saxon lordship boundary of the lost manor of Silsworth can still be traced in the open-field furlong pattern of the present-day large parish of Watford in Northamptonshire (an area which even today has superb ridge-and-furrow in profusion).

Pressure on land was probably the spur to adoption of the open-field system. In Berkshire there is evidence in charters that in the eighth and ninth centuries large Saxon estates were being broken down into small units, some of which might well have found themselves without any woodland or common waste to graze. Overnight this would have created a need for communal control of grazing on fallow arable land, and thus the motive for the township to adopt open-field.

Open-field is a fascinating puzzle in our farming history; it has long since been swept away, except in a very few places. The classic survivor is Laxton in Nottinghamshire, which still retains its vast hedgeless three-field system, a mosaic of strips almost 1,000 years old still controlled by the Court leet. Open-field relics also remain at Soham, east of Cambridge, and at Braunton in North Devon where some strips were recently sold.

Open fields and nucleated villages did not occupy the English heartland overnight; they were just one idea pressed into service when local conditions suited. The system took hundreds of years to spread, and was operated in many different ways in different parishes. Kent and Surrey had blocks of strip fields in a generally enclosed landscape, in East Anglia there were scattered open fields, and on the Breck and other light soil areas the strips were not ridged up and may have been separated by grassy banks.

Although the system started in Saxon times, much of it reached its greatest development long after the Norman conquest. As population increased until the fourteenth century, more and more land was taken into the open fields either by communal forest clearance ('assarting') or from individual 'assarts' later divided into strips as a result of partible (divided between the members of the family) inheritance.

Where the open fields used up all the land very early on, the parish boundary often zig-zags around the edges of the ancient furlongs, as between Great Gransden and Caxton in Cambridgeshire, or Cranoe and Wells in Northamptonshire. In parishes like these, if the people needed more land, there was nothing for it but to make more arable by clearing

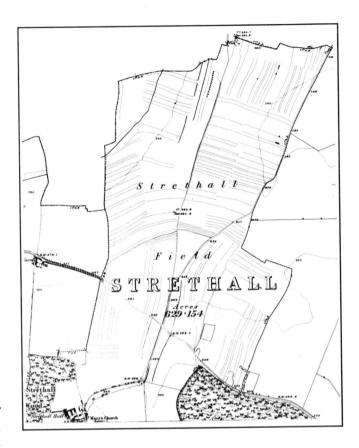

Occasionally, evidence of medieval or earlier open-fields survives even on nineteenth-century maps. The ancient field of Strethall, in north-west Essex, is still named on the 1870 6-inch map, which also shows something of the pattern of ridges and (by their changing direction) of the furlongs into which they were gathered.

part of a nearby forest. These detached exclaves were farmed either individually or in common. In due course, as parishes developed, they became *tithings* of their distant parent parishes and many remained attached to them for more than 1,000 years until the tidy-minded Victorians re-organised the parishes and concealed the evidence. Fortunately, the first edition of the 6-in Ordnance maps surveyed between about 1840 and 1870 was just in time to record them in all their fascinating detail, giving their area, parent parish and even hundred.

DOMESDAY AND THE NORMANS

The Normans retained much of the Saxon land organisation, including the *carucate* as a term for a ploughland, and even adapted the Domesday records to show Saxon hundreds.

Domesday, the great survey of English landholdings ordered by William I, gives a unique insight into the results of 600 years of Saxon land ownership and management, recording the tenancy and value of ploughlands, woodlands and meadows in all the lands held by the king, his secular lords and the bishops. Values are given for 1086 and for pre-conquest times – 'tempore Rex Edwardus', or 'T.R.E.' as the scribe abbreviated it.

Again, the Norman conquest was no catastrophe; there was an orderly transfer of power to the new regime and the boundaries of many landholdings were preserved intact. Parishes survived as the units of administration, and many of the church's vast estates were confirmed to it by the new rulers. The Norman word 'county' replaced Saxon 'shire', but their boundaries hardly changed and the Normans kept the administrative estates (which became 'manors'), ecclesiastical parishes and administrative 'hundreds'.

The pioneer landscape historian W. G. Hoskins has shown how to use Domesday as a guide-book to the Saxon countryside. In nucleated village areas, or in East Anglia with its strange polyfocal settlements, many uncertainties remain. Nevertheless, in places like Devon, with a pattern of dispersed farmsteads, we can often identify the boundaries of individual farms, and in this way put a date on all kinds of hedges, banks, old trackways and woods.

The first step is to find the most important farm of the parish or vill, the *demesne* farm of the lord of the manor. Often this will be the largest farm in the parish, on the best land, with a 'historic' name such as 'church', 'court', or 'great' farm. In Devon and parts of Cornwall the names 'Barton' or 'town' often give away the demesne status of a farm. Hoskins showed how at Kentisbury Barton the large farmstead, lying, significantly, near the church, turned out to be 302 acres (120 hectares) in the Tithe Commutation survey of 1840, a very big farm for Devon. Though the boundaries of such farms do sometimes change, old ones can often be found following an ancient lane, a stream, the edge of an old wood or a long hedge rambling across the countryside, and many will turn out to be Saxon in origin.

Once the demesne farm has been plotted, it may be possible to identify some of the *villein* farms held by freemen and bondmen. These were smaller and more often altered, but if Domesday says there were twelve villeins in a manor, this probably means twelve individual farms. Sometimes, too, the manorial boundary is different in places from the parish boundary, so patient research is needed. In the 'other' England of open-field and nucleated villages, such research is impossible because of course each villein holding was scattered in strips far and wide across the parish.

Under the Norman feudal system, life remained hard; the change from Saxon freedom to feudal servitude made little difference to the average villein or cottar, whose Saxon lords had always demanded work and many other services; for example at Hurstbourne Priors in Hampshire churls holding 1 hide of land (about 120 acres or 48 hectares) each had to 'plough 3 acres in their own time, and sow them with their own seed, and bring it to the barn ..., and give 3 pounds of barley as rent, and mow half an acre of meadow ... and make it into a rick, and supply 4 fothers of split wood as rent, made into a stack in their own time, and supply 15 poles of fencing as rent ... and at Easter they shall give 2 ewes with 2 lambs ... and they must wash the sheep and shear them in their own time ...'.

The agricultural recovery begun by the Saxons continued, and the twelfth and thirteenth centuries saw great land shortages. The remaining woods and forests, and the heaths and moors, bore the brunt of a new wave of clearances. By Domesday, however, the Normans had already begun to establish great royal hunting forests, where woodland felling to clear farmland was discouraged by heavy fines. The reports of the Forest courts are a catalogue of land clearances over much of England as the early medieval open fields and individual assarts ate into the ancient woods and wastes.

The evidence of these clearings still shows on the ground today; individual farms of irregularly shaped fields often divided by great banked hedges rich in woodland plants. The farms have a very easily recognised 'economical' outline, roughly oval with long curving boundaries, leaving between them funnels of unenclosed land, where rights of common grazing often survive today. These farms are particularly obvious in places like the New Forest where they are surrounded by heathland, but with experience their irregular enclosures can also be found in places where the forest has now disappeared completely, as in the Forest of Arden in Warwickshire, and the Weald of Kent. Here the ancient forest has left its mark both in the pattern of the hedges and in their rich plant life; hedges full of flowers like primrose, wood anemone, bluebell and dog's mercury will almost always turn out to be the ghostly outlines of vanished woods.

Another woodland ghost still haunts modern farms in the shape of field names, many of which are hundreds of years old. Both enclosure fields and the furlongs of old open fields were often given medieval names reflecting the clearance of woodland: *sart* (from assart); *wold* (wood) and *stubbs, stockings, riddings* or *stibbings* (all meaning stumps) can still be used to trace earlier landscapes.

Moorland and heath, as well as woods, came under the medieval plough, as new farms were carved out of the acid peaty soils. Here we frequently find sequences of 'intake' fields, usually bounded by stone walls. Not all would have supported cultivation, many were probably summer stock pastures. In the Somerset levels and the silt and peat fens of

RIDGE-AND-FURROW AND ITS CREATION

The great sinuous ridges, such a striking feature of the Midlands clay pastures today, developed over a very long time (probably several centuries) starting in about the ninth century. It is still not quite certain whether the ridges were made as big as possible to encourage drainage, or whether they were an accidental result of the techniques of ploughing, but there are unridged open fields in some places, and at least an element of intent seems likely as many ridges are deliberately aligned up and down slopes.

The mechanism by which the ridges developed has been quite well worked out. The instrument responsible was the Saxon fixed-mouldboard plough, pulled by an unwieldy team of at least four oxen. This kind of plough always turned the soil to the right, so ploughing up the 'left' of a ridge and back down the 'right' would gradually pile the sods progressively more and more to the centre of the ridge, so building it up. Some in Northamptonshire and Warwickshire are over 3 ft (1 m) high, and have survived intact because the land was later converted to permanent pasture.

The most evocative thing about the ridges is the broad 'S' or 'C' shaped curves they make. This happened because the

Ridge and furrow in pasture at Ashby St Leger, Northamptonshire. Notice the change in furrow orientation between furlongs, and the 'butts', mounds of earth, at the ridge ends (foreground and middle-distance).

great plough-team was extremely difficult to turn at the end of the furrow. Hence the ploughman would swing the lead oxen to the left before the plough reached the end of the furrow, then swing right, once the team was on the unploughed headland, to come back down the other side of the ridge. The leftward swing would drag the plough – and thus the end part of the furrow – to the left too, and over the centuries the beautiful swing-swang effect we see today was created. The headland itself is an ancient feature. Each ridge-end was marked by a pile of loose soil, a *head* or *butt*, where the

plough was lifted out. The heads of several ridges together formed a *headland*, known in more than one tenth-century charter in Gloucestershire as a *heafod-land*. Even where later ploughed over, heads and headlands still form recognisable bumps.

COMMON FIELD PATTERNS IN THE COUNTRYSIDE

Most of our field patterns have evolved over many centuries, but usually one particular event, like enclosure, or colonisation of moorland, has had a strong influence on a local pattern. You can pick up important clues to the history of an area by looking at its field patterns, which will help you interpret where ancient vegetation might be surviving. Three main aspects which distinguish different field patterns are:

1) *Field organisation.* Are the fields a planned grid, or haphazard, or obviously developed in a sequence?
2) *Field size and shape.* Are the fields all of a similar size, or a mixture; and are they roughly rectangular, or 'organic' in outline?
3) *Field boundaries.* Are the field edges

marked by hedges, banks, walls, or ditches, and are these straight or curving?

With these points in mind, you will find the commonest types of fields are:

1) *Upland infield-outfield.* Tightly-knit small fields near the farmhouse, usually bounded by stone walls, with larger outfield(s) beyond extending up the moor. Infield walls fairly, but not quite, straight.
2) *Saxon or medieval piecemeal enclosure fields.* Generally small fields with thick, twisting boundaries, often an incremental pattern of sequential enclosure from woodland, forest heath, common, marsh or moor. The organic, rounded fields which 'eat into' ancient moors and commons. Similar fields in west Cornwall may be even older. Ancient hedges with many flowers of old woods or heaths, often embanked.

3) *Early 'enclosure' fields.* Fields of variable size formed by enclosing earlier medieval 'open-field' sometimes with ridge-and-furrow, or subdividing older pastures or downland. Boundaries only rarely straight, but may follow S-shaped strip edges, or furlong boundaries. Mixed hedges botanically.
4) *Parliamentary 'enclosure'.* Fields often of even size, 10–25 acres forming extensive planned grids, to which roads etc conform. Evenly-spaced hedgerow trees, or none. Hedges thin or replaced by post and wire, or now lost. These are the commonest kind of fields in the North East–Midlands–Dorset corridor, enclosed from earlier open-field (*ignoring* the direction of ridge-and-furrow) or from ancient downland or former forests.

In practice, you will find most areas have mainly fields of one kind, but a few of another; a good puzzle is to work out what the odd ones out tell us. For example, old curving hedges, thick and embanked, often occur near villages otherwise surrounded by Enclosure Act fields and represent early Saxon 'closes', 'crofts' or 'tofts' never taken into the open-field, whilst straight-hedge areas subdividing earlier rounded units may show where an ancient park or wood was grubbed out and turned into several fields.

Don't forget there are 'fossil' fields too, like the Iron-Age or earlier square lynchet-bounded fields, or medieval terrace-like strip lynchets; both types are now preserved under grassland. The very earliest are the tiny incremental fields associated with the stone hut-circles of Dartmoor.

ANCIENT OR PLANNED COUNTRYSIDE?

Despite the complex changes outlined in this chapter, it is possible to draw a basic distinction between two types of country-side, which Rackham has recently dubbed 'ancient' and 'planned' countryside. Ancient countryside has long been recognised as 'several' in contrast to 'champion' coun-try; roughly the difference between Devon and, say, Bedfordshire, or what are known in France as *bocage* and *champagne*.

You can see the distinction yourself. Ancient countryside is the landscape of ancient enclosure, either from the wild-wood or from the waste of prehistoric farm-ing, and is shown by:

1) Networks of old lanes, twisting and often deeply sunken, and a profusion of public footpaths.
2) A pattern of tiny hamlets and occa-sional small towns.
3) Dispersed ancient farmsteads sheltering in hollows, often near streams, and some with names like Church, Manor, Hall, Court etc Farm.
4) Many ancient woods, mainly small with irregular outlines.
5) Remains of heaths and commons.
6) Fields of varying sizes, with curving or rambling boundaries.
7) Hedgerows thick, often on banks, rich in shrubs and old coppice stools of ash, maple or oak, full of woodland plants.

8) Saxon or Norse place-names suggesting late-clearance of woodland (p. 81).

Much of Suffolk, Essex, Kent, Hereford, Shropshire, South Hampshire, Sussex and Devon and Cornwall is like this: a landscape of surprising twists and turns. It contrasts with the landscape of planned countryside, laid out on a drawing-table, which has a completely different character:

1) Roads are few, often ruler-straight with wide verges, and they are not sunken.
2) Settlements are large villages, one per parish (ancient parish).
3) Any isolated farms are eighteenth- or nineteenth-century, of Victorian or Geor-gian design, with names like 'New Farm'.
4) Ancient woods are few or absent, but square coverts or linear shelter belts, straight-edged, are present.
5) Hedges are all or mainly straight, lacking coppice stools, thin, sometimes on slight narrow banks. Standard trees may be present, few woodland flowers.
6) Heaths and commons are rarer.

This is planned countryside, and it can be found in Northants, Leicester, Oxfordshire, parts of Cheshire, Lancashire and east Yorkshire, Bedfordshire, Cambridgeshire, much of Wiltshire, and parts of the West Midlands and Dorset. Planned countryside is also typical of the Scottish lowlands.

The distinction sounds clear-cut, and is so in many places where the two systems meet. However, because planned country-side reflects the earlier existence of open-field (or sometimes unenclosed downland), in areas where open-field came late, went early and did not cover a whole parish, mixed landscapes are possible, as in parts of Dorset, Hampshire and Sussex, where though there is evidence of open-field near a village, the same parish may contain one or two ancient, dispersed farmsteads. The endless variations are illustrated by the fossilised fieldscapes of Derbyshire, where you can find stone-walled medieval enclo-sures, post-Tudor enclosures of bundles of S-shaped open-field strips, and the final square moorland enclosures under Parlia-mentary Act, all cheek-by-jowl.

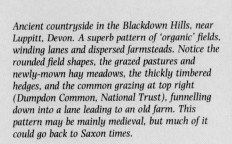

Ancient countryside in the Blackdown Hills, near Luppitt, Devon. A superb pattern of 'organic' fields, winding lanes and dispersed farmsteads. Notice the rounded field shapes, the grazed pastures and newly-mown hay meadows, the thickly timbered hedges, and the common grazing at top right (Dumpdon Common, National Trust), funnelling down into a lane leading to an old farm. This pattern may be mainly medieval, but much of it could go back to Saxon times.

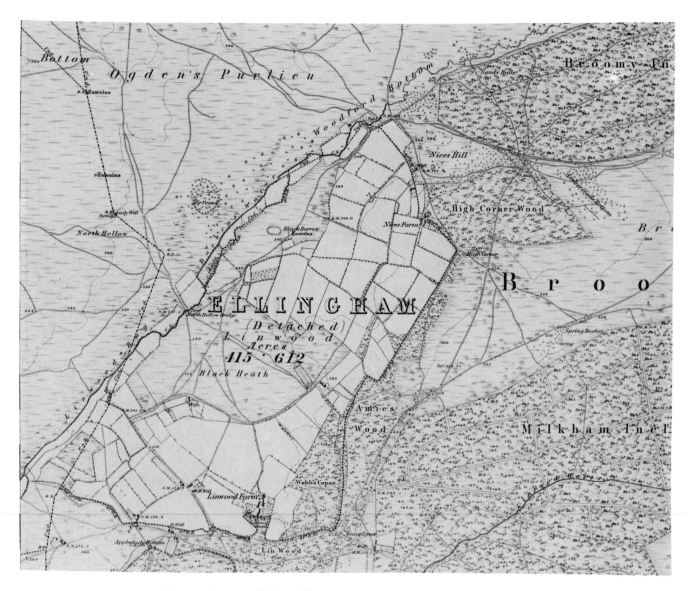

Saxon and medieval land shortages led to a recolonisation of land probably abandoned in the Bronze Age. The 1870 map shows an area enclosed from the heathy wastes of the New Forest near Ringwood. It was obviously carved out of the forest by the men of Ellingham, a hamlet in the Avon Valley – which was itself a daughter settlement of Eling, near Southampton. This is very likely the 'hide' of land called Linwood, mentioned in Domesday; notice that the map shows it as a detached portion of the parent settlement, and the parish boundary almost exactly encircles the enclosed farmland. The name Linwood is interesting: it means 'lime wood', and two ancient small-leaved limes still grow here.

the Wash and East Anglia, similar irregular fields occur, but here they are bounded by winding medieval drainage ditches, quite unlike later straight dykes.

The land hunger of 800 years ago also gave rise to a new sort of unenclosed field; the medieval *strip lynchet*. Strip lynchets are long parallel terraces, usually seen on steep slopes of chalk or limestone in Dorset, Wiltshire, Gloucestershire and Yorkshire, but they can also be found as far apart as Essex and Staffordshire. The name lynchet is confusing because these are not prehistoric features like the lynchets framing the tiny Iron-Age fields we saw earlier. Even so their steep upper and lower edges were formed in the same way; but they differ in their long narrow shape and often taper out into the slope at each end. In Wharfedale they clearly cut right through prehistoric field patterns. At Coombe Bissett hear Salisbury a remarkable flight is still ploughed and harvested (with combine harvesters!) every year. Most surviving strip lynchets, though, are preserved under flowery chalk grassland (just like their Iron-Age precursors) and remain a monument to the desperate need for farmland in the twelfth and thirteenth centuries.

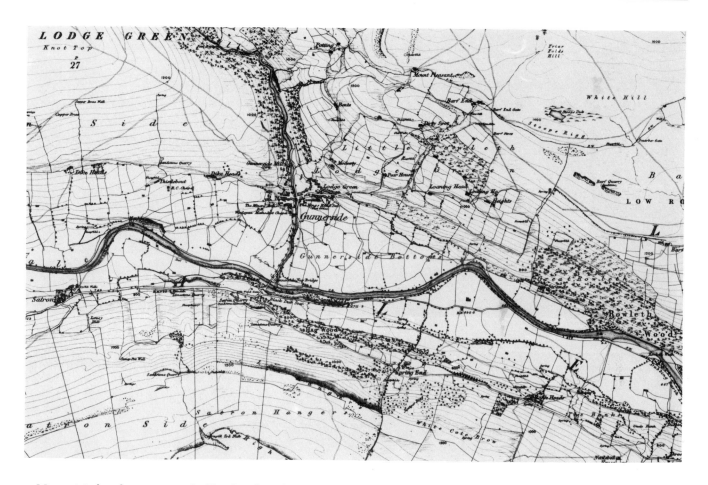

Land enclosure before the days of professional surveyors and imposed field patterns was a haphazard affair; this is the beautiful 'organic' pattern of fields enclosed for pasture – so they did not need straight sides – in medieval times along the flanks of Swaledale at Gunnerside.

Many strip lynchets were probably abandoned to pasture within a century or so, as interest in sheep-farming developed. The woollen industry of Yorkshire was founded on the vast limestone grassland sheep ranches managed by the rich monasteries of Fountains and Bolton. Fountains alone owned almost a million acres, and much of its produce was exported to Italy. From the thirteenth century onwards, stone walls began to march over the high tops, demarcating ownership and enclosing thousands of acres at a time. On a smaller scale, the lowlands showed the same interest in sheep: at the Cistercian Abbey of Beaulieu endowed by King John in 1204, the sheep enterprise is reflected to this day (400 years after the Dissolution) in the farm name *Bergerie*, and in medieval times the Abbot was called to the New Forest *Eyre* court to account for damage to the forest by his sheep. The monastic farms, managed by lay-brothers and local labour, can still be recognised by their title *Granges*. Hyde Abbey, the rich monastery founded at Winchester by King Alfred, owned the manor of Cranborne (Hampshire) where the present-day Hunton Grange farm commemorates the monastic sheep farm, here bounded by a Saxon hedge and where Iron-Age square fields were overlain by the sheep pasture of Hunton Down. Later, nineteenth-century enclosure converted the whole area to arable.

THE LATER MEDIEVAL SCENE – THE BLACK DEATH, RETRENCHMENT AND ENCLOSURE

The great success of Saxon and early medieval farming created the pressure on land which led to the use of the open-field system, the carving-out of ancient enclosed farms from forest, moor and heath, and the ploughing of chalk and limestone soils which had carried grassland for hundreds of years. By 1300 the shortage of land was probably so acute that much of the population was seriously under-nourished. The Black Death, the rat-borne bubonic plague epidemics which devastated the weakened population in 1348–50 and 1361–2, changed the whole face of the countryside. Many villages were abandoned, their fields left derelict, and many more villages shrank

Strip lynchets near Malham, Yorkshire. These are a common form of medieval contour-ploughing on steep slopes as a response to the land shortage of the twelfth and thirteenth centuries. The stone walls date from the eighteenth or nineteenth century – so they are about 600 years younger!

dramatically in extent. Suddenly, there was more land than was needed, but fewer people available to work on it. Marginal land in forests and fens was abandoned again, and a lot of arable farmland was turned over to pasture, which could be worked more economically.

One of the most significant changes was the emergence of a new class of yeoman farmers, as the high wages which landlords were obliged to pay for farm labour allowed many farmworkers to accumulate enough capital to lease or ultimately buy up farmland. The creation of new individual farms out of hundreds of open-field strips meant sweeping new changes in the landscape. A great deal of horse-trading of previously scattered strips had to take place in order to create compact workable blocks, and often the abandoned common-field strips were enclosed with hedges or stone walls and used to pasture sheep or cattle. The most recognisable feature of these fourteenth- and fifteenth-century enclosures is that in many cases the hedges or walls follow the ancient curving strip-edges, and countless examples of these S-shaped stone walls or hedges are known. The Peak District limestone is specially rich in

walled strips; a fine example lies on the south-east side of Castleton.

Even where open fields survived, the strips were exchanged so that individual blocks could be grazed or used for a particular crop, and some strips were combined lengthwise by ploughing over a joint to create longer ridges, perhaps because heavy horses were now more often used for ploughing. In some places the processes of exchange and enclosure left scarcely any common fields at all, especially in Cheshire, Shropshire and Herefordshire.

These early enclosures were usually amicable affairs which rarely made the medieval headlines. After about 1450, however, the rising value of wool, which was still the foundation of the wealth of the monasteries, began to tempt many large landowners to evict their tenants and enclose whole parishes for sheep-raising. This was a sad and sordid business; very often the new owners and the evicted tenants were the children or grandchildren of people who had toiled together in the fields within living memory. This process was obviously easier when a village had been depopulated by plague and had perhaps shrunk to one farm and a few cottages, but in some places it went on until well into the sixteenth century. In Tudor times the Spencer family depopulated the village of Wormleighton, Warwickshire, creating four 500-acre (200-hectare) sheep farms; whilst in 1547 the two original open-fields of Pulteney, Leicestershire were turned into two sheep pastures, 1,000 acres (400 hectares) in extent.

In hundreds of Midlands parishes, deserted villages,

A vanished village; Onley, Northamptonshire, deserted in the late medieval period. Prominent are the rows of house platforms, village streets and pond, and the former open field with ridge and furrow. Most of the site is preserved under the pasture, but the left foreground and the part of the village beyond the further cottage shows signs of the straight narrow ridges of Victorian ploughing.

Ridge-and-furrow, Husbands Bosworth, Leicestershire. Full of interest, this picture shows the medieval ridged fields overlain by straight enclosure hedges which ignore the older pattern. In the large field, notice how the pond is also later than the ridges, how the ridges vary in width, how the soil forms 'butts' or mounds at the near end, and how later ploughing has eliminated some areas of ridge. The ancient landscape survives where it has been fossilised under permanent pasture.

A fossilised medieval landscape at Wardlow, in the 'White Peak' of Derbyshire. The limestone walls follow closely the pattern of strip fields, proving that although most of the land is now pasture it was once open-field arable. The steep flanks of Cressbrookdale are covered in a much older grassland, rich in limestone-loving flowers.

Castleton, in the Hope Valley, Derbyshire. In the foreground is a pattern of S-shaped field walls, between which old ridges still show in the turf.

weakened by plague and depopulated by rapacious owners, lie fossilised beneath the old pastures, preserving the ridge-and-furrow of the old fields and even the streets and house-platforms. These deserted villages are still being recognised further and further afield, and many examples have only been discovered within the last few years as a result of studies in old documents, on the ground or using air photos. More will certainly be found in the future.

AGRICULTURAL REVOLUTION – EARLY DAYS

By about 1600, the population of Britain had climbed back to its level before the Black Death, about 4½ million people (not too different from the population in Roman times!). The seventeenth century was a time of new ideas: crops such as turnips, carrots, new grasses and clover. Clover was especially useful as it enriched the soil and helped the new practice of 'up and down' or convertible husbandry: fields put down to pasture for a few years to rest, then ploughed up again.

Though these innovations took the edge off the demand for land, they also encouraged enclosure of open fields. In the marginal open-field counties, common fields soon vanished, and even in the heartland enclosure by agreement continued, so that groups of strips could be hedged and put down to grass; in some areas their long curving boundaries still survive. Where the landlord was strong and the tenants few or weak, whole parishes were enclosed, as in Wimpole in Croydon and other West Cambridgeshire parishes owned by the Chicherley family, where there are still spreads of roughly rectangular fields with somewhat undulating sides, unlike nineteenth-century straight hedges.

Elsewhere, open fields were kept, but re-organised into more and smaller units to improve rotations for new crops. By now many of the early 100-acre (40-hectare) sheep-pasture enclosures were unwieldy, and were divided into smaller 20-acre (8-hectare) fields; whilst at the other end of the scale clusters of the ancient tiny assarts made by smallholders around the edges of forests and commons were gathered into new larger fields of a more workable size. These re-organisations left many poorer people

An abandoned medieval lane, Sheephouse Copse, Hampshire. This old track led from a tiny hamlet deserted in the fourteenth or fifteenth century. Despite 500 years of disuse, it is still clearly visible, and has not yet been colonised by woodland flowers, perhaps because of the thick beech litter which collects in the sunken track-bed. England is full of these ancient features.

Fenland, like this at March north of Cambridge, is a vast expanse of reclaimed peat or silt. Such areas lack ancient roads, woods, watercourses or vegetation, following complete clearance within the last 300 years. This is the landscape of 'improvement', drawn up by professional surveyors.

more than 2,000 acres (800 hectares) of farmland; and Melchet in Wiltshire was disafforested in 1610 and the land turned into a pattern of irregular fields, which still exists.

The Fens, too, came under renewed attack; there had

destitute, as the great commons and wastes where their stock had grazed were ploughed up. The Crown itself was selling royal forests wholesale in the seventeenth century; for example the forests of Melksham, Gillingham (Dorset) and Chippenham were legally disafforested and reduced to one twelfth of their size between 1624 and 1650, making

Watermeadow management involved the creation of miles of carefully levelled channels, like these mapped in 1870 at Breamore, Hampshire. The meadows were flooded with warm, silt-rich river water in early spring to improve grass production for sheep grazing. Un-channelled areas, at bottom, were probably managed for hay; note the detached pieces of Fordingbridge parish (and hundred) in Breamore's hay meadows (see p. 134).

The landscape of enclosure near Burford, Oxfordshire. The planned pattern of fields and plantations with straight or smoothly curved, narrow hedges set with well-spaced 'standard' oaks points to an eighteenth- or early nineteenth-century date. In the foreground, wild flowers and insects might yet be found in the uneven permanent pasture, if they have not been driven out by 'chemical agriculture' – fertilisers and herbicides.

been Roman and later drainage works, especially in the silt fens, but in the seventeenth century a more systematic assault on the peat fens began, with the establishment of the Bedford Level Corporation in 1630. The work was interrupted by the Civil War, and involved the construction of massive water channels to carry the fen waters away to the sea, and to carry the rivers Great Ouse and Nene across the fens. Though not completed until well after 1650, these channels and the rigidly rectangular pattern of drainage ditches which feeds them still dominate the fenland landscape today. Sadly, only a few tiny patches of the original peat-fenland remain now, gems of ancient vegetation like Wicken, Chippenham and Woodwalton Fens; islands of richness in a desolate sea of vegetable crops. Wind erosion of the friable dried-out peaty soils is a constant menace; a post sunk deep into the peat at Holme Fen records the shrinkage of the drained peat.

While water was being got rid of in East Anglia, it was used in the chalklands to create irrigated water meadows, in which warm chalk-spring water was allowed to flow over grasslands to give the ever-popular sheep an 'early bite' in spring. The vast flocks were then used to manure the arable land created by enclosing the ancient downland pastures. These old irrigation channels still stripe the valley floors in Dorset, Hampshire and Wiltshire (p. 134). There is a

DRY STONE WALLS

Dry stone walls can tell us a lot about the way the countryside has evolved as the land has been put to different uses over the centuries. They are an ancient feature of the mountains and moorlands, where trees are scarce and thick stock-proof hedges impossible to establish in the rocky ground.

The earliest walls (and still some of the most impressive today) were the massive banks of stones cleared from the ground by prehistoric farmers. The best examples of these 'consumption' walls (designed to consume as much stone as possible) are in west Cornwall and at Wasdale Head in Cumbria. Such walls often twist and turn to exploit rock outcrops, and are frequently based on a straggle of giant boulders rolled off the moorland fields.

Wall-building skills gradually improved, as the need for stock-proof enclosures and the discovery of the properties of different kinds of stone developed. Today there is a vast range of styles evolved over the centuries as the tens of thousands of miles of stone field-walls have been constructed. Walls last a very long time, but building them is a tough job; after a day's wall-building, usually about 20–25 ft (6–7 m), the waller will have lifted about 12 tons of stone an average of 3–4 feet. Because of this, stone was never carted very far, and walls reflect the bedrock under the waller's feet to a remarkable degree; in the Yorkshire Dales the mid-Craven fault can often be pinpointed to a few yards by the sudden change from bright silvery limestone to dark gritstone in field walls.

A dry stone wall is much more than a pile of stones; it has a carefully-designed internal structure. In most walls, two parallel walls of stones are built up on a solid footing, each stone being set crosswise to the run of the wall. The space between is packed with rubble, and the two sides are tied together by throughstones. Heavy copestones, set vertically, form the top of the wall; their weight is important in holding the wall tight together, and copestones dislodged by a careless rambler or a jumping sheep will soon lead to a progressive collapse.

The details of wall-construction technique vary greatly (it is said that experts can tell who built a particular length), but good technique is shown by individual stones as well as complete courses being laid horizontal to allow correct drainage. As you travel about Britain, you will see a remarkable range of styles: Mendip limestone walls are rather unrefined; Cotswold walls are built with the stones lengthwise; Scottish 'drystone dykes' range from the north-eastern walls of squared granite blocks to the precarious-looking Galloway dykes where a double-wall base is topped with a single wall of glacially-rounded moor-stones; Welsh walls are of many kinds on slate or gritstones; in the Lakes the walls in naturally slabby sedimentary rocks in some areas contrast with those on the volcanics, and in the Pennines too the available stone and its bedding characteristics determine the nature of the wall.

There is another reason why walls are not all the same, and that is the prevailing technique at the time they were built. Given a little maintenance, walls last for hundreds of years, and were seldom moved or re-organised. Both the style of the individual wall, and the pattern they make, are highly characteristic of each period of construction and enclosure. The Peak District, the Lakes and the Pennines of Yorkshire have mile upon mile of straight nineteenth-century walls, lots of eighteenth-century walls (many straight and others less so), and still quite a few from the sixteenth- or seventeenth-century (or even earlier) enclosures from waste or open-field by individuals (p. 62). The older fields tend to have foundations of great boulders, and to form

A dry stone wall in North Yorkshire. Mainly of limestone, with obvious bedding planes, but incorporating some rounded or angular Silurian gritstones. The left part is well-coursed and has a recognisable coping; but the right half has been hurriedly repaired and is more chaotic.

irregular patterns with rounded, organic shapes. Superb examples can be seen around Gunnerside in Swaledale and in Nidderdale (Lofthouse), and many other villages in the Dales have a few of these older fields near the settlement itself. The 2½-inch maps of the Peak District are

particularly worth looking at to see the contrast between ancient enclosures, walled-off S-shaped (ridge-and-furrow) open fields, and the grids of square parliamentary fields made much later.

In some places the differences between these types of walled fields have been used to unravel the history of how the land in a township has been used. One fascinating example is the story of Linton, near Grassington in Wharfedale, worked out by Arthur Raistrick. The Enclosure Award for Linton, dated 1792, shows that near the village the land was already in 'ancient enclosures'; further out lay the common fields and beyond these the common pastures. The 1792 Award carved the common fields of Linton into 8-acre (3-hectare) fields enclosed by straight stone walls built 6 ft (2 m) high, battered from 3 ft (1 m) thick at the base to 14 in (35 cm) at the top, and with 21 throughstones per rood; these walls can still be seen today. A little later the common pasture was enclosed too, into long 30-acre (12-hectare) strips. It is the 'ancient enclosures' near the village which are most fascinating, however. Here, a pattern of organic fields forming a 'drunken irregular maze' seems to match exactly the area of 2 carucates (150 acres, 60 hectares, or so) at which Linton was assessed in Domesday. Clearly these are very old, though undatable, fields which may perhaps have been an 'infield' in 1086. Even more astonishingly, Raistrick has shown that about half this ancient field, around 70 acres (28 hectares), is ringed by a stone wall of the most massive construction, built upon great boulders up to 3 or 4 ft (1–1.2 m) across – obviously the result of early land clearance. This wall is extremely old and later walls butt up to it but never break through; it must be the earliest wall ever built at Linton and is quite likely to be the original Anglian wall, created when Linton was carved out as a separate settlement around the eighth century.

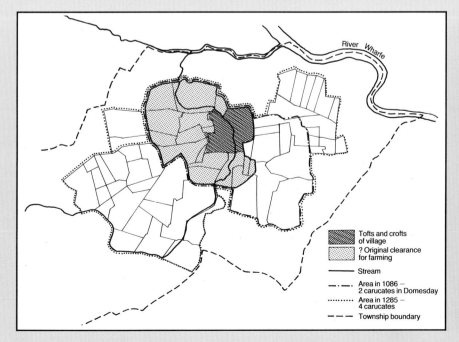

Tofts and crofts of village

? Original clearance for farming

——— Stream

—·—·— Area in 1086 – 2 carucates in Domesday

·········· Area in 1285 – 4 carucates

– – – Township boundary

The development of Linton in Wharfedale can be worked out from the ages of stone walls, which reveal its gradual expansion from the Anglian settlement of about 70 acres (28 hectares) to a township of many hundreds of acres. The diagram is based on work by Dr A. Raistrick.

From the air, the square Georgian enclosure fields around Over Haddon, Derbyshire, can be seen to have been flung down like a net over the land by the enclosure commissioners, ignoring valleys or rock outcrops.

beautiful series just north of Dorchester in the Frome Valley.

The seventeenth and eighteenth centuries were not a period of wholesale change in the landscape; but the work of enclosing open-field, forest and heath, and downland went slowly on, creating a farmscape of fairly regular fields, whose hedges still showed links with medieval practice, following slopes and streams, and never truly straight. Even so, this period created the basic social and economic upheavals which later brought about more far-reaching changes in the landscape. It was the new crops, husbandries and machines evolving in the seventeenth century which set the stage for the massive replanning of the countryside in the great age of enclosure which followed.

THE AGE OF IMPROVEMENT – PARLIAMENTARY ENCLOSURE

The first Act to enable a landlord to enclose his land despite the peasant tenants' wishes was passed in 1602 for Radipole, near Weymouth, but from 1700 they came thick and fast; 208 Acts were passed by 1760, and a further 2,000 by 1800. By 1860 the process was complete, and the enclosure of nearly half of England and large parts of lowland Scotland had been achieved.

Enclosure by Act led to the development of surveying; at

Parliamentary enclosure; stone-walled fields near Kendal, Cumbria. The regular rectangular pattern is characteristic. Notice the variations in the dry stone walling, resulting from rebuilding at different times. On the right, the carpet of dandelions betrays a field heavily manured and grazed, but not treated with herbicides.

The Malham area has many superb old field systems. Here, close to Malham Cove, fields of at least three ages are superimposed. On the slope at left can be seen the bones of prehistoric rectangular fields beneath the limestone turf with its blue moorgrass and other flowers. In the right middle distance are the parallel terraces of medieval strip lynchets, whilst overlying these ancient fields are the rectangular stone-walled fields of eighteenth- and nineteenth-century enclosure. There is a strong National Trust presence in the Malham area and Upper Wharfedale.

least 3,000 English parishes were affected, and for each one 'before' and 'after' plans were drawn up, showing the old situation and then all the proposed new roads and fields, stream straightenings and so on.

An Enclosure Award (a document sharing out the new fields between the larger original tenancies) was also drawn up, but in the process those with only a few common rights received nothing. The statistics of enclosure are awe-inspiring; in Scotland alone 30,000 plans were prepared, in England 200,000 miles (320,000 km) of quickset hedges were planted in about 100 years, consuming at least one *billion* plants of hawthorn and other species for which nurseries had to be established. Occasionally, where wooded commons were destroyed, oak and ash were planted in the hedges to give future timber; it is these trees whose disappearance has caused so much concern in recent years, as Enclosure Act hedges have been bulldozed out again by modern farmers. In Scotland 19-year, and later 30-year, leases were often granted, with clauses requiring the land to be completely walled with dykes or hedges, as the old Scottish townships, with their medieval run-rig fields and impoverished undrained out-pastures, were swept away. In the uplands of Yorkshire and the Peak District, stone-walls were built across miles of former sheep-pasture, creating the distinctive pattern of square fields punctuated by out-barns; the walls were such an enormous

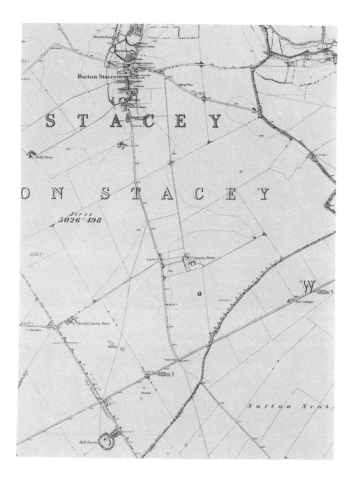

Nineteenth-century enclosure of downland, Barton Stacey, on the chalk plateau north of Winchester. The only ancient features here are the old tumuli and the rambling parish boundary known as Barton Stacey belt, probably a pre-Saxon estate boundary. Everything else, even the field-corner clumps, is planned. This, though, is ancient not recent clearance of woodland; there were no woods here in 1086. 1st Edition 6-inch Ordnance map.

final enclosure of the rump of the open-field system; 90,000 acres of pasture were enclosed in Durham, Northumberland and North Yorkshire in only 35 years. For a while much of this stayed as privately-owned pasture, but the corn price-scares of the Napoleonic wars led to widespread ploughing up of ancient chalk and limestone grasslands for corn-growing, as Cobbett and others lamented:

Between Winchester and Wherwell we came by some hundreds of acres of ground that was formerly most beautiful down, which was broken up in dear corn times, and which is now a district of thistles and other weeds. If I had such land as this I would soon make it down again.

Enormous forests like Rockingham in Northants, Delamere in Cheshire, and Bere Portchester in Hampshire, all of them great wooded commons, were destroyed. In the case of Bere the Crown was anxious to replant the part of the forest which it received as its share of the carve-up with timber for the Navy. Again, Cobbett voiced his displeasure, this time at the destruction of Waltham Chase, ancient hunting forest of the Norman Bishops of Winchester:

Besides sweeping away two or three hundred cottages, besides plunging into ruin and misery all these numerous families, here is one of the finest pieces of timber-land in the whole kingdom going to be cut up into miserable clay fields for no earthly purpose but that of gratifying the stupid greediness of those who think that they must gain if they add to the breadth of their private fields.

undertaking that many were built by gangs, often of out-of-work miners, employed directly by the Enclosure Commissioners. Enclosure, by Act or agreement, of the vast upland sheep ranges or the remaining royal Forests dwarfed the

In the face of opposition like this, it was, rather unusually, 40 years from the petition to Parliament until actual enclosure.

It is the Enclosure Act period which we have to thank for the rectilinear landscape of central England and elsewhere. Its effects are visible all around us: ruler-straight roads, walls or hedges, and watercourses, and the many new Georgian or Victorian brick farms set among their fields, not in the village, with contemporary names like Botany Bay or Waterloo, and the prosaic 'New Farm'.

3 · Ancient Woods and Forests

IGHT THOUSAND years of woodland clearance for farming have destroyed almost all of Britain's primeval woodland cover, and created the fields, heaths and grasslands we look at later in this book. Our present 5 million acres (2 million hectares) of woodland, covering a mere 7 per cent of Britain, is not all it seems. More than 4 million acres (1.6 million hectares) of it is plantations, mainly on sites which have been farmed. Even of the 750,000 acres (300,000 hectares) we still possess of woodland which is both ancient and semi-natural in origin, very little probably has any direct link with the wildwood.

WHAT IS ANCIENT WOODLAND?

Within our old woods lies a wealth of fascinating, unique, historical and ecological information about the history of these islands; the greatest storehouse of potential know-

It is difficult to imagine the 'wildwood' of 6,000 years ago; the nearest we in Britain can get is fragments of ancient 'primary' forest like Mark Ash Wood in the New Forest. Here no trees are felled and none are planted, and dead wood from collapsed trees lies on the wet forest floor, supporting thousands of insects and fungi; lichens and mosses grow luxuriantly in the damp atmosphere, and grazing animals keep sunny glades open. This is an extremely rare sight; most British woods are managed by clear-felling and have a very different wildlife value.

Anses Wood is one of several wooded areas in the New Forest which are thought to be 'primary' woodland, a term which means they have never been cleared for farming at any time during the last 10,000 years. These marvellous old woods have been open to grazing cattle, deer, ponies and pigs for centuries, and today are dominated by unpalatable trees like oak, beech and holly.

wildwood, we usually talk about woods as *ancient* or *recent*. Ancient woods are those which developed before about 1700 (it is usually impossible to be precise); whilst recent woods are those less than about 300 years old!

Some ancient woods *are* descended without interruption from the prehistoric wildwood; these are the primary woods, and they include parts of the New Forest or the Weald, woods in deep gorges like the Avon and the Wye, and many of the East Anglian boulder clay woods. In fact many counties can boast a few relics, like the cliffs or ravines of the Yorkshire Dales or the Peak District, the wooded valleys of Devon, or parts of the woods of the Lakes or south-west Scotland.

Of course, these are not undisturbed post-glacial woodlands, they have changed quite a bit over the last 10,000 years, both because the climate has changed and because man has felled trees or grazed his stock. Nevertheless they have one very important characteristic: they retain undisturbed, unploughed brown forest soils, and have acquired, and kept, a wealth of flowers, ferns, mosses, lichens, and even snails, slugs and insects, which live nowhere else.

All other ancient woods, by far the majority, are growing on what was once farmland. These are the secondary ancient woods. Even so, some are very old indeed and many have acquired some, but not all, of the natural richness of primary woods; they can also tell us a lot about the way woods change, and why, and about our own use of the land in the Bronze or Iron Ages, or the Dark Ages, since when many of them have developed, overlying Bronze-Age barrows, Iron-Age fields or even medieval ridge-and-furrow.

Recent, post-1700 woodland is of course all secondary, and includes the oak and birch woods growing on old abandoned common grazings, or plantations like the Chiltern beechwoods or the conifers of Kielder Forest.

ledge we possess. Despite its small extent our semi-natural forest is a remarkably diverse one. The green ink on the Ordnance map conceals a range of woods of many sorts: coppices and groves; forests, wooded commons, deer-parks and scrubs; ashwoods, oakwoods and alderwoods; woods of maple, lime or hornbeam; beechwoods, yew woods, hollywoods and birchwoods; elmwoods, chestnut woods; plantations of all sorts – the list is long. This chapter is about how to make sense of woods both as they developed in historical and prehistoric times, and as they are today.

Because it is often difficult to prove that a wood is *primary* woodland with historical continuity from the pre-Neolithic

TREES IN ANCIENT WOODS

It is the behaviour of trees which gives woods their character. Most trees of our ancient woods are native, part of the flora which colonised Britain naturally, and they can usually reproduce themselves and spread; though one or

two, like wild service tree and small-leaved lime, may only do so very infrequently, and even beech and oak may only have a full establishment of saplings to replace themselves once a century or more – which is quite enough of course.

In a strange way, however, man has been prolonging the life of individual trees for hundreds or even a thousand years, oddly enough by cutting them down every few years! When cut down most of our trees do not die, they simply send up new shoots, either as *coppice* from the stumps (ash, hazel, oak, maple, birch, lime, hornbeam, alder and wych elm are coppicing trees) or as a thicket of *suckers* from the roots (aspen, wild cherry, English and smooth-leaved elms and wild service tend to sucker).

In this way a crop of wood can be cut from the stump which becomes a 'stool', or from the sucker shoots, again and again without endangering the survival of the tree. In fact coppicing stops the tree from becoming top-heavy and splitting or blowing down, so all the oldest trees in Britain are coppice stools, though you might not think so at first glance. At each cut, the shoots spring from the outer edge, so the stool gradually expands. An ash stool 6 ft (2 m) across on a fertile site may be 400 years old; on a poor site it would be much older. In fact stools twice as big are not unknown, and they can be of ash, maple, wych elm or other species, but it is hard to guess their age because they are always hollow-centred, an ancient ring of living wood growing imperceptibly outwards. Some stools of small-leaved lime are so large that they have become groves of new trees; one such ring on the Dorset-Hampshire border is more than 20 ft (6 m) across, and must have been alive long before the Norman conquest.

Coppicing has another effect: it maintains the ancient woodland composition. Many a coppice has been cut up to

Some of the finest 'primary' woods in Britain can be seen on the remarkable cliffs along the lower Wye Valley in Gloucestershire and Gwent. The gentler slopes have mostly been changed by planting new tree species, but the steeper parts are an almost overwhelming series of transitions from one native tree community to another. Wych elm, small and large-leaved limes, ash, beech, oak, rare kinds of whitebeam, and other trees form endlessly varying mixtures in these superb ancient woods.

This ancient 'stool', or coppice stump, of ash in Felshamhall Wood, Suffolk, was last cut two years ago, and new shoots are growing from the old base. The stool is probably at least 400 years old – and could even be twice that age. Most of our native trees will form these ancient living stumps if repeatedly cut, and they are the most obvious way of identifying an ancient coppice.

100 times even since Domesday; and its pattern of trees, even the plants of the woodland floor, may have changed only a little in that time. There are many ancient records of lime, for example, growing just where we still find it today. Trees which coppice can also be 'pollarded', which is really coppicing 'up in the air', where browsing deer or cattle cannot reach the tasty young shoots. Pollarding is hard work, and is characteristic of sites where medieval circumstances dictated that trees had to be grown in the presence of grazing stock; Epping forest with its hornbeam and beech, and the pollards along old droveways, are two examples.

Other trees in our woods were introduced by man; some, like sycamore, are now naturalised, others like horse-chestnut or Norway spruce can grow only where planted and do not spread.

pollen sequence can be correlated with radio-carbon-dated woody material to give us an impression – misty but still revealing – of the major changes in our forest cover.

From ancient pollen, which is made of woody lignin and is extremely enduring, we know that Europe's climate has been cyclically warming and cooling for at least half a million years. Each warm interglacial has seen an initial invasion by birch and pine, then an expansion with alder, elm, lime, hazel and oak, followed by a change to hornbeam, beech and spruce; then as the climate cools pine, birch and moorland return.

Our present 'Flandrian' interglacial, which succeeded the last or 'Devensian' ice age about 12,000 years ago, is no exception. The dusty, rubble-strewn tundra, with its frost-heaved soils and constantly shifting watercourses, began to be colonised by blue-green algae (which can make their own nutrients), sub-arctic mosses, rushes and sedges. The

WOODS IN PREHISTORY

WHERE DID WOODLANDS COME FROM?

Practically all the evidence we have about the beginnings of our woodland can be found in peat bogs, pickled in the acid waterlogged bogmoss remains, which have preserved in their successive layers a perfect time sequence of the pollen rain falling on to the bog over thousands of years. This

This diagram shows how bare rock, ice and tundra gradually gave ground to forest cover, first of birch and pine and then of other trees. In Atlantic times more tree species expanded their cover, but peat bogs began to grow too. From the Neolithic onwards elm and lime, and later other trees, declined dramatically as man began to create farmland, so that woodland now covers a tiny percentage of Britain. N.B. The dates are radiocarbon dates, which progressively underestimate true dates as you go further back in time.

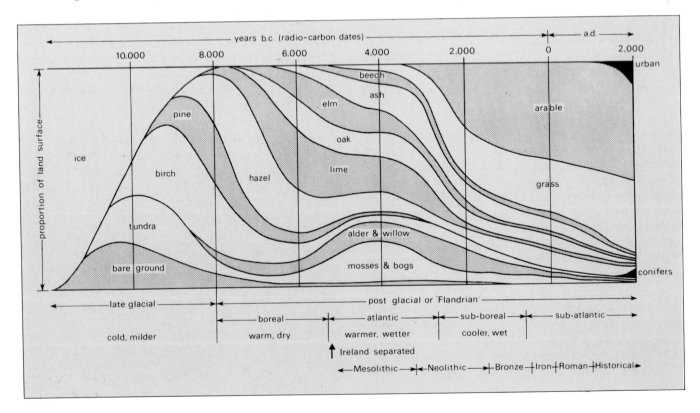

Morrone Birkwood National Nature Reserve, near Braemar, Deeside. Birch and juniper were amongst the first trees to colonise Britain. As the climate improved, they retreated northwards and birch/juniper woods are now found only in the uplands of northern England and Scotland.

English Channel was only a river, draining parts of north-west Europe, and trees soon gained a toehold in Britain's developing vegetation.

First to arrive were the cold-tolerant birches spread by wind-borne seeds; initially the tiny Arctic or dwarf birch, only 2 ft high, which still lives in Scotland. Dwarf willow and juniper were also early-comers. Then followed the larger birches, and in the south-east the pine, forming 'proto-woods', open groves of trees in stable areas.

Around 10,000 years ago, the climate warmed rapidly, and the pine and birch forest spread north, together with rowan and aspen. Birch rapidly enriches the soil because it concentrates any calcium in the subsoil into the surface humus year by year, creating conditions suitable for other trees like hazel, which soon invaded, followed by alder and lime.

Analysing the pollen in peat bogs across Britain charts the spread of forest trees, showing that by 10,000 years ago oak and wych elm were common at least in the south, and pine and oak had already reached Ireland. The sea cut Ireland off from Wales, however, before many of the other woodland species present in southern England arrived there; Ireland has oak but lacks lime, beech, hornbeam, dormice or purple emperor butterflies for example.

England was severed from France and then Holland about 8,600 years ago, and though by then the great English forests of lime, oak, elm, hazel and alder were supplemented by late arrivals such as beech, ash and maple; others were excluded, and England lacks some species such as sycamore which actually do very well when introduced. The succeeding climatic period is named the Atlantic, after the waters which inundated the channel, and made our climate wetter, and it was these times which saw the full expansion of the 'wildwood', covering at least two-thirds of Britain.

THE WILDWOOD

The vast Atlantic forest was not a uniform ocean of oakwoods, but a very complicated mosaic of stands of wych

79

elm, ash, hazel, birch, lime and other trees, each stand a particular mixture specially adapted to local climate and soil conditions. Oak and hazel dominated the north and west of England and south Scotland. To the north lay the Scottish highlands where pine and birch held sway, but the north coast of Caithness was beyond the permanent forest line. Woods with elm grew on the base-rich limestones and moist chalk soils; and much of south-east Britain lay in a province dominated by lime and hazel. As time passed, later arrivals expanded their ranges; beech on the freely-drained chalk and gravel sites, hornbeam displacing lime in the Thames basin, and maple, whose history is rather obscure.

The wildwood was quite unlike almost any woods we have today. Free at first of human influence, it could have had trees of all ages, from multitudes of saplings struggling for light to huge senescent forest giants, with trunks 70 or 80 ft (21–24 m) to the first branch, like some of the 'bog-oaks' dug out of the East Anglian fens by modern farmers. Dead trees would either stand and rot, like oak; or blow down like beech, creating glades for new seedlings and for woodland flowers and grasses. Browsing deer would maintain the glades and make them even grassier, gradually forming a patchy forest, rather like parts of the New Forest today. The New Forest, in fact, is about as close as we can get to the lowland wildwood, a mosaic of woods and grassland, never clear-felled and having, therefore, a very high humidity which allows a luxuriant growth of lichens and mosses which festoon the trees. Even so, there are many differences: the New Forest now lacks lime, one of the most remarkable features of the Atlantic forest; for though we still have all the other wildwood trees in abundance, lime has now declined to a relict species, growing only as a few ancient individuals, or an acre or two of coppice, except in a few special parts of England.

EARLY MAN AND THE CLEARANCE OF THE WILDWOOD
Even while the wildwood was still evolving its complex mosaic, Mesolithic men were nibbling at its upland margin to create deer-hunting glades. Neolithic farmers began a more systematic onslaught, starting in the lowlands on the light sands and alluvium of the river valleys. As their nutrients were used up by crops, or leached by rainwater, the infertile sands soon turned to heathland, whilst the clearance of wych elm from the most fertile alluvial soils of the valleys led to the great 'Elm Decline' visible in the pollen record about 3500 BC. Perhaps only about one-sixth of the forest was destroyed in the Neolithic – we shall never really know; but the losses accumulated through the Bronze Age, when round barrows were sited, for visibility, on cleared ridges, and a complete fieldscape covered many parts of England. We can be sure that many of the surviving woods

were regularly coppiced for fuel or poles, such as those recovered in the long-buried 'Sweet Track' across the prehistoric wetland of the Somerset levels. Beech and hornbeam colonised gaps in the canopy, and ash, hazel and oak invaded abandoned fields.

In the Iron and Roman periods, clearance moved to the heavier soils, with their lime, oak and maple woods. The great Roman ironworks and potteries, and the centrally-heated public buildings and villas, used vast quantities of coppice wood; Henry Cleere has calculated that, in the Kentish Weald, 84 tons of wood were needed to smelt 1 ton of iron, and just six furnaces produced 550 tons of iron each year. These furnaces would have been fuelled by the yield of about 23,000 acres (9,200 hectares) of coppices, cut on a 10-year rotation, and like all other wood-using industries would have carefully preserved their wood sources. It is not wood-burning ironmasters but stump-grubbing farmers who threaten woods! The Romans of course needed both woods and fields, but they may well have begun the process of protecting some woods from stock, to allow regeneration.

The Roman period was a critical, and still largely unexplored, time when the woodland pattern was starting to settle down. By the time the Romans left, the endless forest was only a dim memory, except in Scotland.

WOODS THROUGH HISTORICAL TIMES

THE DARK AGES
The Saxon settlers shared with a demoralised British population a landscape which was probably about 30 per cent wooded, but the woodland was already very unevenly spread across Britain. The core of England with its fertile clays was even then nearly devoid of woods in a great belt from East Yorkshire south-west towards Wiltshire. In Wales and Scotland, and the north and west Midlands, and in the Home Counties, there were still extensive forests, and many smaller woods survived in the West Country. This was a profound contrast, and it has in the end given us the present contrast between the 'planned countryside' of the east Midlands, and the wooded, organic, 'twisty' ancient countryside of peripheral England (p. 59).

Much of the remaining forest was already being managed for fuel wood, and as a grazing area for cattle and pigs. Saxon names for some great forests are recorded; 'Andreadswald' (Germanic *wald*) for the 80-mile (130-km) forest of Kent, Sussex and Hampshire, on the heavy soils which are still called 'Wealden'; the 'Wolds' of Lincolnshire and Yorkshire, and the 'Cotswolds' which combines the British *coit* (Welsh *coed*) with the Saxon *wald*.

Some woods kept their old British names – Selwood

Although wild swine had vanished from England's forests by about 1260, domestic pigs are still turned out in the New Forest, continuing the ancient medieval tradition of pannage, under which pigs were allowed in the autumn to forage for the green acorns and beechmast, which were poisonous to deer and cattle.

Maple is a common tree in coppices on chalk and clay, and an attractive one with its lobed leaves, elegant habit and knobbly bark. It has an obscure pollen history, but was well-established by the Iron Age. This lovely old chalk ash/maple wood is called Mascombe Copse, a name which perpetuates its ancient British title, Masan Combe, which means 'maple valley'.

Forest in Somerset was called *Coit Mawr* or Great Wood. In old English *coit* may have become *chet*, an element that crops up time and again in forest names – such as Melchet, Chute and Penchet (later Clarendon), all on the Hampshire–Wiltshire border. Celtic names for small woods are rare in England, though of course they are common in Wales; but a Hampshire charter of 863 records the name *Masan Combe* (maple valley) for one small wood which is today known as Mascombe Copse. Remarkably, it is still a maple wood too!

DOMESDAY WOODLAND

The best guide for the Saxon woodland pattern is William the Conqueror's great taxation inventory of England, Domesday, whose woodland complexities have been teased out by many workers, especially H. C. Darby and more recently Oliver Rackham. Domesday was compiled from returns collected by the commissioners on several circuits of parts of England; though it has little to say of England north of Craven. In the early south-eastern circuit, woodland was recorded by swine-renders, the rent (in pigs) due to the woodland owner from those who fattened their swine on acorns and beechmast in the woods. Because the rate varied from 1 pig in 7 to 1 in 10 or more, in the midland counties estimates of the total herds of swine were sought, but these too were mainly notional, as the mast crop varied enormously, so that finally in the western circuits woods were recorded by acreage, or if very large by leagues.

Rackham calculated that Domesday records about 7,800 woods, in 6,200 out of the total recorded 12,580 settlements. So by late Saxon times virtually half of all English estates had no woodland left; the intensive late Saxon farming had reduced woodland cover to perhaps as little as 15 per cent (or about twice what we have now). Domesday confirms the impression that woods were distributed very unevenly; the woodless settlements tended to lie on barren light soils like the Breck or the chalk downs, which by now were grassy or heathy places; or in the intensive farmscape of the Midlands.

The most wooded counties were probably Staffordshire, Derbyshire, Cheshire and Worcestershire, where four vast woods each up to 150,000 acres (60,000 hectares) accounted for much of the total. Contrast these with Lincolnshire, where Kesteven had only 4 per cent of woodland in 1086, whilst Holland could scarcely show a wood at all. Only 8 per cent of settlements in east Yorkshire had wood for building materials by the time of Domesday, and Huntingdonshire, Cambridgeshire and Northamptonshire were all poor in woods, and had probably been so since Roman days. Their few remaining woods were carefully managed, however, and many of them are with us today,

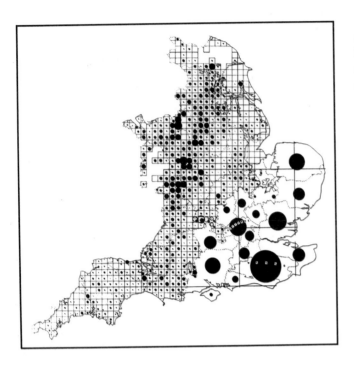

Distribution of woodland in England, as recorded in Domesday. Each black circle represents the area of woodland at the scale of the map; Domesday settlements have been aggregated to 10-km squares in the western counties, where the areas or extents of woods are recorded in Domesday. In the south-east, areas are less accurate, being recorded as 'swine-rents', and aggregated to county. Separate figures are calculated for the Weald and the Chilterns. By kind permission of Oliver Rackham.

It is fascinating to reflect on what Domesday tells us about Saxon woods, and woodland clearance. All told, between 550 and 1050 the Saxons managed to halve the area of England's woodland to about 15 per cent; that is equivalent to grubbing out 30 acres (12 hectares) of ancient woodland every day for 500 years! They had special names for settlements made in forest clearings – *lēah*, *hyrst* or *feld* (as in Tadley, Billingshurst or Lichfield) – which give a clear impression of the location of Dark-Age forest. The interesting point is that the areas with many Saxon clearance names are exactly the same as those where there was *still* woodland in Domesday, whilst these Saxon clearance place-names are absent from areas which Domesday shows to have had very little woodland – Breckland, the central and east Midlands, east Yorkshire and non-Wealden Sussex for example. Similar evidence exists in East Anglia, Leicestershire and Lincolnshire, where although there are several places named after woods there are remarkably few named after clearings.

All this almost certainly means that the Saxon settlers in the Midlands and eastern England found a landscape with few surviving woods, but in peripheral England there was still plenty of woodland to clear, and much of it remains even now. In other words, the basic pattern of English woodlands was created by farmers not just before the Norman conquest, but at the *latest* by Roman times; and, from what we are now finding out about Iron-Age and Bronze-Age farming, it could be much older still.

gloriously rich wildlife habitats in what is in some ways an agricultural desert. Surprisingly, Devon was another place with few woods, and half of those were less than 14 acres (5.5 hectares); but then as now Devon must have been a county of thick, timber-filled hedges.

Many counties showed a 10 to 20 per cent cover of woodland, and Domesday recorded woodland where medieval records later showed royal forests; for example the Wiltshire forests of Chippenham, Melksham and Saver-nake. Nevertheless, there are mysteries too, which only detailed research can solve, arising from the way the records were collected by estate. For example Domesday reveals no woods belonging to the settlements in what later became the Forests of Melchet, Clarendon or Grovely, but instead these large woods (which certainly existed in 1086) were recorded under the giant royal manor of Amesbury, a downland estate which is most unlikely to have had much woodland. In the Weald, too, Domesday records much of the woodland under the ownership of non-Wealden estates, which must have owned detached exclaves in the forest.

THE ORIGINS OF WOODLAND MANAGEMENT

If the broad pattern of woodlands in our countryside goes back as far as Roman, Iron-Age or Bronze-Age times, at what point did the actual boundaries of our existing carefully-demarcated copses, groves and woods begin to form? Firm boundaries are always the result of a conflict of interest, and the less woodland is left the more it needs to be protected from trespassing cattle or neighbours, and care-fully managed to produce a crop of wood. It seems likely, then, that in relatively woodless parts of England bound-aries may well have been defined by or even before Romano-British times, but in 'ancient countryside' where much woodland or waste remained through the Dark Ages, boundaries are often Saxon or Norse.

The Saxons used banks and ditches to define the edges of woods, estates or tenancies, and many existing woodbanks were recorded in Saxon land charters, which often refer to woods, to their owners, to 'hanging' woods on steep slopes, to groves or to individually-described trees. A charter of Edward, dated 1046, granted the estate of Hoddington in Hampshire to the Bishop of Winchester; the account of its

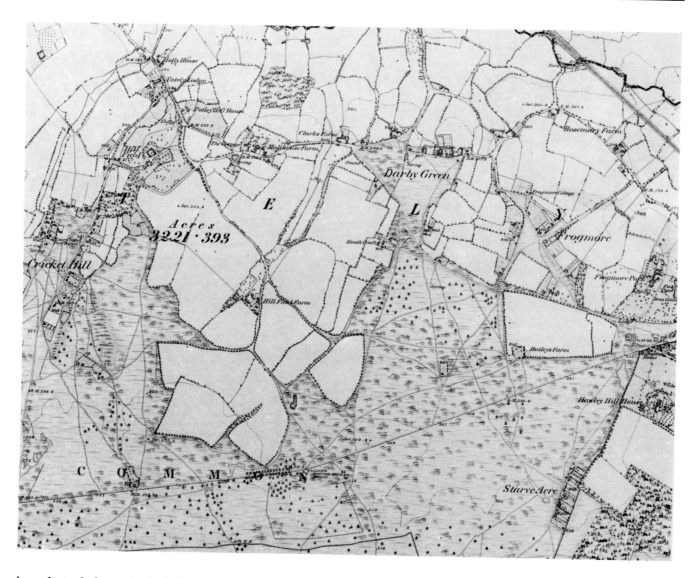

In Saxon and medieval times, vast areas of wooded forest and heathy 'waste' were cleared to make new farmland. In this case the fields were carved out of what was known in the Middle Ages as Eversley Forest, part of the vast Forest of Windsor. The pattern is typical; irregular-shaped fields are formed, leaving tapering funnels of unenclosed land, and, as the farms coalesce, small triangular 'greens' like Darby Green. Apart from suburban development in the north, much of this 1858 landscape is recognisable today as Yateley Common, Hampshire. 1st Edition 6-inch Ordnance Survey.

bounds includes a typical description: 'Andlang Rewe innan Humbaling-graf Westweardne' or 'along the row of trees to the grove of the family of Humbeald on its west side'.

Although there are written, theoretical, Roman descriptions of woodland management, we know that the Saxons established several different practical management traditions, and legislated to protect woodland which was becoming scarce as clearance went on. For example, we read in the Laws of Ine, king of the West Saxons in 688, that: 'if anyone fells in the wood quite a number of trees, he is to pay for three trees at 30 shillings each'.

This concern (30 shillings was a great deal of money in 688) reflects the fact that the Saxons built with wood, and used great quantities for fuel and all kinds of wattle-work and crafts, and are likely to have needed more and more from a diminishing area of woodland. In this way the need to manage particular woods for particular purposes arose. A later Saxon charter in which Burgred, king of Mercia,

granted pasture for 70 pigs, five wagons of rods, one oak for building, and wood for the fire, every year from Wolverley Common in Worcestershire, tells us a lot about what was happening there. The 'leah' place-name indicates woodland clearance, but the remaining woodland of this estate must have been an early compartmented pasture-woodland, because a regular supply of *rods* could only have come from a coppice, protected from the commoners' cattle. This quite sophisticated management has a critical importance for understanding medieval woods, and in fact the distinction between *silva pastilis* or pasture-woodland, *silva minuta* or coppice, and *silva pastilis per loca*, a wood pastured in some parts, is frequent in Domesday records for Lincolnshire, Derbyshire and Nottinghamshire.

From records like these, we know that late Saxon times saw much of the ancient, probably rather ill-defined pasture-woodlands, usually part of the common waste of the village, being converted either into sorely-needed farmland, or into enclosed coppices where wood was grown more intensively.

After the Norman conquest, the distinction between pasture-woodlands, where there was still grazing, and the protected coppices became much more formal, establishing two basic kinds of ancient woodlands in our landscape, both of which can still be seen in many places today. Where woods were scarce, trees were also grown in hedgerows, especially in counties like Essex, Devon and Kent.

COPPICED WOODS AND THEIR MANAGEMENT

A coppice was managed to produce a continuous supply of small wood products by felling the trees every few years and allowing the cut stumps to put out new shoots, which would then provide the next crop of wood. Cattle love the juicy coppice re-growth, and stock had to be rigorously kept out of the wood by a ditch and massive woodbank supporting a hedge, paling or brushwood fence.

The coppiced trees, grown for poles for craft uses or for fuel, formed the underwood; in some coppices there was also an overwood of larger trees maintained for timber. This was the medieval origin of what we now call coppice-with-standards. The underwood was made up of whatever species the wood had inherited from the wildwood itself, or from later colonisation, and could include ash, maple, hazel, aspen, lime, elms, hornbeam, oak, birch, alder and more rarely beech.

In most years, part of the wood, termed a cut, coupe, cant, fell, panel or whatever local custom had it, was felled, yielding poles and brushwood. Many an ancient coppice still shows traces of these panels, either as low banks (possibly once topped by a brushwood dead-hedge to exclude stock) or in the form of 'cant-marks', often pollard trees at compartment corners, like those still visible in Ham Street Woods National Nature Reserve in Kent.

Usually the panel was clear-felled, regardless of the species it contained, and the stumps or stools allowed to regrow. In this way the distribution of the different tree

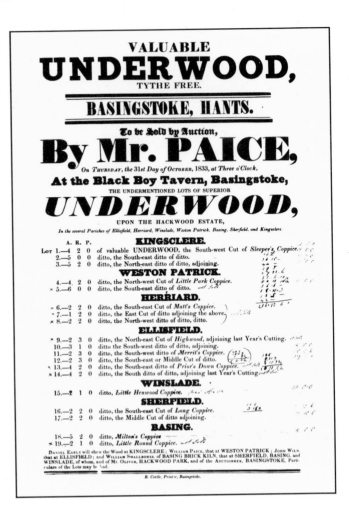

Coppice sales poster from Basingstoke. Coppice was sold at auction here until about 1950; this particular sale was held in 1833 and the poster advertises 19 fells or 'cuts' situated in coppices on the Hackwood estate.

species in the wood was kept the same over hundreds of years; this is a great help to woodland ecologists because it means that the pattern of tree communities may have direct links to ancient times, and occasionally even to the wildwood.

Species like ash, often wanted in larger sizes, could be left to grow on until the next cut. Similarly stems wanted for timber could be selected and left uncut for two, three or more rotations, a process called storing. Sometimes this involved singling; cutting all the poles except one or two from a stool. Even oak for building was usually felled when only 6 to 9 inches in diameter; the 300 oaks in a medieval house were not the large trees we see in woods today. If giant oaks were needed for mill posts or special buildings

A medieval coppice would have looked much like Monk's Park Wood, Bradfield St Clare, Suffolk. This section of the wood, called 'Pear Tree fell', has been almost clear-felled, yielding great stacks of poles of ash, lime, alder and birch, which are piled against the ancient coppice stools, so that the only visible stumps are those of self-sown young birch, a few left uncut.

year rotation produced an income of £63 a year. Most coppice went for fuel, however, and the volume could be astonishing; the earliest-known record is given in the Account Book of Beaulieu Abbey for 1269 and lists from 1 acre (0.4 hectare):

400 dozen bundles of small burning wood (about 20 wagon loads)
500 bundles of 40 vine stakes or fencing rods
4,000 oven-faggots

like castles or cathedrals they were usually bought from special woods where they were carefully grown from saplings selected for good form.

Hazel was the universal fuel and craft tree. It was thought to lose its suppleness after 12 years' growth, and was usually cut small for wattle work and faggots. In the fourteenth century it was much in demand for sheep-hurdles, and many a chalk-country coppice (Cranborne Chase for example) is still dominated by hazel which was selectively encouraged in mixed coppices even in those days. At Quarley in Hampshire, in the eighteenth century 112 acres (45 hectares) were valued at 9 shillings per acre per year – cutting 7 acres (3 hectares) annually on a 16-

a total of about 40 tons per acre on a 20-year rotation. This was the only form of energy or craft material available in most of medieval England, so the coppice was a sort of power station-cum-DIY shop.

In many coppices, the landlord owned the ground and the timber, but let the underwood out to someone else, with strict instructions to allow new saplings or single more poles for timber at each cut. At Southwick in Hampshire, Richard Norton leased the underwood of Rowe Coppice to a wheelwright subject to a penalty of £5 (in 1719!) for every 'young heire' cut by mistake, and of 'forty shillings for every heire or timber tree' damaged by the carters removing the 'underwood stuffe'.

AN ANCIENT COPPICE: BRADFIELD WOODS, SUFFOLK

There is still one place, in Suffolk, where you can experience a medieval coppice in all its glory. A few miles south-east of Bury St Edmunds, down a maze of twisting lanes, lie the Bradfield woods. Their medieval owner, the great Abbey of Bury St Edmunds, was destroyed in the Dissolution, but the woods, miraculously, have survived. One of them, Felshamhall Wood, is a normal coppiced wood; its name comes from the ancient word *halle*, a 'corner'; it is the wood in the corner of Bradfield St George parish next to Felsham. Joined to it by a narrow neck along the parish boundary with Bradfield St Clare is Monk's Park, also now a coppice but once containing the grassy *launds* of the Abbot's deer park. Each wood is still surrounded by its massive medieval (or much earlier) bank. Felshamhall's bank is 15–20 ft broad, tapering on the inside, away from the deep ditch, and topped with old pollard boundary trees of many species. Monk's Park's boundary is different, more symmetrical in profile, like other deer-park banks, and has been lost where two-thirds of the wood was bulldozed after 1966, leaving a raw edge to the south-west. Monk's Park also has traces of internal banks, relics of its deer-park days, when it was compartmented so that the deer could be kept out of the recently-coppiced areas.

A visit to the Bradfield woods leaves an overwhelming sense of productivity and order; great stacks of ash, alder, hazel, birch, lime and other poles awaiting conversion to scythe-snaiths, mallets, thatching spars, rake-handles, bean sticks and other products. The brushwood, once bundled up into oven-faggots, is now burned in carefully selected spots, and the wood-ash sold to potteries for making glaze. Nothing is wasted.

The woods are divided into panels, here called fells, such as Pear-tree Fell, each area being cut once every 10–11 years. The records of coppicing go back to 1252, which means that each part of the wood will have been clear-felled, except for a few small oak or ash standards, at least 70 times since then! In fact the Bradfield woods are far older than that; research on their soils suggests they have never been farmed, and are primary woodland, developed 8,000 or 10,000 years ago. Their present (pre-1966) shape is probably as old as the Dark Ages, when the Saxons settled the area.

Their great age and continuous history of management means that the Bradfield woods are an extraordinary repository of wildlife. Their vegetation alone has kept researchers busy for decades, and although most invertebrates have hardly been looked at the wood is noted for its white admiral butterflies and bush crickets. It also has a strange flora of fungi, which includes many species which have to be identified from continental material! Bradfield woods are also renowned for their rich vascular plant flora, which runs to 370 species or more; and it is certainly easy to believe as you walk down the grassy rides full of flowers, and insects, and marvel at the floral richness of the cut coppices, bursting with water avens, oxlips, bugle and violets, orchids and garlic and spreads of herb

Oxlips in Monk's Park Wood, West Suffolk. The true oxlip is confined to a small area of East Anglia, though the 'false-oxlip' occurs widely where primrose and cowslip grow close together. The oxlips bloom spectacularly, like other coppice flowers, in the second year after coppice cutting, as here in the Bradfield Woods and in other East Anglian woodland nature reserves.

Paris. Because the woods are so carefully managed, and because of their soils, there is a wonderful sense of renewal about them; there is none of the thick bramble tangle of some woods, but a carpet of seedlings of trees, a tremendous potential for the future.

Though the bulldozing of two-thirds of Monk's Park was a conservation disaster, it triggered off action by the County Council and, later, purchase of the remaining woods by the Royal Society for Nature Conservation and their subsequent management by the Suffolk Trust for Nature Conservation as a living monument to East Anglia's ancient woods.

NATURE AND THE COPPICE CYCLE

Coppicing has an important effect on the plants and animals which live in a coppiced wood. For most of the years in the coppice cycle, the plants of the woodland floor are deprived, by the coppice re-growth, of the energy-rich summer sunlight. Most woodland plants like bluebell or anemone can tolerate this, largely because they avoid being shaded by coming into leaf, and usually into flower, long before the trees. They form a 'pre-vernal' community. Others, like violets or ground ivy, are similar, but are more or less evergreen. Another group of plants puts up with the shade, either by photosynthesising in low light-levels, as in enchanter's nightshade, or by supplementing photosynthesis with food obtained from mycorrhizal relationships with soil fungi, as in some woodland orchids. It is the first group which is commoner in managed coppices, and the vigorous growth they make in the intense sunlight in the first season after the coppice has been cut enables them in the second season to produce that spectacular blooming which carpets the coppice floor with the yellow splashes of primrose or oxlip, the pink spikes of early purple orchid and sheets of dog violet and bugle. Bluebell is relatively independent and can actually decline after coppicing, though in most years it will still produce those incredible hyacinth-scented seas of blue, which are actually rare anywhere else outside Britain.

After this spectacular second spring, the new coppice shoots and disturbance-herbs like willow herbs and thistles begin to shade out the ground plants in late summer. Brambles begin to flower abundantly, and their nectar-rich flowers provide food for many woodland butterflies. Neglected coppices may have only the common speckled wood, or very occasionally the rare wood white, which feeds on vetches in shady woods, but regularly-coppiced woods support white admiral and the woodland fritillaries which feed on violets. All of these have gone steadily downhill since coppicing declined, especially the pearl-bordered and small pearl-bordered fritillaries. The high brown is now becoming rare in many former haunts, though the silver-washed is still widespread. The comma, on the other hand, has extended its range.

This rich insect life supports birds, which also use the thicker stages of coppice regrowth in which to breed; so the coppice gives both food and breeding sites in close proximity. Shrews too need a constant supply of insects to maintain their body temperature, whilst the woodmice and bank voles are more omnivorous. The common dormouse (which is now far from common) avoids recent coppice and uses the later thicket stages to move nimbly from bush to bush, feeding and breeding in the shrub layer, and even the canopy trees, seeking nuts and berries and cavities for nest-building.

Thus coppicing affects different species in different ways, but is responsible for keeping many of our woodlands rich in flowers and insects. Although few woods are now coppiced for purely commercial reasons, many are cut over for the produce, and for thickening up cover for pheasants.

Pearl-bordered fritillary feeding on bugle. The rather strong-flying fritillaries are amongst the most difficult butterflies to photograph. They are strongly dependent on flowers favoured by coppicing or moderate grazing (particularly violets), and as these traditional practices have declined these gorgeous insects have become rarer and rarer.

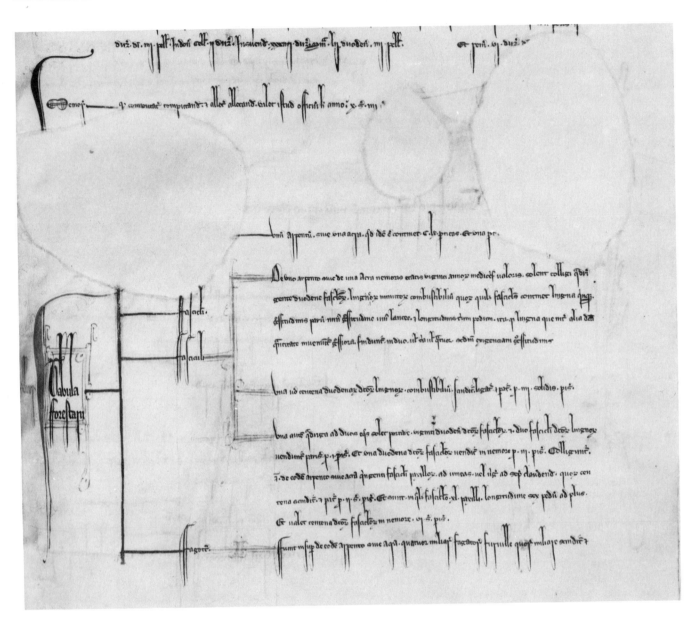

A page from the account book of Beaulieu Abbey, showing in medieval Latin the 'Tabula forestarii', one of the earliest records of the value of coppice, prepared in 1269. The holes in the manuscript show where a Victorian child cut out the colourful illuminations to embellish her scrapbook! (British Museum.)

Particular species were of course used for special purposes: ash for wagons and gates, beech for furniture, maple for domestic items like bowls, and alder or ash for hop-poles. Hornbeam, the hardest wood, was used for mill gear-teeth, and hornbeam and beech from the Chilterns fuelled London's hearths for centuries.

Even in medieval times, favourite species were encouraged and unwanted ones cleaned from coppices, but from the late seventeenth century onwards coppices began to be 'improved' by actually planting new species into them, or radically improving the content of oak for tanbark, or hazel. In the Industrial Revolution new coppices were planted in some areas where woods were few, for example in the north Midlands where there was demand for charcoal for iron smelting and tanning. From the eighteenth century, coppicing declined as alternative fuels became accessible, and it became difficult to get labour for woodland management. Coppices were cleared and replanted as high forest, or were further improved with chestnut and other species. At the same time, the management of the overwood changed away from a continuous promotion of

saplings, and towards the planting of well-spaced oaks amongst the coppice stools. This trend was especially strong after the Napoleonic wars and has created many of the coppice-with-standards woods which until recently were finally being felled, and often cleared for farming. Strangely, there are now signs of a revival of coppicing, as experiments are carried out into producing renewable supplies of woody material from which to produce fuel or chemicals, but hopefully these will not allow the introduction of alien trees into Britain's ancient woods.

One of the commonest forms of lowland woodland structure is 'coppice-with-standards'. Winterdown Copse, on the Hampshire chalk, is a hazel coppice, cut two years ago and now regrowing. The 'standards' or timber trees are oak and ash, which may have been 'promoted' from coppice stools, although the oaks are probably nineteenth-century plantings. Many of these chalk ash/hazel woods arose in the Dark Ages on abandoned Romano-British fields.

MEDIEVAL PASTURE-WOODLANDS

Pasture-woodlands contrast with coppices in that they combine growing trees and grazing cattle in the same place. This is a poor compromise for both uses, because the trees shade out the grass which the cattle need, and the cattle eat the young saplings or coppice shoots, so that trees are not replaced. Sometimes a balance was struck between these competing interests by pollarding the trees so that poles could be cut above the reach of grazing stock.

It may seem strange that such a system ever developed, but its origins lie deep in prehistory when animals were pastured and sheltered in natural woodland cover. As woodland cover shrank, the rights to this rough grazing and source of wood became concentrated in the remaining common waste of Saxon times. Under the Normans these became the 'wastes of the manor' where the lord owned the soil and timber, but the peasants still had rights to grazing, bracken and firewood, and these rights have prevented the complete destruction of pasture-woodlands on commons right up to the present day, so they are still a living part of our countryside heritage.

In medieval times pasture-woodland was much more widespread, and besides being found in wooded commons it formed great tracts of royal forests, where the king's deer grazed or browsed along with the commoners' beasts;

Pollards are trees cut higher up than coppice, so that the new shoots are safe from browsing stock. They are an indicator of ancient pasture-woodlands, like this one at Seatoller, in Borrowdale, where old pollard ash, holly and wych elm grow on a steep, flushed slope. This wych elm is rather unusual – pollards are usually oak, beech or other species typical of more acid soils – but wych elm flourishes in this damp climate, and the old trees are covered in 'old forest' lichens and mosses. Seatoller Wood is one of a number of beautiful National Trust woods in the Lake District; others include Great Wood, Borrowdale, with giant wych elms, Johnny's Wood, and oak coppices in the Duddon Valley.

chases, which were not royal but otherwise like forests; and the smaller enclosed parks where the deer were fed or sheltered.

WOODED COMMONS

These are the oldest kind of pasture-woodland, where the ancient customs of seeking wood or running cattle and pigs became defined, and rationed, as common rights long before the Norman conquest. Once codified, common rights were very complex and were administered by manorial courts. They included rights of *pannage* of beechmast and acorns for pigs, and *estovers*, a general right to wood for fuel and other uses including *ploughbote*, *hedgebote* for fences, *housebote* for building, and *firebote*. Partly as a result of later enclosure many rights also became attached to wood or timber in hedgerows, for though the rights were vigorously defended they were not strong enough everywhere to prevent enclosure.

Pre-conquest commons were often vast; the Weald of Kent was a common for all Kent, and Sherwood ('shire wood') probably filled the same role for Nottinghamshire. Wooded commons, like others, are vestiges of unenclosed land surrounded by enclosed farmland or woods. Their boundaries are created entirely by their neighbours and their outlines are characteristically rambling and concave, funneling into corners where tracks emerge.

Most commons, after centuries of grazing, little or no regeneration, cutting of wood, bracken or peat, and burning, were treeless places. Larger commons were often partly wooded, however, and a few were divided into compartments, some coppiced and some grazed; and even fewer, such as Naphill Common (Bucks) and The Mens and Ebernoe (Sussex), retained some tree cover throughout the historical period.

The management problems are illustrated by a large compartmented common at Hurstbourne Tarrant in Hampshire, also known as Doles Wood. Once part of Chute Forest, the common covered 779 acres (311 hectares). By 1670 it had shrunk, when the Chancellor, asked to adjudicate, declared: 'there are 600 acres... of Dowles Coppice, some of which has been cleared for pasture... known as the Grubed

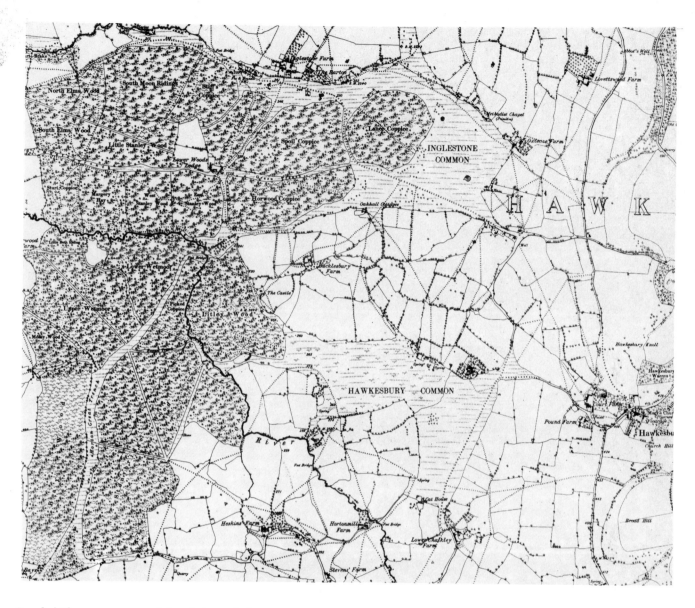

Compartmented commons were relatively unusual. This is Inglestone Common, near Hawkesbury in Gloucestershire, with a fine pattern of enclosed rounded coppices and straggly unenclosed grazing land. The Cotswolds is still a remarkably rich area for commons and other unimproved grasslands, and is noted for its woodlands too. 1st Edition Ordnance Survey.

Lands.' The commoners claimed: 'to us belong common of pasture, . . . upon the said Dowles Coppice and Grub Lands for our horses and other beasts levant and couchant on our several lands in the parish.' Of the twelve coppices, those under eight years' growth 'should remain enclosed until they be of a growth of eight years, and then afterwards eight of the twelve coppices should always be common and four only enclosed'. Its later history is typical; it was reduced by Act of 1818 to 200 acres (80 hectares), the remainder becoming farmland, and the rump was largely requisitioned and ploughed by the Ministry of Agriculture during the last war. It is now a beech plantation.

Other commons were uncompartmented, and bore pollards, as at the Wildgrounds, Gosport, now a nature reserve, where a few ancient shells of pollard oaks are treasured, and Frithsden Beeches, in the Chilterns, with its

magnificent grove of beech pollards, on the edge of Berkhamsted Frith.

One of the best surviving wooded commons is the Mens, near Petworth in Sussex, whose name may come from the Germanic *gemaene* meaning 'common to everyone'. Here a pattern of eighteenth-century compartments, and recent woodland of holly, beech and oak, conceals the elements of a very ancient pasture-woodland phase, with old pollards, hazel and hornbeam, and rarer species diagnostic of ancient woods like wild service tree and midland (or *woodland*) hawthorn.

FORESTS AND CHASES

Today, most people think of a forest as a great expanse of woodland, often of conifers. Yet the word had a quite different meaning in medieval times when a *Forest* was a place set apart by the king for the protection of the 'beasts of the forest' including the king's deer (initially red and roe, but later fallow as well) collectively called the 'venison', and their habitat, known as the 'vert'. Special courts were set up to administer Forest law to protect the vension and the vert. At first, Forests were mainly royal demesne land, and coincided more or less with the actual physical woods and heaths where the deer lived, but under Henry II and Richard I the legal boundaries of the Forests were pushed out to cover one-third of England; mainly in order to raise revenue from fines for infringements against Forest law. Both legal and physical Forests were very unevenly spread over England. Hampshire, where the Norman capital of Winchester lay, was almost all parcelled up into 11 different Forests; the only exception was Waltham Chase, hunted over by the Bishops of Winchester. Some Forests like Chute and Clarendon (Wilts) had Saxon origins, but many others were not recorded until the thirteenth century. In all there were 66 Royal Forests, ranging from Allerdale and Inglewood in Cumberland to Trivel in Herefordshire, Rockingham in Northamptonshire and New and Wolmer in Hampshire. There were also 77 chases in private hands.

The physical forests lay mainly on sands, gravels, clays or other infertile tracts of land, poor farmland but good territory for deer, and their pursuers. Surprisingly, Forests do not go hand in hand with places where great tracts of woodland remained at Domesday; there were none in the Weald or the Chilterns, for example. Most Forests were in partly-wooded areas like Hampshire, Wiltshire, Shropshire and Lancashire. They were usually managed as wooded commons; the king could not afford to suppress the local graziers entirely, even though he reduced the taxes of owners of Forests which he did not own personally. They were grazed by the commoner's cattle as well as royal deer; and it is the common rights which have helped to ensure the preservation of one or two of them, especially the New Forest.

What sort of woodlands were there in these forests? Most had some pasture-woodland, and because they were not

Epping Forest, known in olden days as Waltham Forest, survived a nineteenth-century attempt at enclosure to become the property of the City of London; but misguided attempts to 'preserve' it have favoured beech over hornbeam, and many other species have been lost. It retains, however, its straggly 'common' outline, and it is not too late to initiate better conservation management.

HATFIELD FOREST, ESSEX

Five minutes from the M11 motorway, and uncomfortably close to Stansted airport, lies the Forest of Hatfield Broadoak, Essex, owned since 1923 by the National Trust and one of those all too rare places where you can still feel the Middle Ages around you and see almost all the features of a working medieval forest in action.

Hatfield was a royal manor, taken over by William I from King Harold. Later, as Oliver Rackham has described in his recent book, the Forest was owned by Robert the Bruce, tussled over by the Morley and Barrington families, and, from the eighteenth century, conserved by the Houblons, founders of the Bank of England.

The physical forest seems to have been about 1½ square miles (4 km²) in extent as far back as Domesday. Just before it was enclosed and slightly reduced in 1857 – the last former royal forest to be enclosed – Hatfield was just over 1,100 acres (445 hectares) with 65 acres (26 hectares) of purlieu woods adjoining. It then had the usual straggly outline of a common. The 1st edition 6-inch Ordnance Survey map printed here, however, shows Hatfield just after enclosure in 1875–76, squared off with straight boundaries to north, east and south, and shorn of about 200 acres (80 hectares) of peripheral pieces which were allotted to those who had previously owned common rights on the forest.

But in comparison with most enclosed Forests – which were unceremoniously grubbed out root and branch – Hatfield escaped lightly, and what the National Trust now cares for is the whole of the medieval core. Essentially, Hatfield has changed little. Though no longer an actual common, it is still a compartmented Forest, divided by permanent woodbanks into a fixed pattern of coppices separated by open 'plains'.

Originally there were 17 coppices; although only 12 now survive as such, there are traces of the others; for example the eastern three were converted in about 1760 into open tracts of pollarded trees, mainly hornbeams and maples, on what became 'Bush-end Plain'.

Today, Hatfield still has its complement of up to 160 fallow deer; and the grassy plains are still grazed from May to October by 300 cattle, which are excluded from the coppices in the old-fashioned way. The coppices, despite a few exotic plantings and one or two minor dalliances with 'modern' forestry in the 1950s and 1960s, retain their ancient tree and shrub composition, descended directly from the Wildwood, and many of the individual stools of oak, hornbeam, maple and other native trees are real giants. In spring recently-cut coppices are brilliant with patches of ancient woodland flowers, including a few oxlips, and support a rich fauna of insects and birds.

Once richer in flowers and insects, the grassy plains sadly were sporadically 'improved' with chemicals after the Second World War in a misguided attempt to increase their productivity, and were later damaged by vehicles. All is not lost, however, for many areas were too wet or inaccessible in the scrub to improve, car parking has been controlled, and now, after some 40 years, the grasslands are recovering their lost riches of native grasses, sedges and herbs.

As a result, we can still stand on a coppice-bank in Hatfield Forest and look either inwards into an ancient coppice with its giant stools of maple, oak or hornbeam, or out into the open plain, studded with centuries-old pollards, which include ancient thorns, crab-apples and hollies as well as the hornbeams and maples; and thus compare the ecological effects of the two main traditions of medieval woodland management, the coppice and the wood-pasture. Hatfield is one of the glories of England's's ancient woods, and should not be missed!

Hatfield Forest, as it appeared in about 1860. This was a compartmented Forest, with a fixed pattern of grassy launds with isolated pollards, and enclosable coppices for wood-growing. 1st Edition 6-inch Ordnance Survey. Essex Sheets 23 and 32.

AN ANCIENT ROYAL FOREST – THE NEW FOREST

By far the best surviving pasture-woodland in Britain is the New Forest in Hampshire, a remarkable complex of habitats which still covers 90,000 acres (36,000 hectares) (much the same as in 1250) and includes not only our greatest tract of heathland and valley bogs, but an extraordinary wealth of woodlands, plants, birds and animals. The whole forest is the most extensive uncultivated area in lowland England, and is visible even from space as an island of ancient vegetation, with something of an upland appearance, in an ocean of agricultural and urban development. It is also the best place to see how a Norman hunting forest worked, and how centuries of management, first for deer, but later for timber, have produced woodlands quite different from those elsewhere in the countryside, containing unique clues about the evolution of our woods from prehistoric times.

By the Bronze Age, much of the forest was under cultivation, perhaps in a shifting pattern, and a great deal of the woodland and the fertility of the soils was destroyed, so that now heathland is the commonest vegetation. Pollen studies show, however, that there has always been woodland present too, and there are still 9,000 acres (3,600 hectares) of beautiful old woods, known since Victorian times as the 'Ancient and Ornamental' woodlands, often referred to as the 'A and O'.

In structure, these old woods resemble the wildwood, and they still contain thousands of species of insects and other invertebrates, lichens, mosses and fungi, many of which must have been common in the prehistoric forest where there were many glades, dead and dying trees, and countless small streams, trickles and pools, but which outside the New Forest have succumbed to coppice management, drainage or replanting. Today the New Forest is of outstanding importance for its richness in species associated with dead or dying wood, holes in trees, and a humid atmosphere. Numbered among these are 13 out of our 15 species of bats, including specialists in wood-pasture like the noctule, barbastelle and Leisler's bat, and numerous birds including tawny owl, treecreeper, the woodpeckers, redstart, wood warbler and so on. The insect fauna is specialised but outstanding; more than 1,500 species of beetles, as well as flies, hymenopterans and others, use the dead-wood habitats.

The 'A and O' woodlands have an incredibly complicated ecology, though to the casual visitor they may look rather uninviting with their prickly holly, wet ground and rather few woodland flowers and butterflies. Here we can do no more than look at these woods and raise a few pointers to the history of royal Forests in general, and the 'Ancient and Ornamental' woods of the New Forest in particular.

THE 'ANCIENT AND ORNAMENTAL' WOODS TODAY

You can recognise the 'A and O' woods easily enough. On the map they have ancient 'wood' names like Pinnick Wood, Gritnam Wood, and so on, and have no mapped boundaries. On the ground you will see that they have in fact no boundary banks; they are unenclosed, and gradually peter out into the open heathland.

The minute you walk into one of these beautiful old woods, you are overcome by a feeling of antiquity. They have all the signs of ancient wooded commons, with beech and oak of all shapes and sizes, sometimes growing thickly, sometimes with broad glades, or thickets of grazing-resistant holly, some of which form great groves or rings. Many of the trees have been pollarded, others are forked, leaning at angles, calloused at the base, stag-headed or otherwise not quite what a forester might wish. There is no coppice layer, and palatable trees like hazel are virtually absent, whilst even the holly shows a distinct browse-line about 6 ft up, below which everything has been eaten or at least nibbled. Nor is there much of a woodland flora; just a few species like spurge, butcher's broom and, in some places, wood sorrel and bluebell. Deer, cattle and ponies are everywhere, and in the autumn you may even meet a family of pigs, turned out to forage on beechmast and acorns. The overall impression is one of lack of human interference; there is certainly no sign of management – no cut stumps nor

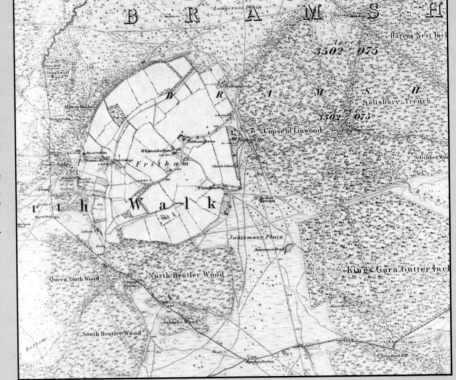

A detail of the 1858 6-inch survey of the New Forest. This marvellous map shows many of the 'typical' forest features; the vast open heaths and 'plains', the many watercourses and the pockets of farmland. The contrast between the straight-edged, fenced enclosures and the old open woods grading into heath is clear, though the old woods of North and South Bentley were fenced in an older, more 'organic' pattern and re-sown with oak.

planted trees. Appearances, as usual, though, are somewhat deceptive, and in fact these woods have changed a great deal over the last 6,000 years.

ORIGIN AND HISTORY OF THE 'ANCIENT AND ORNAMENTAL' WOODS

Today's oak- and beech-dominated woods are quite different from the primeval forest which grew here; its pollen still exists in the New Forest's valley bogs and shows that 6,000 years ago the forest was dominated by small-leaved lime, hazel, oak, elm and alder. Today, oak and alder are still common, but elm and lime have vanished altogether, and hazel is very rare, though it is common just outside the forest in un-grazed woods.

The loss of hazel and perhaps lime is well accounted for by frequent medieval records of cattle damaging coppices in the forest, and elm growing on fertile soils may have been cleared preferentially by early farmers. There is another change, however, that from oak towards beech, which was hardly represented in the Iron Age, was still less dominant in 1299 (when a bank called the Lyndhurst ridge was built over a soil surface where beech pollen was rare), but expanded dramatically from about the fifteenth century. These changes can be related to management practices in medieval, or earlier, times, but there is still the question of whether the present old woods are of natural wildwood origin, or have at some stage been cleared and later replanted.

Even in Saxon times, of course, much of the Forest was heath, so the private estates would probably have grown wood in some enclosed coppices, as well as having grazed woods in the common waste in the stream valleys and on the heath. It would be useful to know which, if either, of these kinds of woods ultimately became the present 'A and O' woodlands. Fortunately we have plenty of evidence to consider.

Firstly, there are many records of coppice management in the Forest; and of under-wood being damaged; for example, 'The wood of Henry, the son of Aucher, pertaining to Biketon, was newly wasted of under-wood by the same, therefore in mercy and let the wood be taken into the King's hand. Afterwards Henry came and was fined one mark. . . .' (1280).

Secondly, an Act of 1483 extended from three to seven years the period for which 'encoppicements' were to be enclosed to prevent grazing of the new shoots, whilst in 1543 Henry VIII in the 'Statute of Woods' laid down a working plan for coppices in royal Forests. Such evidence strongly suggests a compartmented Forest, where some areas were set aside for wood production. Were the 'encoppicements', however, the ancestors of the A and O woods? Nineteenth-century foresters mistook the term 'encoppicement' for 'plantations' and wrongly believed that this meant the ancient unenclosed New Forest woods had been planted; as Lascelles wrote in 1915, 'Every one of the beautiful old woods . . . is the result of such a process of enclosing, encoppicement and cultivation as is prescribed in those Acts' (of Henry VIII).

In this view, the old foresters were wrong, having done neither the documentary research in the Public Record Office, nor the biological work in the field, which present-day historical ecologists have undertaken. The third clue is found in sixteenth-century records of the 31 sites known to have been encoppicements. Only five of these can be related to the present unenclosed woods. The remainder have been lost (seven) or lie in what are now statutory enclosures. No mention is made in the records of most of the great 'A and O' woods – Brinken, Pinnick, Redshoot or Frame Wood, for example; and the fourth clue is that the king's surveyor, Roger Taverner, in 1565 carefully distinguished ten *coppices* from the remaining 136 *woods*, many of which bore 'great old oaks'.

If the 'A and O' woods were not ancient encoppicements, however, what *was* their origin? Clues 5 and 6 come from the woods themselves. Studies of soil profiles prove that many of the ancient unenclosed woods grow on undisturbed 'Acid Forest Brown Earth' soils which would have been destroyed if the land had ever been farmed. (Others are easily distinguished, such as Matley, which clearly overlies a cultivation site, and may have been replanted in medieval times – it has old decayed coppice banks.)

Finally, a clue comes from the lichens which clothe the ancient forest trees. Lichens are extremely sensitive to being either dried-out or over-shaded. Many of them can survive only in woods never coppiced nor clear-felled, but with some glades, giving both light and humidity. Overall the New Forest woods have around 300 bark-living species of lichens (more than anywhere else in Europe) and some individual woods have more than 130 different species per square kilometre. Significantly, large numbers of these are the sensitive 'Old Forest Indicator' lichens, like the lungworts *Lobaria pulmonaria* and *Lobaria laetevirens*, which are common enough in humid west Scottish woods, but extremely rare in south-east Britain.

All this evidence forms a pretty convincing case for saying that the wonderful old 'A and O' woods of the Forest are indeed

Lichens are lower plants in which a fungus and an alga form a stable association. They require both light and humidity, and in the south the most demanding species are confined to a few ancient pasture-woodlands. In the north-west, woods tend to be much damper and more lichens flourish. The photograph shows Lobaria laetevirens (with orange fruiting-bodies, left), and the tree lungwort Lobaria pulmonaria, growing on a beech at Airds Wood, Appin, Argyllshire.

The Knightwood oak, a famous pollard oak in the New Forest. This tree has a girth of about 20 ft (6 m), and although it has shed some of its lower branches is still growing well. It is now about 350–400 years old, and could well live at least as long again. It exemplifies the 'pre-A' generation trees in the forest, most (though not all) of which are pollards.

beginning to be concerned about timber conservation, mainly to maintain revenues from letting coppices and selling timber.

Many of the unenclosed woods recorded by Taverner in 1565 as oakwoods are now dominated by beech, and it is the Crown's various timber surveys which give us the basis for understanding this change. Timber was increasingly felled for great buildings and defence works, and from about 1570 for naval shipbuilding. A famous survey of 1608 revealed 123,927 trees (197,405 loads) fit for the Navy and another 118,072 loads of 'doddards' (ancient decayed trees). The high proportion of 'doddards' shows the lack of replacement, caused by the grazing. From the outbreak of the Civil War many of these trees were being rapidly felled, whole woods being stripped of their oak. Even doddards were cut wholesale to provide 'knees' and 'crooks' used in ship frames.

Charles II initiated the re-enclosure of ancient encoppicements and started the system of making new enclosures for growing timber. Nevertheless, the open woods were still suffering, branches up to 2 ft thick being cut for firewood under the guise of providing deer-browse. Finally an Act of 1698 made further pollarding illegal; so if you see an old pollard in the Forest it is probably older than that.

The heavy fellings and subsequent management go a long way towards explaining the present dominance of beech. Oak has a very uneven age-distribution today. Fewer than 25 individuals of more than 350 years growth (17 ft, 5.2 m girth, or so) survive. These are known as the 'pre-A generation', and are often exceptional trees for relict lichen populations. Much commoner are the 'A' generation of trees which arose between 1650 and 1750, following widespread fellings. It was at this time that beech increased in abundance; especially in

descended directly from the wildwood, and have been open to grazing since time immemorial. This has left its mark on the tree flora, with the loss of palatable hazel and lime, and on the ground flora too. There is some evidence, however, that a good check on which woods are 'primary' is given by the presence of butcher's broom, growing with wood spurge.

There is one more aspect to consider. What has caused the dramatic increase in beech over the last 400 or 500 years? Both oak and beech seem able to hold their own in terms of regeneration. Yet something, other than grazing, must have favoured

beech. Again, the answer lies in management history, described in ancient records.

Royal Forests were run by two courts, the lower 'Court of Swainmote' and the upper 'Justice in Eyre', which the king established to impose penalties for offences against the 'venison' or the 'vert' and to carry out the 'Regard' of the Forest (in other words to check on whether illegal felling [assarts] or enclosure for farming [purprestures] were taking place). Many of the ancient records of these courts can still be seen in the Public Record Office, and they show that by the fifteenth century the Crown had lost interest in deer, but was

areas where oak was completely clear-felled. Where oak was only selectively removed, both oak and beech regenerated, and in isolated wet woods like Pinnick and South Ocknell, where there was little felling, oak still predominates today. It is the latter woods which still have the richest flora, with rarities like bastard balm, and other plants which are grazed or shaded out in most of the 'A and O' woods, such as wild daffodil.

The later history of the New Forest is one of an increasing number of Crown enclosures, now totalling 20,000 acres (8,000 hectares), and enclosing within their new plantings a number of old pockets of 'A and O' woodland. 9,000 acres (3,600 hectares) of these enclosures had been established by 1850 when the Commissioners concluded that further tree production could only be achieved by removing the deer from the

Only a few hundred years ago, oak was much commoner in many New Forest woods now dominated by beech. The complex reasons for this change include selective felling of oak for the Navy, more effective colonisation of felled or disturbed areas by beech, changes in soil and climate, and grazing pressure. The grassy clearing has been made and kept open by cattle, ponies and deer.

Forest. This was legislated for in 1851, and the resulting reduction in grazing pressure on the open forest initiated a massive surge of regeneration leading to what is known as the 'B' generation of trees, abundant in the Forest today, so that the 'A and O' expanded from 5,000 to 9,000 acres (2,000–3,600 hectares), although the deer have since increased again.

In 1871 the Forest escaped total enclosure and destruction when a Bill to disafforest it was, fortunately, withdrawn; mainly due to public pressure. Conservation for philosophical and aesthetic reasons prevailed over economics, and our last and largest medieval forest survived. Today it is managed by the Forestry Commission,

Pinnick Wood is one of the least disturbed of the ancient woods in the New Forest, and has remained an oakwood, unaffected by beech invasion. It still has a rich flora, and a primeval feel which is rare in lowland England.

advised by the Nature Conservancy Council, and has Verderers, who control the grazing carried out by the commoners. We are extremely lucky that it still exists, with its incredibly rich wildlife, so that we may walk in it and ponder what John Wise called, in 1862, its 'thousand significations'.

coppiced they often grew outsize oaks, very useful for building palaces and churches. After the Assize of the Forest in 1184, the king tried to control the grazing and pannage to help the woods regenerate, but in many forests his own staff were also the local commoners, and, not surprisingly, little was achieved! However, a few forests were compartmented, like Hatfield, Essex, with its remarkable pattern of coppices, enclosed when necessary for regeneration, and 'launds' or lawns for grazing, all of which can still be seen today. Elsewhere, originally protected coppices fell into disrepair and were damaged by grazing. In the uplands, of course, some forests had little woodland and were moorland, like Langstrothdale Chase.

Since forests were usually grazed in the Middle Ages, they developed a quite different structure from the protected

Evening sun illuminates the ancient pollard hornbeams and maples, and the cuckoo flowers in the old grassland, of Bush-end Plain in Hatfield Broadoak Forest, in Essex. This is the last of England's medieval forests to retain all its ancient forestal features.

coppices. As on commons, wood supplies could only be protected from the cattle by pollarding. Ancient pollard trees are an evocative feature of forests, like the extremely old oaks of Windsor, the New Forest, or the Forest of Dean. Pollard beech and hornbeam dominate parts of Epping Forest, a wonderful medieval survival in north London.

Regeneration of trees from seed had to wait for the odd occasion when grazing pressure happened to be low, and the trees in some forests are in narrowly-defined age-bands. The grazing had other effects which you can still see today. It favoured beech and oak, and especially holly, over the tastier trees like lime, ash and hazel which were often gradually eliminated. Lime, for example, disappeared from the New Forest about 500 years ago, yet its pollen record shows it was common in earlier times, as Saxon place-names like Lyndhurst and Linwood remind us. In a remarkable demonstration of the effects of human management. two ancient lime stools still grow in a coppice within yards of the forest-edge at Linwood. On the other hand, grazing and felling of timber trees have favoured the invasion of beech in many southern forests.

The second effect has been on the flowers of the forest floor. Many of the plants we would expect to find in a wood, like primrose and bluebell, are often absent or extremely suppressed and not flowering.

A few tough or prickly specialists may be quite common, however. One is butcher's broom, a strange member of the lily family; this has tiny green flowers, and later on enormous brilliant red berries, borne on what look like leaves but are actually part of the stem. In the New Forest in Hampshire, the association of butcher's broom and wood spurge seems to be specially common in the primary woods, the oldest part of the forest. Other typical forest flowers are bilberry (on acid soils) and cow wheat.

Pasture-woodlands have another important feature – humidity. Because the woods are not coppiced, and often grow on poorly-drained soils, the atmospheric humidity is high, and many kinds of mosses and lichens, which can only live in these conditions, grow luxuriantly all over the trees and on stumps, deadwood and the ground. In general, the warmer, wetter west of Britain has a much richer moss and lichen flora, but in forests there can be an extremely rich range of these plants; the New Forest, despite a moderately low rainfall, has more lichen species (about 300) than any other site in north-west Europe.

The forests we have today are only a tiny flavour of the medieval forests. Gradually, the kings lost interest in deer, and only awoke to the need for timber conservation in the seventeenth century. In the intervening years, vast acreages of forest had been sold for farmland, and from then on this process accelerated, forests being enclosed, and destroyed, sometimes leaving the Crown a part of the land which was planted up with timber. The first edition

Staverton Park, Suffolk. A superb medieval deer park dating from about 1280. Here, thousands of old oak pollards, like elephants' feet, rise from the sandy forest floor with its bracken and sand sedge.

Ordnance Survey 1-inch map gives a remarkable impression of the last surviving forests, many of which were enclosed soon afterwards. For example in Alice Holt (Hampshire) in 1565 the 'maine wood (was) set with oaks of very great age, and with thorne, maple and some beech, beside the waste plots'. In 1812, however, the Crown purchased the common rights and its Office of Woods planted the whole forest with oaks. Rockingham Forest (Northants) was disafforested in 1796, leaving the Bedford Purlieus, amongst other traces; Wychwood was not enclosed until 1857, and the vast Forest of Bere around 1816. The surviving Crown woods passed to the Forestry Commission in 1923.

The actual process of enclosure is well shown by the Forest of Neroche in south Somerset, where both in Domesday and on the ground today there is almost no evidence of a forest ever having existed. In Domesday the area around Neroche is curiously blank, but careful work reveals that surrounding it are several settlements with extensive ploughlands, to which are assigned far bigger woods than they could have accommodated.

In fact, it appears these woods were all detached wooded commons, actually situated at Neroche. Their total area of about 17,000 acres (6,800 hectares) agrees well with the space left 'empty' in Neroche. In the eighteenth and nineteenth centuries this mysterious forest was enclosed in stages, and now only a few small commons survive.

PARKS

Parks, in the pasture-woodland and not the Corporation Parks Department sense, were medieval enclosures for keeping deer. Unlike forests they were private demesne land of the Lord of the Manor. A few were in existence at Domesday, or even before (Ongar in Essex and Earnstray in Shropshire), but they became much more popular in the twelfth and thirteenth centuries. Anyone could own a park,

Savernake Forest, Wiltshire. An ancient royal Forest now mostly destroyed by conversion to agriculture, or replanted with beech. Even so, some pasture-woodland fragments remain, and numerous old oak pollards live out their lives in the fields and plantations; many will no doubt outlive the great nineteenth-century beech avenues which line the forest roads.

but if it lay in a forest permission had to be sought from the king to enclose it, and the Close and Pipe rolls abound with references to emparking in the thirteenth century. In 1258, for example, Patric de Cadurcis obtained licence to enclose his woods at Weston (Patrick) in Hampshire and make a fence ('Weston Boscus, Vocat Headon et Haselmangrove, includ et hayam facere'). The '*haya*' of most parks was a massive bank, often topped with a cleft-oak paling, which served to keep the deer in, and was sometimes provided with 'deer-leaps' where deer could jump into the park, but not out. The deer themselves were usually fallow, probably introduced in the twelfth century, and occasionally roe or red. In the winter they were fed in the park by the keeper or 'Parker'.

In all, there were probably more than 3,000 parks in England, only 20 of which were Crown property. The king owned the giant 1,000-acre (400-hectare) park of Blagdon which unusually straddles the Hampshire-Dorset border,

and a park at Lyndhurst in the New Forest, whose park pale still survives, and pollen studies on the soil buried beneath it have given much data on the thirteenth-century forest in that area.

The characteristic shape of medieval parks is an 'economical' outline, rectangular with rounded corners, or roughly oval, in order to minimise fencing costs per unit of park area.

Early parks were usually enclosed from woods and waste, but, later on, many were formed from pre-existing fields, like the renowned Sotterley Park in Norfolk, its origins betrayed by the stranded village church and slight traces of old field boundaries.

Around half the pasture-woodland parks had some system of compartmentation to allow woodland regeneration, but even in those which didn't the trees often held their own both as pollards and as a result of the infrequent regeneration allowed by collapses in the deer population. Staverton Park in Suffolk has hundreds of ancient oaks, though none is much older than 400 years, and a great deal of regeneration must have occurred at intervals; the park is at least thirteenth-century in date, occupies unpodsolized sandy soils (see p. 156), and is likely to be an enclosure direct from the wildwood.

Other remarkable parks include Moccas in Herefordshire with its rich fauna of beetles, akin to that of Windsor Great Park, where more than 2,000 of Britain's 4,000 beetle

species have been recorded, and Melbury in Dorset. Melbury is especially rich in lichens and bryophytes, as is the ancient park of Boconnoc near Lostwithiel in Cornwall.

Deer parks which were abandoned and enclosed for farming in medieval times can still be traced on maps; the farm was often called Park or Old Park Farm. Park Lane, North Park Wood and so on often turn out to be clues to this ancient form of medieval land use. Even today, the modern 1:50,000 map with its magenta 'bridleways' can reveal the outline of long lost parks; these rights of way are incredibly enduring features and an oval pattern of old lanes is often a telling hint to those on the lookout.

DISCOVERING ANCIENT WOODS

How can you tell whether the wood where you walk at weekends is ancient? Fortunately the ancient origins and long management history of most ancient woods have left all kinds of clues which you can decipher and chew over to help you decide.

One group of clues can be found in the wood itself, but others will need to be extracted from maps and documents in your county Record Office or library. They range from obvious things like the name of the wood, or its position in the parish, to more subtle clues such as the presence of

The Forest of Bere Portchester, Hampshire, survived as a vast series of wooded commons and heaths, and enclosed woods until about 1816, when it was 'disafforested' and converted into enclosed farmland, Crown plantations and privately-owned coppices, many of which remain today.

certain flowers or the balance between the tree species present.

In the first place, the name of the wood can be very helpful. If your wood is named after the parish (or vice versa!) and lies along the parish boundary, it is almost certain to be very old indeed. Woods with names like Spring, Cuts, Coppice or Copse are also likely candidates. Grove can be ancient too, but Plantation, Covert, Belt, Furze, Scrubs etc may turn out to be nineteenth-century in origin.

The local Record Office will have thousands of old deeds, estate papers, wills, bills of sale and accounts which contain references to old woods. You will need to be careful in interpreting some of these; particularly when they refer to area, because the medieval woodland perch was longer at 18 ft (5.5 m) than the statutory $16\frac{1}{2}$-ft (5-m) perch used for arable; so medieval acreages of woodland tend to be under-estimates. For instance, the Wood Book of the Chapter of Winchester Cathedral gives the acreages of its woods at Manydown in 1667, including the following.

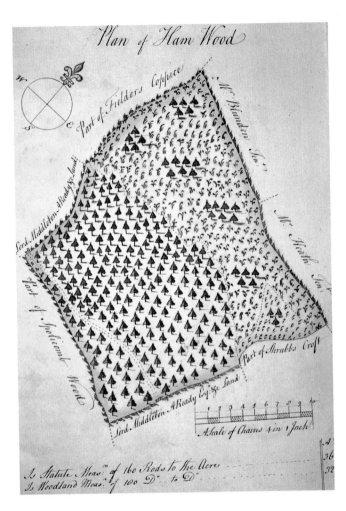

A 1773 survey of Ham Wood, on the Froyle estate in north Hampshire. The ownerships, trackways and gates and the age of the trees are all carefully shown. Surveys like this are an invaluable source of information; note the 'statute' and 'woodland' measures of the size of the wood.

Coppices in the Hands of the Church 1667	
Well Coppice	18 acres
Bottom of Worthwood Coppice	24 acres
... Also coppices let to Mr Wither	
Cowdown Coppice	11 acres
Pardown Coppice	8 acres

All these can be traced today, but Cowdown Copse is actually about 14 acres (5.5 hectares), still within its original banks.

When looking for old woods, it is often best to start on the map. Modern maps are useful for car trips or walks, but practically no help for any kind of historical or ecological work. The exceptions are the excellent 1:25,000 'Path-finder' and 'Outdoor Leisure' Ordnance maps which still show old tracks, field boundaries and parish boundaries. For more detailed work or to check what a wood was like a century or two ago you will need to use estate maps or other old maps from the Record Office, or the various reprints of the 1st edition of the 1-inch Ordnance Survey, dated around 1800–1820 (see p. 53 for details). The later 1st edition 6-inch maps are quite superb, the zenith of English cartography, showing all kinds of features, ditches, fences, hedgerow trees and meadows or rough grazing, which have been destroyed by twentieth-century farming. The 1-inch maps of 1800 or so predate the last phase of enclosure of royal forest and are excellent for telling enclosed woods from unenclosed pasture-woodlands (and heaths and downs), though small copses were often missed altogether.

Maps also show the shape of woods. Ancient woods often have sinuous curving boundaries, frequently following streams, old winding lanes and tracks and so on. Even where these features are absent, however, an old wood edge is never straight. Straight edges and rectangular corners are the work of nineteenth-century surveyors; but beware of old woods cut back to a straight edge by a modern farmer or a Victorian military man clearing the field of fire, as to the north of the Portsdown Hill forts in Hampshire.

Armed with a few of these ideas, we are ready for a little fieldwork, which should aim to look at three main things:

1) The physical features of the woods; woodbanks, compartment banks, ditches, streams and ponds, archaeological remains like barrows, and so on.
2) The structure of the wood; whether it has old coppiced trees, or pollards, saplings or standards etc.
3) The composition of the wood, both in trees and shrubs and in the flowers growing on the woodland floor.

BOUNDARIES, BANKS AND BARROWS

The boundaries of woods are of special significance. Medieval or earlier woods are usually bounded by an ancient woodbank, broad and curving, made from the spoil dug from the ditch outside it, which marks the legal extent of the wood. The bank is always inside the ditch, because the silt cleared from the ditch was placed on the wood-owner's property, and a woodbank has a characteristic profile, steeper on the ditch side, sloping away more gradually on the wood side, and the older the wood, in general, the broader the bank; up to 20 feet (6 m) is not unusual in heavy soil areas.

By contrast, recent woods have steep-sided tall narrow banks and are often found in areas of common land or royal forest broken up into compartments and enclosed in the

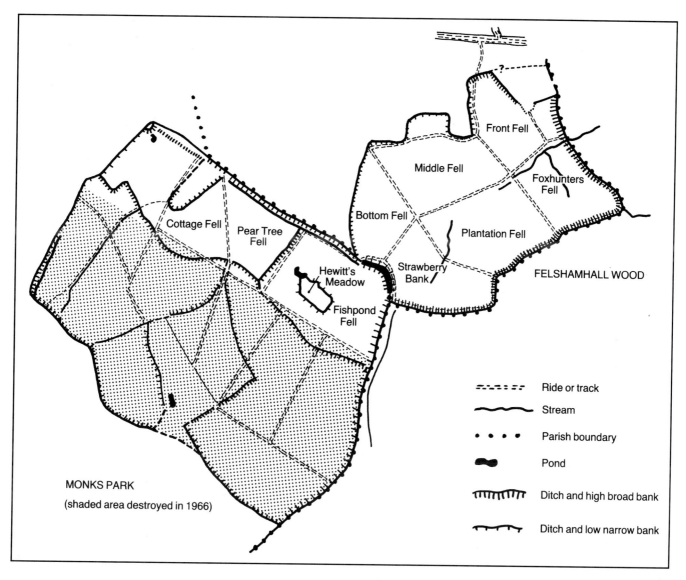

Ride or track

Stream

Parish boundary

Pond

Ditch and high broad bank

Ditch and low narrow bank

MONKS PARK

(shaded area destroyed in 1966)

FELSHAMHALL WOOD

Front Fell

Middle Fell

Foxhunters Fell

Bottom Fell

Plantation Fell

Strawberry Bank

Hewitt's Meadow

Fishpond Fell

Cottage Fell

Pear Tree Fell

One of the best ways to understand the history of a wood is to draw a map of the banks and ditches around and within it. The Bradfield woods have been formed from two ancient woods lying in two different parishes in west Suffolk. About two-thirds of Monks Park was destroyed for agriculture in the 1960s, but survives as documentary records and soil marks.

nineteenth century. Shelter belts and fox coverts often have no bank at all, and of course in the rocky uplands where no ditch was either necessary or possible, woods are often bounded by vertical rock outcrops or by stone walls.

Occasionally, the ditch appears to be inside the bank. This may mean the wood originally lay on the adjoining land, or it could be that you are looking at a deer park bank, where the inside ditch helped stop deer jumping out. Such parks had high, broad banks, symmetrical in profile, and the park outline was often rectangular with round corners, or vaguely oval.

Woodbanks were expensive, and have tended to survive in the landscape. If the bank lies well inside the wood, the wood has probably spread outwards in a farming lull; look for colonising hawthorn, ash, birch or oak scrub which will probably not have been coppiced. Woodbanks were originally topped with a stockproof hedge or brushwood dead-

hedge. Nowadays you will often find outgrown coppice stools of ash, maple, oak or hazel, less often beech or hornbeam, and very rarely lime. Standard oak or ash grown for timber also occur, as well as rarer incidental trees like wild service tree. If cattle were kept in the next-door pasture or used an adjoining droveway, there may be pollards of various species.

If some woods have grown beyond their banks, in others

Woodbanks are amongst the most enduring landscape features. This is the ancient, probably Saxon, bank round Felshamhall Wood, West Suffolk; it follows a gently winding course and, as is usual, slopes more steeply on the ditch side. Like many woodbanks, this one carries pollard trees and has been colonised by woodland flowers, notably dog's mercury; in many woods the bank offers varied conditions of light and drainage, and has a specially rich flora and fauna. The ditch still forms the boundary between the parishes of Bradfield St George and Felsham; Felshamhall Wood is in Bradfield and its name means 'the wood at the corner near Felsham'.

the wood is younger than the boundary, for example where woods have colonised prehistoric fields bounded by lynchets. Archaeological features can help date a wood; if a Roman villa, a medieval moat or castle lies in a wood, then the wood is later than the archaeological remains. Bronze-Age barrows, built on chalkland ridge tops, now often lie buried in Dark-Age secondary woodland. Motley Copse in Hampshire has an old earthwork castle now covered in twisted maple stools, but this woodland can be no older than twelfth century. Elsewhere a decline in farming has allowed woods to spread over medieval ridge-and-furrow.

Topography can give clues too: woods on steep un-farmable sites or specially rocky places are often old; places like the Wye Valley or the Avon Gorge, Ling Ghyll in Ribblesdale, or the Kentish sandstone gullies, are all examples, but even in farmscapes a ribbon of old woods often runs along tiny stream valleys.

on the way the wood has been managed and which species of trees are present; for example, beech casts a heavier shade than ash. In practice, most ancient woods you come across will be one of the following.

1) *Simple coppice*, where multi-stemmed coppice trees dominate the wood. Usually of several species, they are not overtopped by a high canopy of timber trees.
2) *Coppice-with-standards*, where a coppice has timber trees in it, but they do not form a complete canopy.
3) *High forest*, where there is a more-or-less complete canopy and the coppice layer is suppressed or absent. Semi-natural high forest will usually have several kinds of trees, but not all in the canopy. In pasture-woodland high forest there are often pollards, grazing-resistant shrubs like holly, and a grassy woodland floor.

The most obvious indications of age in all these ancient woods are the massive old coppice stools or pollards.

The other kinds of woodland you may meet are plantations, a few of which are ancient (in parts of the New Forest for example) and scrub, which is young woodland of pioneer trees like birch, sallow, hawthorn or ash, usually on old common grazings or fields or recent sites like railway embankments. These are usually betrayed by patches of heather or bracken, or chalk grassland plants along rides. Remember too, that many old coppices were bulldozed or poisoned and planted with conifers or mixtures, so don't be too surprised by an ancient bank round a stand of Douglas fir!

WOODLAND STRUCTURE

Woods that are ancient have had time to develop layers: hugging the ground are the mosses, lichens and fungi of the *ground* layer. Above this we find the woodland flowers of the *field layer*, then the shrub layer or *understorey*, with the high *canopy* trees towering over everything else.

The relative development of each of these layers depends

WOODLAND COMPOSITION – TREES AND SHRUBS

The range of tree and shrub communities in ancient woods, and of ground flora communities, is very wide. At the simplest level climate affects the trees which grow in different areas; lime and maple are absent from Scotland, wych elm prefers the warm damp west, beech and hornbeam the south of Britain. Then changes in soil acidity, texture and nutrients bring further contrasts: hazel avoids the most acid soils, beech needs free drainage, and so on. Finally, after these natural factors, has come man, looking after or neglecting woods, grazing stock and thus favouring unpalatable beech over tasty elm or lime.

Woods, then, are remarkably individual; subtle differences in the range or ages of the trees, the state of the coppice and the woodland flowers, give every part of each old wood a distinctive identity. How can we go about working out which aspects are natural and which the results of management? This is a woodland heritage detective story, for which we need some kind of 'identikit'.

The first woodland identikit, devised by Sir Arthur Tansley before the war, used the tallest trees, the canopy, to define woodland types. In fact Tansley envisaged a sort of ideal climax oakwood, into which all his 'ashwoods' or 'beechwoods' would evolve unless diverted or prevented by climate or human interference. This approach overemphasises the canopy trees, and particularly the dominance of oak and beech, which was often the result of planting in the nineteenth century, or of the older practice of treating oak and beech in natural woods as timber trees, promoting them into the canopy and relegating all the other species to the second division in the understorey. Most woods are in fact naturally mixed woods, in which the dominant species varies as soils and drainage dictate.

Now, though, after years of heavy wartime and post-war felling of oak and beech, and neglect of coppicing other species, it is much clearer that many of those 'oakwoods' or 'beechwoods' are really woods of lime, hazel, ash, maple, hornbeam or other trees in varying mixtures.

More modern ways of classifying woods sometimes take an imaginary 'column' through the wood from canopy to ground layer, and define recognisable types reflecting all the layers. These methods, the Merlewood 'plot type' and the National Vegetation Classification, require detailed work on large plots, and a knowledge of mosses and liverworts. For our purposes they are not much help.

In this book, we use the 'stand-type' system, developed by Dr G. F. Peterken, chief woodland scientist in the Nature Conservancy Council. The stand-type system classifies woods according to the species present as coppice (where coppice is present) which as we have seen is the most enduring and probably the most natural feature of woods. This copes well with mixed woods, with the effects of historical management, and with the ecological processes of succession, whereby ash for example may succeed beech before beech takes over again.

The Peterken system classifies woods into over 40 different types in Britain (Appendix I). but this is a three-stage process and it is not difficult to learn how to divide woods into the basic twelve stand groups, as shown on p. 106.

Although it may seem complex, it is quite easy to use, and you will soon find yourself on weekend walks looking out for the tell-tale indicators of different kinds of woodland. Before we look at the wealth of woodlands still left in Britain, however, we must also look briefly at the flowers of the woodland floor, because they can tell us a lot about woodland history and ecology.

Coppicing allows light into a wood, giving those magnificent displays of woodland wild flowers. In this coppice cut last year, bluebell, early purple orchid and primrose are prominent. The dominance of dog's mercury betrays a lime-rich soil, and in the distance near the cut ash-stool the angled stems and white bells of Solomon's seal strongly hint that this wood is in central southern England or Kent.

WHAT SORT OF WOOD IS THIS?

Knowing something of woodland history is helpful, but you will soon want to know something about the way woods vary in their tree composition. The Peterken stand-type system is designed to help sort out ancient semi-natural woods into types, known as stand types. The system works by analysing the trees present as coppice, or in pasture-woods as ancient trees or pollards. This means you cannot use the system for recent woods, for obviously *planted* coppice (rare) or sycamore or chestnut woods (common). Also, pine does not coppice, but true pine stands only grow in Scotland.

The system defines stand *groups*, split into stand *types* and *sub-types*. Here we look only at the first stage, which is enough to tell you whether you are in a beechwood, maple-wood or whatever.

USING THE SYSTEM

First, make a list of all the trees in your stand. A *stand* is a reasonably uniform area of woodland; big woods will usually have several different stand types as the soil changes from place to place in the wood.

Then look at the chart which summarises which trees occur in each type of woodland. Compare your tree list with those listed in the row of boxes running diagonally from top right to bottom left of the chart. Whichever of your species is nearest to the top right, that species defines the stand; the name of the group appears on the right, and to the left are marked the boxes showing (at top) the names of the other trees which could be present. (Subsidiary trees like willows, aspen, wild service and so on are ignored for the present.)

Notice that the *most significant* tree, nearest to top right, in your list, *not* the commonest tree, defines the stand. Thus, if you found ash, oak, birch and maple, the stand is a Group 2 stand *ash/maple*, even if maple was less common than ash. If there are only one or two individuals, ignore them, but a systematic scatter of a species, say wych elm, along a slope, is best treated as a stand.

You can also see that 'non-associating' trees are singled out for attention and given priority. This is because though they rarely grow with each other, they can grow with other 'associating' species. However, it is the non-associating species, e.g. beech or alder, which defines the stand; thus a mixture of ash, hazel and alder is an alder stand.

If there are no non-associating trees, you will see that the remaining groups, 1 to 6, and 12, form a series from wych elm to birch reflecting more and more acid soils. Group 1 ash/wych elm stands only grow on deep rich soils: Group 4 or 5 lime stands or Group 2 ash/maple stands grow on rather less rich sites: and so on down to the acid oak/birch Group 6, and the leached, poor soils where only birch and rowan can be found.

Notice that the stand group is given by the most nutrient-demanding tree present. Thus an 'ash/maple' wood can also have hazel, birch or oak; but it must not have any lime, wych elm, beech, alder, hornbeam, pine or English elm or it would be a different stand type.

The second stage of the classification breaks the groups into types, sometimes geographically, e.g. upland or lowland oak/birch woods; sometimes by acid or lime-rich soils; sometimes by the other trees present (e.g. hornbeam with sessile oak 9B, or pedunculate oak 9A).

Finally, in the third stage, sub-types are decided, usually in a similar way to the types themselves; for example on soil characteristics. You will find details in Dr Peterken's book, and clues can be gleaned from the stand-type names in the list in Appendix I.

All this sounds horribly complicated, but make a list of the trees in a wood, work through the key or check the chart, and you will be surprised how quickly you can pick it up. Better still, why not go on one of the many guided walks run by County Nature Trusts and local authority countryside departments; that way you can get an expert to help you.

Group	Betula spp. (birch)	Quercus petraea/robur (oak)	Fraxinus (ash)	Acer campestre (maple)	Tilia cordata or platyphyllos (lime)	Ulmus glabra (wych elm)	Alnus (alder)	Fagus (beech)	Carpinus betulus (hornbeam)	Ulmus procera (English elm)	Pinus (pine)	Common Name of Group
11	×	×	×	×	×	×	O	O	O	O	Pinus sylvestris	Pinewoods
10	×	×	×	×	×	×	O	O	O	Ulmus procera		English Elm Stands
9	×	×	×	×	×	×	O	O	Carpinus betula			Hornbeam Woods
8	×	×	×	×	×	×	O	Fagus				Beechwoods
7	×	×	×	×	×	×	Alnus					Alderwoods
1	×	×	×	×	×	Ulmus glabra						Ash/Wych Elm Woods
4 or 5	×	×	×	×	Tilia cordata							Lime Woods
2	×	×	×	Acer campestre								Ash/Maple Woods
3	×	×	Fraxinus									Ash/Hazel Woods
6	×	Quercus spp.										Oak/Birch Woods
12	Betula spp.											Birch (Rowan) Woods

ASSOCIATING TREES — NON-ASSOCIATING TREES

Key: [Tilia cordata] Must be present by definition.   [ ] Must be absent by definition.

× May be present or absent.   O Usually absent. If present, stand is intermediate between groups.

INDICATOR PLANTS OF ANCIENT WOODLANDS

Plants which can only spread very slowly from old woods to new ones are good indicators of which woods are ancient. This has been a matter of folklore for a long time, for example: 'Our original woods may ... be readily identified, because every wood containing the wild hyacinth I take to be such. Outside the wood, bluebells rarely appear in the hedgerow, if so, they proclaim a woodland that has disappeared.' (Beevor, 1925.)

In recent years, however, this idea has been tested as historical and archaeological data on the age of individual woods has improved. Rackham studied oxlip in Hayley Wood in Cambridgeshire, and found it spread into adjoining secondary woodland only very slowly, and it seems incapable of leapfrogging across fields. Peterken studied ancient woods and wood-ghost hedges in Lincolnshire and found that the following were virtually confined to ancient woods:

pale sedge	bitter vetch
hairy woodrush	May lily
greater woodrush	bird's-nest orchid
cow wheat	yellow pimpernel
herb Paris	small teasel
smooth-stalked sedge	pendulous sedge
woodruff	– and the trees
wood horsetail	wild service and
toothwort	small-leaved lime

In addition, many other flowers were strongly associated with, but not confined to ancient woods:

wood anemone	primrose
nettle-leaved	yellow archangel
bellflower	wood melick
lily-of-the-valley	wood millet
wood sorrel	greater butterfly
early purple orchid	orchid
barren strawberry	

In practice, many of these flowers can sometimes be found in younger woods – it

depends partly how close an old wood is. No one species is foolproof, but if you found quite a few of this list, almost anywhere in Britain, you could be virtually certain the wood was very ancient indeed. The exact list of these 'Ancient Woodland Indicator Species' varies from region to region as some species change their habitats quite a lot when the climate changes; for example greater woodrush is a good indicator in the south and east, but is quite catholic in its tastes in the north and west. Dog's mercury is a good indicator in the east but can invade recent secondary woods in Hampshire or Dorset. The northern coral root, creeping lady's tresses and one-flowered wintergreen are confined to the ancient pinewoods of the Caledonian forest (p. 119).

Because individual species are unreliable, ecologists usually count how many of these ancient woodland species (including small-leaved lime, wild service, maple and wych elm) occur in a wood. The list of species for southern England is given in Appendix II. Most ancient woods score 15 to 30 of these species; the richest woods may have 45 to 65. Included in the list are a number of ferns which are also characteristic of ancient woods – hard and soft shield ferns, and narrow buckler fern, for example. Other ferns, however, form part of the group of plants which have no affinity with ancient woods at all:

male fern	herb bennet
broad buckler fern	(wood avens)
ivy	lords-and-ladies
	ground ivy

These species are almost characteristic of secondary woods; if you find them, but few or no ancient woodland species, you may well be in recent woodland.

Early purple orchid in a southern oak/hazel wood. This is one of the wild flowers regarded as 'indicators' of ancient woodland, but since its main dislike is soil disturbance it can also be found in several kinds of ancient grassland, on chalk or limestone pastures and in hay meadows. In whatever habitat it is always a pleasant 'find', strongly associated with old, rich, habitats.

WOODLAND PLANTS

Around 250 different wild flowers, sedges and grasses are mainly found in woods. They do not occur there purely by chance, and the exact communities of plants in a wood are often very complex, and stable over hundreds of years. Different species have different reasons for living in woods in general, and individual woods in particular.

Soils are important, of course. Some woodland flowers, for example, require strongly lime-rich soils of chalk or limestone; these include the common dog's mercury and rarer species like the astonishingly blue purple gromwell of Mendip woods, or the Jacob's ladder and mezereon of the Peak District. Others require acid, freely-drained sites, like bilberry, Forster's woodrush or white fumitory; while another group needs heavy soil – wood sedge, bugle or oxlip are examples. A few behave differently in different places; lily-of-the-valley is a calcicole (thriving on lime) in the north (e.g. Dovedale) but a calcifuge (lime-avoider) in the south, in Pamber Forest in Hampshire, or St Leonard's Forest in Sussex, for instance.

Even when these soil preferences are satisfied, plants are subject to other pressures, such as grazing or competition; so water avens, pignut, narrow-leaved lungwort or greater woodrush can all be found outside woods so long as grazing pressure is low, in meadows or lane-banks, for example. Some flowers can tolerate shade, but not competition (wood sanicle); or, like primrose, need light to flower, but prefer years of shade to weaken more competitive grasses, so they favour coppiced woods. Another group is quite capable of withstanding grazing but avoids competition; these, like the prickly butcher's broom, the unpalatable wood spurge or the ground-hugging yellow pimpernel, are commoner in pasture-woodlands.

Of course, there are also a few flowers which actually require trees or their leaf-litter; toothwort, which parasitises maple and other trees, bird's-nest orchid and yellow bird's-nest (which are saprophytes, living on decaying organic matter) are examples. Whilst many of these woodland flowers are sheltering from grazing, there is another group of lower plants which is extremely susceptible to desiccation. These are the epiphytic lichens which live on tree trunks and branches, and the tiny filmy ferns of damp rocky gullies; they need a constant high humidity and many are confined to ancient pasture-woodlands where there has been continuous woodland cover and very little coppicing, such as the New Forest.

Continuity is an important aspect of old woods; many of the plants which live in woods take many years to find their way into new woods, and can in fact be used to show which woods are ancient. These 'ancient woodland indicator species' (see p. 107) are an important aspect of old woodland which has been studied a great deal in recent years. It is not just individual species which remain in one spot for centuries, like the green hellebore growing near Selborne in exactly the same place where Gilbert White knew it 200 years ago, but whole communities of plants are known to have changed little over 30 years or more, and there is every chance that in primary woods some ground-flora features stretch back as far as the wildwood, just as the coppice layer does.

They reflect the detailed composition of the soil from place to place. For example, Rackham discovered a transition from wet to dry ground in Hayley wood characterised by a succession of plants: 1) pond sedges, oxlip, sparse meadowsweet and tufted hair grass; 2) oxlip and bluebell; 3) bluebell dominant; 4) bluebell/mercury patchwork; 5) dog's mercury.

All this means that looking at woodland ground-flora composition is a fascinating business, and it can tell you much about the way in which a wood has been managed, how long the site has been wooded, and which semi-natural stand-types are present, but be careful before adopting conclusions from one part of Britain in another!

TYPES OF WOOD

Up to now we have looked at where woods came from, and why they survived clearance for farming and became coppices or pasture-woodlands, but we have said little about where different kinds of woods grow, how to recognise types, and how to tell whether a particular composition is reasonably natural. So we must now sketch in a bit of flesh on the bones of our identikit, and look at which kinds of woods grow where, and to some extent how man has altered them.

Because our identikit is based on the species present as coppice, we will start not with the usual 'traditional oakwood' (which is largely a nineteenth-century artefact) but with the various sorts of woods which contain ash coppice.

Ash and its common companion hazel are two of the most widespread trees in Britain, growing on all but the most acid soils. On the most base-rich sites we find ash, hazel, maple and wych elm, on neutral or slightly calcareous sites, ash, hazel and maple, and on less-rich soils only ash and hazel.

Spring flowers in a Dorset coppice. Ash/hazel woods are common in much of Britain. Here the flowers visible early in the year are primrose, bluebell (leaves) and lesser celandine. Note the small poles on the hazel (centre) and the three large stems on the once-coppiced ash at left.

Thus there are:
1) ash/wych elm woods;
2) ash/maple woods;
3) ash/hazel woods.

ASH/WYCH ELM WOODS (GROUP 1)

Wych elm, the commonest elm of ancient woods, strongly prefers deep moist soils, either rich in bases or flushed with base-rich water.

Wych elm stands are therefore common on the Jurassic, Silurian and Carboniferous limestones from the Mendips through the Welsh borders to the Craven District, or on the chalk; but they also grow on lime-rich clays in the Midlands, and frequently in places in the valleys of north-western England where lower slopes collect nutrients flushed down from above.

Until you have got your eye in, healthy wych elm can look remarkably like hazel with its large-shouldered toothed leaves, but wych elm forms very large stools and nowadays many of these have been killed by Dutch elm disease; and their white skeletons collapsing into piles of iron-hard dead wood stand out in many ash/wych elm woods. Surprisingly, some stands seem unaffected; these may be resistant and are worth propagating to replace lost elms in other woods.

The disease is carried by tiny *Scolytus* beetles, and one good way of protecting old stools is to coppice them regularly so that they never develop the fissured bark which the beetles recognise, until the epidemic has died out, but we must leave enough each year for the white letter hairstreak butterfly caterpillars. Most wych elm stands are managed as mixed coppices of ash and elm; but, in some, oak or ash were kept as standards.

In the Lake District there are calcareous elm stands on limestone, as at Low Park Wood, Kendal, but the commoner type is small stands along the foot of flushed slopes. These occur in fact from Cornwall to the Scottish highlands, often at the lower edges of upland oak/birch stands. In the oakwoods of Loch Sunart at Resipole there are small streams which have cut down into rather base-rich igneous rocks intruded as dykes into acid schists. Each deep gully is marked by a streak of base-demanding ash/wych elm woodland winding through the main oak/birch stands, showing how the stand type changes as the rocks change.

To the south-east, ash/wych elm stands can be found on heavy clays where there is some base-richness as at Great Sorrell's Copse near Basingstoke in Hampshire (a wood with an extremely rich flora even though part of it seems to overlie medieval ridge-and-furrow) and on lighter soils in East Anglia and Lincolnshire.

ASH/MAPLE STANDS (GROUP 2)

Where the soil is not deep or rich enough for wych elm we may find ashwoods with maple, a tree which is often thought of as hedgerow tree. Certainly in hedges it forms an elegant tree with beautiful golden and russet leaves in autumn, and was noted as a boundary marker in charters by Saxons, who called it 'mapuldur' (as in the place name Mapledurham). It is common too on woodbanks where it exploits the nutrients released by the ditch-silt piled on the boundary bank, but it is abundant in many a coppiced wood on a range of soils from heavy clay to well-drained chalk loams, growing with ash, hazel and oak.

Ash/maple stands are mainly southern; the tree does not get into Scotland though it occurs in Cumbria. In the south-east its distribution is limited by the presence either of hornbeam, which is a stronger competitor on the heavy clay sites in the Thames basin and the Weald, or of beech which tends to dominate on better-drained soils. In many old coppices maple has probably been favoured because it responds vigorously to coppicing.

Ash/maple woods are a British speciality; they have an international significance. They grow on the calcareous soils of the Hampshire-Dorset chalk, on the oolite of Lincolnshire and Wiltshire, and on the Mendip limestone, at Rodney Stoke for example; they are also the commonest sort of woods on many poorly-drained Midland and East Anglia clays; and are well represented at both Monks Wood, Abbots Ripton, Cambridgeshire, and the well-known Hayley Wood, near Cambridge. Occasionally ash-free maple woods can be found, but these are rather rare.

Maple can form giant stools (size for size a maple stool will be much older than an ash stool) and also occur as pollards. Pollard maples seem to be particularly characteristic of wooded commons like Hoegate Common, a surviving part of the Forest of Bere Portchester, Hampshire. Rockingham Forest and Hatfield Forest both have an abundance of maple.

ASH/HAZEL STANDS (GROUP 3)

These are 'ashwoods' where wych elm and maple are absent, so they tend to occur in north-west Britain beyond the geographical range of maple or lime, or elsewhere in England on sites too nutrient-poor for maple or wych elm. Several ash/hazel types occur in the lowlands on light or heavy acid soils, such as Wealden clay, boulder clay in East Anglia, or the clay-with-flints of the Hampshire and Dorset downs where ash/hazel forms the core of the vast hazel coppices of Cranborne Chase and the Hampshire chalk. This is the greatest concentration of hazel woods in Britain, and here the hurdle-makers and thatching spar-makers still ply their craft. Many look at first like oakwoods, as standard oaks were planted into them in the nineteenth century.

There are also calcareous types on the Oolite of Northants and Gloucestershire, and in the north-west, where sessile oak is an accompanying species, on limestones. These northern ash/hazel woods are some of the most interesting woods in the country; examples include Gait Barrows on Carboniferous limestone in northern Lancashire, Rassal ashwood on Durness limestone in Scotland, the deep valley of Castle Eden Dene in Magnesian limestone in Durham, and the various high-level ashwoods around Ribblesdale, of which Colt Park Wood is the richest example, which grow in the pavements of Great Scar limestone. Related types occur in the Peak District as well. The uplands also hold examples of more acid ash/hazel woods, with birch and rowan; these occur both in west Scotland and the Lake District, where they form transitions to upland sessile oak/birch woods, and further south on Exmoor.

In the extreme north and west, where exposure is greater, there may be hazel woods without ash. These are known to occur on Skye and at Drimnin in Argyllshire where there are wind-pruned hazel stands only 8–12 ft (2.5–3.5 m) high in places, which still shelter a true woodland flora with woodruff, sanicle and wild garlic.

Ashwood flora

Apart from the more acid clay ash/hazel stands, which are often dominated by bramble, bluebell and yellow archangel, most ashwoods occupy base-rich sites where a rich woodland flora grows. Some species are dominant or widespread: wood false brome, primrose and dog's mercury, for example. Others are much more specialised and vary from region to region, giving our various ashwoods a great deal of diversity and fascination.

The south-western limestones of Somerset, Avon and Gloucester are the home of meadow saffron, fingered sedge and angular Solomon's seal, and a few Mendip woods can offer the intense blue of purple gromwell. Spiked star of Bethlehem, once collected as 'Bath Asparagus', still grows in Avon and Wiltshire, and the spectacular lady orchid in the dry ash/maple woods of Kent, whilst common Solomon's seal is widespread in southern chalk ash/maple and wych elm woods. Other frequent plants are the poisonous herb Paris, with its glossy black berry and four rigid leaves, woodruff, and on moist sites wild garlic with its prolific white starry flowers and strongly-smelling leaves – you always know when you are in a garlic wood in spring!

Many hazel, elm or maple stools are parasitised by toothwort, a strange member of the broomrape family, which pushes its ghostly pink flower spike up through the soil in April – it was once called 'corpse-flower'. In Cambridgeshire, the beautiful yellow oxlip carpets some heavy-soil ash/maple stands, whilst the northern limestone woods shelter mountain melick, wood fescue and lily-of-the-valley. Here the nettle-leaved bellflower of southern woods is replaced by giant bellflower, and other northern flowers like baneberry, globeflower, wood geranium and (in the Peak District and Craven only) Jacob's ladder occur.

LIME WOODS (GROUPS 4 AND 5)

Woods which still contain coppiced lime are some of the most interesting in Britain. Since its wildwood dominance in much of England, lime has been gradually eaten out by cattle depastured in woods, and has suffered from competition from hornbeam as its own reproductive capacity has waned in the cooling climate over the last 2,000 years.

What this does mean is that if you find true small-leaved lime as old coppice in a wood, the wood is likely to be a wildwood relic. Although lime can still be found in a scatter of sites over much of its former range, in most of them there are only a handful of very ancient stools, often several feet across – a few along the Hamble river in Hampshire are 12–15 ft (3.5–4.5 m) in diameter. In a few places there are still woods dominated by lime coppice; in Lincolnshire, north Norfolk, and the Suffolk–Essex border, as at Paul's Wood, Black Notley, a relic of a once-larger wood called Lindris which, Rackham suggests, comes from Saxon *linde* (lime) and *hris* (meaning underwood or coppice).

Other limewoods grow in the Hampshire basin, in the Meon and Hamble valleys and in what was once Waltham Chase, the now-enclosed relics of the Bishop of Winchester's hunting grounds, where Bishops' Inclosure and many other woods still have lime. In the New Forest, its decline is charted by the reduction in soil pollen in Saxon times, but two ancient stools have recently turned up within yards of the open grazed forest in a coppice at *Linwood*! In the west and north, small-leaved lime is frequent in the limestone gorges of the Wye Valley and Peak dales, growing as far north as Rainsbarrow in Cumbria, and is occasionally joined by the even rarer large-leaved lime. (Common lime, the more awkward tree of towns and churchyards, is the hybrid of these two, and can occur naturally.)

These limewoods grow on a variety of soils; ranging from light acid sandy or gravelly places (as at Hamble, at Swanton Novers Great Wood in Norfolk and at Shrawley Wood in Worcestershire) through clay of various sorts in Lincolnshire and Suffolk, to the strongly calcareous, poorly-drained, thin soils over the western limestones, such as the Carboniferous limestone of the Wye Valley and the Wenlock limestone of Shropshire, as at Tick Wood.

Lime comes second to wych elm in the Peterken hierarchy (p. 106) which means that stands called 'lime' stands can also have maple, ash, hazel, birch and either sort of oak. Appendix I lists several types, basically split on the presence

THE UPLAND ASHWOODS OF INGLEBOROUGH

Ingleborough in north Yorkshire is the best place in England to see upland ashwoods developed on the Carboniferous Great Scar limestone, a massive pure stone formed 300 million years ago from the remains of countless billions of microscopic sea animals and subsequently uplifted above sea-level. The hard limestone weathers only slowly and is very resistant to abrasion by glaciers, so that today a vast tableland of Great Scar limestone forms a plinth for Ingleborough Hill, its surface scoured clean by the ice and later partly covered in boulder clay and peat.

The limestone outcrops as low cliffs fringing vast areas of bare stone weathered into

Baneberry (Actaea spicata) *growing in the Colt Park Wood National Nature Reserve, North Yorkshire. The month is June, but the ash trees have still not come into leaf at 1,200 ft (365 m). The other flowers here are red campion and mossy saxifrage. They survive here because sheep are kept out of the wood.*

the strange 'limestone pavements', where the slightly acid rainfall has slowly dissolved out the weaker joints in the rock, forming beautifully-sculptured gullies, deep narrow cracks called 'grikes', and fluted 'sink-holes' where streams from the overlying Yoredale series of rocks disappear down into potholes in the fissured limestone.

For many hundreds of years, the moorlands and valley side limestone or boulder clay grasslands were grazed by great flocks of sheep, and woodland is now very rare in the area; but in parts of the limestone pavements with their deep grikes sheep were often excluded, because they frequently died trapped beyond reach; and here there has developed a special kind of upland ashwood, two examples of which near Ribblehead are now national nature reserves.

The ecology of these northern calcareous ashwoods is remarkable. In one wood there are areas of bare pavement, tussocky grassland on thin drift clay and about 15 acres of dense ashwood, forming a canopy about 30–40 ft high, with hazel, birch and rowan present too. The flora of the open grikes is actually much richer than the shaded area of the ash canopy. This is because it is growing down in the fissures of the pavement, two or three feet down, sheltered from the wind and the occasional intruding sheep, but in a humid, well-lit environment. These shallow grike areas are awash with unusual plants, such as the beautiful globeflower (or butterboxes as it is known in the Dales), giant bellflower, green spleenwort, a rare fern of mountains, and lily-of-the-valley. Other more frequent woodland flowers abundant here are wild garlic or ramsons, dog's mercury, and wood sorrel. The surfaces of the limestone blocks, which are known as 'clints', are bare, but where rainwater has dissolved shallow depressions a little humus may collect, and here typical limestone grassland flowers like mossy saxifrage and the strange blue-flowered blue moor grass can

scrape a living, protected from competition from more vigorous species which need deeper soil.

Both these last species are abundant at the other wood, near Chapel-le-dale, but here there are differences too. Nowhere does the ash form a closed canopy, and the limestone blocks are exceptionally large, many metres across and sometimes as smooth and bare as a billiard table. Near the scar edge (a cliff of 10–13 ft, 3–4 m, down to the pasture below) the grikes are extremely deep; further back the grikes are shallower and fewer, and at the back margin there is a complex zone of grassy depressions adjoining the moors, which stretch, purple-brown, up the flanks of Ingleborough itself. The limestone pavement here is quite different; several thousand years ago it became covered in vegetation which laid down a layer of peat, the remains of which now form acid islands on the strongly lime-rich clints, making for an extraordinary assemblage of plants. On the peat islands grow acid-loving species (heather, billberry, cowberry and even the rarer crowberry), but poking through them are plants more typical of calcareous soils (such as lily-of-the-valley, wild angelica, grass of Parnassus, saw-wort and globeflowers. Growing in the grikes themselves are, again, woodland flowers, including dog's mercury, herb Robert, and hart's-tongue fern, but also rarities like baneberry with its spike of white flowers, and ferns including wall-rue, maidenhair spleenwort and green spleenwort. In the limestone grassland at the rear grow other treasures: the pink of bird's-eye primrose, yellow of alpine cinquefoil and the purple heads of melancholy thistle.

Trees are surprisingly scarce. There are patches of ash growing from the grikes and a few sycamore, colonisers from the not-so-far distant shelterbelts of the isolated farms of Kingsdale, hazel, and the rather uncommon birdcherry.

These upland limestone woods are extremely atmospheric places, with the breeze constantly blowing and the great panoramas of neighbouring Ribblesdale, Pen-y-ghent and Whernside. Though richer than many, they are otherwise typical of the fascinating ash/hazel woods on the Carboniferous limestone of northern England, many of which have probably never been thoroughly surveyed.

or absence of ash. The ash types include acid ash/lime/birch, a common type in the Lincolnshire limewoods, and ash/lime/maple stands either on neutral or mildly calcareous soils, again in Lincolnshire and East Anglia, or else on well-drained western limestones such as at Salisbury Wood, Gwent. The remaining ash/lime type includes stands on thin soils over limestone where sessile oak occurs.

The other limewoods are oak/lime; in other words ash is absent. The oak can be pedunculate, mainly in eastern limewoods, such as Hockering Wood in Norfolk; or sessile as in the Hamble in Hampshire, and Collinpark Wood in Gloucestershire. Generally the flora of the limewoods is rather poor, particularly in the acidic sites, where wood millet, soft-grass, bracken, bluebell and anemone are common. On the calcareous clays and the limestones there is often a much more diverse flora rather like that of the ash/wych elm woods which also grow in these places.

An ancient coppice stool of small-leaved lime in Paul's Wood, Black Notley, Essex. Lime is a relict tree most often found as old stools, many of which are enormous – up to 25 ft (7.5 m) in diameter in a few cases – and are probably more than 1,000 years old. This particular one might date from around Tudor times. In the Middle Ages Paul's Wood was known as 'Lynderswood', or in Latin boscus de lindris *which comes from the Old English* linde *(lime) and* hris *(underwood or coppice).*

There is always a particular pleasure in finding lime in a wood, especially if it was previously unrecognised! As more woods are actually surveyed in detail, rather than simply written about as though they ought to fit a generalised description, more lime sites turn up, and it is amazing where they do. Several hectares of lime stools were recently found beneath larch and other conifer plantations in Forestry Commission woods in southern England, where the thin poles had been pressed down flat under the weight of larch brashings. No doubt they will survive, and once the larch crop is gone the stand can be restored to its former glory. The time to look for lime is in the spring when its beautiful pale-green heart-shaped or 'cordate' leaves (hence *Tilia cordata*) are very obvious in mixed woods. True small-leaved lime leaves have thin petioles, almost as long as the blade, and the underside of the leaf bears tufts of russet hairs in the axils of the veins. You could start your search by visiting a known limewood to get your eye in!

OAK/BIRCH WOODS (GROUP 6)

What should we count as an oakwood? We are interested in ancient semi-natural woods and their likely ancient composition, which is why we are using the Peterken 'identikit' to classify coppice stands into various types. We must take care, then, not to count as oakwoods every wood where oak is the most obvious tree in the canopy. Oak plantations or woods of ash/maple or ash/hazel into which oak was planted in the nineteenth century are not 'real' oakwoods. We are interested in those where oak was part of the original natural composition, where for example oak was common enough to be coppiced, where ancient oak coppice has grown out to high forest, or where oak has always been present in pasture-woodland stands, as in the New Forest.

In practice, the oakwoods are confined to sites too acid or nutrient-starved for ash, maple or wych elm, where birch is an invariable part of the community and is often abundant either as coppice or as invading saplings after the oak has been cut, hence the name oak/birch woods. There are several types of oak/birch woods, and they tend to grade into one another. First, there is the geographical split into upland oakwoods, where the soils tend to be thinner and the climate and flora more oceanic, and lowland oakwoods, often on deeper soils. Cutting across this is the split between sessile and pedunculate oakwoods, for the two species have slightly different ecological preferences; not that these are clearly expressed, because hybridisation is almost invariable.

In the uplands there are many sessile oakwoods on acid freely-drained slopes, like the Birkrigg and Keskadale oaks near Keswick, and the dramatic Lodore woods of Borrow-dale. Birkrigg is extremely acid, but on richer soils hazel may be present in addition to birch. However, most of these woods were cut for fuel, charcoal and tanbark, and hazel was often weeded out. The most acid upland oakwoods are closely akin to the highland birch/rowan woods (p. 125) and have a flora dominated by wavy hair-grass, bracken, bilberry and common bent-grass. Boulders and outcrops are often carpeted with mosses; especially obvious are the shining green round cushions of *Leucobryum glaucum*. In the oceanic north-west where the climate is humid, the air unpolluted and coppice management less or absent you will find these oakwoods festooned with lichens, including beard lichens and the rather anatomical sheets of tree lungwort. The lichens in upland woods nearer to industrial areas are nothing like as rich.

Most upland oak coppices have long been neglected, which does little harm, and thrown open to shelter sheep, which do much harm by preventing natural regeneration. Fortunately the need to re-enclose these is now recognised; in the Derbyshire Peak District Padley Gorge and Brock-holes Wood, Crowden, show what can be achieved.

There are also *pedunculate* oak/birch woods in the uplands from Devon to almost the north of Scotland, and many of these are very rich woods in many ways. They include the famous Wistman's Wood on Dartmoor, a fascinating place which has changed since it was opened for grazing. Once impenetrable, you can now walk beneath many of the ancient stunted oaks, still dripping with lichens and mosses. The ground is a tumble of moss-covered rocks and 'waterfalls' of greater woodrush, and remarkably Wistman's Wood is actually spreading, despite the grazing. Experimental enclosures are wired off to see what effect the sheep are having, comparatively, on the rest of the wood. Holystone Oaks in Northumberland is another excellent high-level pedunculate oakwood, and further north there are many around western Scotland, especially in the area around Loch Sunart in Argyll, where transitions between sessile and pedunculate oakwoods are frequent. In places these have a rich flora with species like pignut, anemone, primrose, yellow archangel and dog's mercury, although all the typical acid flowers like bitter vetch, wood sorrel, stitchwort and barren strawberry are still to be found.

Nevertheless, you do not have to go to the uplands to find

Oak coppice growing in the valley of the Duddon in Cumbria. On these acid rocks, where soils are thin and leached by rainfall, oak and birch dominate, and in the past were often coppiced, in the case of oak for tanbark. Few wild flowers grow in these woods, and the ground is often covered in mosses like these green cushions of Leucobryum glaucum *characteristic of the acid, free-draining soil. (National Trust.)*

Wyre Forest, Worcestershire and Shropshire. In parts a heathy forest on acid soils, where the present oak timber has been grown by singling from coppice stools which once provided fuel for charcoal, and tanbark. The forest still contains some primary woodland, rich in tree species, flowers and insects, and is one of the most important woodlands in the West Midlands.

Forest where hazel may well have been present until grazed out. Sherwood Forest is a fine example of the birch type, though its structure and composition has remained intact only in small areas.

Commoner in the lowlands are the pedunculate oak/birch woods, though even these are restricted to sites too dry or acid to support ash; the majority of lowland 'oakwoods' are in fact ash/hazel (oak) woods! Pedunculate oak/birch can be found in the New Forest as pasture woodland, and is not infrequent on the most acid silty clay-with-flints over the chalk, where many such woods were used as commons. Where there are sufficient nutrients hazel may occur too, and many of these woods were managed as oak standards over hazel coppice.

Good points to watch out for in identifying these old oak sites are: absence of ash; sandy, gravelly or acid rocky sites; oak either coppiced or very old (pasture woodlands); plants of acid, not calcareous, sites (except in uplands); ancient forests or commons (in the lowlands). If you follow these guidelines you will soon be able to distinguish true oak-woods from the impostors where oak has been planted.

ALDERWOODS (GROUP 7)

Alder grows wherever there is water moving, not stagnant, in the soil, so it avoids heavy clays, preferring the easy-draining silt or alluvium brought down by rivers and deposited along flood-plains. Because the distribution of alder is so clearly related to topography, it is usual to distinguish alderwoods of valleys, springlines and flushes, plateaux and slopes.

Alder has been a common tree since at least the Atlantic period, and has probably been affected very little by the activities of man, though it has often been coppiced, providing the wood for clogs and brush-backs. In medieval times its light straight poles were used for scaffolding.

You will find alderwoods most commonly along stream-sides, growing on the well-drained banks or in the organic ooze of abandoned meanders. In the peaty places lady fern and marsh marigold, and the tiny spreading greenish-yellow golden saxifrage, are common. Away from the streams on the flood-plain itself more extensive stands grow; often these are a carpet of wild garlic in spring, and a dense bed of nettles in summer, for this rich alluvium is the

true oakwoods. Various stands with sessile or pedunculate oak grow on light strongly acid soils in most of the lowlands, from Kent to Dorset, in East Anglia, and less commonly in the Midlands where such soils are rarer. The sessile oak stands seem to occur in well-defined areas where ancient forest survived until late enclosure; they can still be found in Wyre Forest in Worcestershire, an area with an exceptional flora and fauna, and in Sutton Park in Birmingham. Again, there are sub-types with or without hazel, though this can be difficult to assess in places like the New

Alderwoods are characteristic of valleys, floodplains or other flushed places. The flora can include hemlock, water dropwort, marsh marigold, nettles and yellow iris, and is sometimes dominated by the great mounds of tussock sedge (Carex paniculata).

ANCIENT WOODS OF SCOTLAND

Looking at the vast moors of the highlands and the well-managed farms and great houses of the lowland chequerboard landscape of Scotland today, it is difficult to believe that most of Scotland was once covered in dense forest of oak, pine, hazel, birch, alder and willow, in some places up to around 1,800–2,000 ft (550–500 m) above sea-level. The main tree missing was spruce, which did grow in Scotland in earlier interglacials but in this one did not colonise Britain before the Atlantic flooded the English Channel.

The great forest of Boreal times, perhaps 8,000 years ago, has been destroyed partly by climatic change, which caused peat bogs to spread to lower altitudes during the Atlantic period, overwhelming the ancient mountain pine-forests, whose bleached stumps, unrotted in the acid waters, can still be seen emerging from beneath the peat of places like Rannoch Moor, where they are characteristically covered by the pale green woolly cushions of the moss *Rhacomitrium lanuginosum*.

Man has completed the job. Major clearances probably did not start until after AD 700, much later than in England, but during the Dark Ages and in medieval times the forest was attacked from the glens and straths upwards, creating farmland, and was perhaps burned to eradicate wolves and other predators; Scottish woods with much pine, heather and bracken do burn, unlike their lowland mixed deciduous counterparts, but the extent of burning in what were basically mixed oak, birch, pine and hazel stands has probably been exaggerated, with frequent tales of Viking raids.

Natural changes were more important in the highlands, but in the lowlands man's impact was greater. After the conquest the Cistercian order founded monasteries in the southern uplands, such as the great abbeys of Melrose, Kelso or Lindores, and created vast sheep ranches, just as in Yorkshire.

As late as the fifteenth century, although much of the lowlands and the highland straths had been cleared, several large woods remained in Perthshire, Argyllshire and even east of the Cairngorms. Nevertheless, the process of attrition went on; after the 1715 rebellion land forfeited by many old Scottish families was purchased by speculators like the York Buildings Company, which set about exploiting its land for timber and minerals. Good timber was extracted from the Abernethy forest on Speyside and floated to Speymouth for ship-building; charcoal-fired iron-foundries, emulating the earlier one at Furnace near Letterewe, Loch Maree, consumed great quantities of wood; and regeneration was prevented by cattle and sheep grazing. It was the highland lairds who began the clearances of the small clachans for sheep ranches in the highlands, but between 1740 and the mid-nineteenth century vast areas of potential forest regeneration as well as farms and settlements were destroyed. Later the upland moors became sporting 'deer-forests', though they were not Forests in the English, legal, sense.

Today, only fragments of Scotland's ancient woods survive, but those that do exist are magnificent places, treasures full of wildlife richness. Around the west coast are extensive coastal oakwoods, mixtures of sessile and pedunculate oak and birch, grading uphill into purer birchwoods, and on basic soils into ash/hazel/oakwoods. These are beautiful places, dripping with lichens and mosses, and though many have had some coppicing others have remained humid enough to keep rich populations of the most sensitive lichens.

More often recognised as ancient are the tiny fragments of the old pinewoods, which can still be found around Loch Maree, at the Black Wood of Rannoch, and on Deeside and Speyside. The most southerly is at

Rannoch Moor, Scotland. Here the peat of the blanket bog is being eroded to reveal the remains of ancient pine forests, overwhelmed in a deteriorating climate four or five thousand years ago. The old stump and some peat hags are thickly covered in the woolly moss Rhacomitrium lanuginosum.

Coille Coire Chuilch, near Tyndrum, which is typical of the more open pinewoods where deer-browsing prevents seedling establishment. Most of these ancient pinewoods are actually birch/pine stands, with occasional juniper or rowan but few other trees, except alder along the rushing streams. The balance tips in favour of birch where the soils are better or the climate warmer and damper, as in Glen Affric, and towards pine where the climate is more continental, colder in winter and drier in summer, as in Speyside.

The soils of the pinewoods are usually coarse, full of boulders, and made up of acid siliceous rock debris. They are usually leached of nutrients, creating a podsol (see p. 156), with an impermeable 'pan' at a lower level. In the more open woods, heather and bracken create gorgeous purple and gold in autumn; often the boulders, the bare ground and the heather stems themselves are encrusted in lichens, especially the ground-living *Cladonias*, which include the 'reindeer moss'. In the more closed, shaded woods grows a carpet of bilberry, with its green and pink flowers and black berries, and wavy hair-grass. Less common are cowberry and, in peaty places, crowberry. The most ancient parts of the woods, where a closed canopy has persisted, are the home of many rare species, like dwarf cornel, the lesser, medium, and one-flowered wintergreens; and the beautiful twinflower and chickweed wintergreen which are boreal relict species. The pinewoods also have two or three orchid specialities, like creeping lady's tresses, lesser twayblade, and the straw-coloured coral-root.

These ancient northern woods, knee-deep in heather and bilberry, are wonderful places to search for wildlife; they still have several rarer woodland mammals, including red deer, wild cat, red squirrel; and, in the lochside outliers of the north-west, the otter and the pine marten. Special birds live here as well; crested tit, capercaillie, and the crossbill, which is specially adapted to feeding on pine seeds. It is sad to report that even in our 'enlightened' times it is still necessary to guard against destruction of these old woods with their marvellous craggy ancient pines, such as happened recently at Abernethy.

A surviving fragment of the great Caledonian pine forest on the flanks of Glen Affric. Several such ancient forest fragments can still be found in Scotland, especially on Deeside; they are the remnants of the once-vast forests destroyed by climate and human folly. Most have been exploited at some time, and ancient trees are very few, but when deer are fenced out regeneration will still take place.

Sword-leaved helleborine, a spectacular orchid of beech and other woodlands. With the exception of early purple orchid and violet helleborine, orchids are not especially good indicators of ancient woods, but their ecology is fascinating and they have a special conservation importance.

Bradfield woods (p. 86) have a great deal of this sort. Sometimes, alder forms stands away from valley sides on steep slopes where there is drainage parallel to the surface; it is quite novel to find alder on the upper slopes at Glasdrum Wood in Argyll, for example, where the bedding of the rocks runs closely parallel to the slope surface, so that water drains downslope, not into the soil. There is another strange kind of alderwood in a few upland places within birchwoods, and in Norfolk. This is the bird cherry/alderwood which occurs in Wayland Wood and a few other sites.

Alder is quite an easy tree to recognize, especially as its old cones persist on the tree through the winter, and it has a distinctive, almost Japanese, branching pattern. If you are looking in a wood which generally lacks alder, you will often find streaks of alderwood along streams and flushes; these will be a different stand-type to the other areas without alder (p. 106).

BEECHWOODS (GROUP 8)

Beech has been a later developer in Britain, and in north-west Europe generally. It was present in England for several thousand years before it suddenly became more competitive in the damper, cooler 'sub-Atlantic' climate of the late Bronze Age onwards, and expanded dramatically, perhaps invading farmland. It is a tree both attractive and highly prized for timber, so it has frequently been planted almost throughout Britain, well beyond its natural limit which is south of the Carmarthen-Wash line.

It has always been thought of as a tree of the chalk downs, and it grows well on thin calcareous soils, such as those of the chalk 'hangers' of Hampshire and Sussex, but it actually does better on the acid silty clays and gravelly soils of the southern tertiary deposits; the common factor is good drainage, and beech avoids heavy neutral soils.

nettle's real home. Small alder stands can often be found round springs and down flushes within many other woodland types; these form distinct communities, again with golden saxifrage, but also broad and narrow buckler ferns and the large smooth-stalked sedge (*Carex laevigata*).

The most extensive alderwoods of all are probably those of the Norfolk Broads. These are technically sump alderwoods, where the water table is always high, but water is moving upwards or downwards within the ooze. Here there is also a great deal of grey willow, and the native blackcurrant is common too, whilst much of the vegetation is like a shaded marsh with swards of lesser pond sedge, yellow flag, and tussock sedge.

Alder is actually quite good at colonising valley-floor meadows; some were let for both grazing and coppicing in historical times. Elsewhere, alder also grows on clay plateaux where the soil impedes downward drainage; the

Chalk beechwood, forming the steep edge of the ancient common of Doles Wood in north Hampshire. The beech stand contains ash and wych elm, and the calcareous soil is covered with dog's mercury. Other beech stands occupy equally well-drained, but acid, soils developed on gravel and silt. Similar beechwoods, at Selborne, were studied by Gilbert White, and are now owned by the National Trust.

Because it makes excellent timber, but coppices rather weakly, it occurs naturally, and has been encouraged by man, as high forest; or as standards in mixed coppice, where, however, it tends to shade out the other species. On the other hand, it can put up with being pollarded, its seedlings are tolerant of shade and it is pretty well down the menu for most woodland herbivores; which means it tends to be favoured in grazed woodlands. Hence it is well-represented on many ancient wooded commons and royal Forests on acid soils, such as the New Forest, Dean, Epping and Windsor, and the vast and ancient common of the Chilterns.

Most Chiltern beechwoods today are plantations made since enclosure in the nineteenth century, but a few unenclosed pasture-woodland fragments still survive, like the beautiful pollards of Burnham Beeches, and Frithsden on Berkhamsted Common, Herts.

The stand-type system separates beechwoods into those with ash, mostly on the calcareous sites; and those with oak but not ash, mainly on the acid sites. The acid beechwoods include those with sessile oak, which can be found in South Wales and south-west England, and those with pedunculate oak, rather more common in the south-east. The New Forest is extremely rich in both types, and the ancient New Forest beechwoods are probably the finest semi-natural acid beechwoods in Europe. Not only do they have a richer flora than the usual rather limited communities of bracken, bilberry, hard fern and wood sorrel, but they are also extremely rich in lichens (p. 95).

The ash/beechwoods on mainly calcareous sites are quite different. Their tree and shrub composition varies, but they often have a very rich flora indeed. The commonest kind is the variant with maple, which grows on the chalk scarps of the Downs and the Wealden edge where Gilbert White knew it on Selborne Hanger. Most of these stands are high forest, but coppice survives at Hillocks Woods in Buckinghamshire, and Chatcombe Wood in Gloucestershire; yew is frequently present too. On limestone sites, such as James Thorn and other places in the lower Wye Valley, there are ash/beechwoods and a rich tree and shrub flora generally, whilst on the deep combe-bottom soils at the base of chalky slopes can be found similar woods with wych elm. On the Hampshire Wealden edge you can study the subtle changes in stand-type up and down the slopes; with drier ash/beech/lime/wych elm above, ash/beech/maple on the main slope, and ash/beech/wych elm at the foot.

The flora of the beechwoods on lime-rich soils is often dominated at first glance by dog's mercury, but search reveals a multitude of other flowers, and these woods have an extremely rich flora, with wild garlic, anemone, wood sedge, yellow archangel, sanicle, toothwort, hart's-tongue fern, and many more. The Hampshire chalk has rarities like box, lime, Italian lords-and-ladies, and the rare orchid sword-leaved helleborine, whilst the woods around the Cotswolds have other specialities.

Mention must also be made of the strange beechwoods with ash and sessile oak, in the Wye Valley, where endless combinations of beech, ash, lime, wych elm and sessile oak grow on successive layers of limestone and sandstone, usually on steep bluffs where many trees grow in pockets of soil in rock-clefts; the trees here also include rare white-beam species, and wild service.

Beech is a popular tree, and argument has always raged about how natural certain beechwoods are or are not, such as the beech pollards at Felbrigg in Norfolk, and the various Welsh beechwoods on Carboniferous limestone; both these are perfectly respectable. Even on Noar Hill in Hampshire, once part of Wolmer Forest and where there are good records of beech being felled as long ago as 1334, there have been suspicions that the existing beech stands were planted. Succession is complex on these sites, however, and most likely the fact that the woods now look even-aged is a result of grazing pressure suddenly being reduced, giving a great flush of saplings a hundred years ago.

It is often extremely difficult to decide if a beech stand is natural. It is partly a matter of getting to know woodland soils and flowers, but the fact that beech was not often coppiced means that plantations and ancient semi-natural stands look very much alike. Local peat pollen records can help; at Airds Wood, Appin in Argyll, there is what looks like a respectable ash/beech/wych elm wood on Cambrian limestone, with all the right plants; but the fact that it is of planted origin is betrayed by the lack of beech pollen in local deposits – and perhaps by the fact that the wood grows on a steep slope overlooking the long abandoned carriage-drive to the local mansion!

HORNBEAM WOODS (GROUP 9)

To see hornbeam woods, it is best to go to the area round London, especially the swathe from the Chilterns through Hertfordshire to Essex; or else to Kent, because like beech, with which it is often confused, hornbeam is a tree of the south-east. In its stronghold around London half of all woods have some hornbeam; there is a thin scatter of sites as far west as Somerset and the Welsh borders, and it has been planted beyond those limits, often in hedges from which it has since spread.

Hornbeam is a tree of continental climates; the hornbeam coppices in Kent along the motorways to the channel ports look remarkably like many northern French woods. It was one of the last trees to arrive in Britain and did not flourish until after the Neolithic decline of elm. The pollen record at Epping Forest where there are famous hornbeam pollards suggests its expansion there was in the Dark Ages,

Hornbeam woods are commonest in the Home Counties, and there are several fine examples in and around Greater London. The tree has a characteristic fluted grey bark, and its extremely hard wood was once used for gear teeth in mills. This wood is in Hampshire and grows on the great flint lynchet bank of an Iron-Age field.

and in Hampshire it is certainly only common in the area of Ashmansworth, where stands of twisted hornbeam stools grow on Iron-Age or Roman flint lynchet banks over clay-with-flints. Here hornbeam is a tree of ancient secondary woods, and in the east it may have taken over sites formerly occupied by lime, perhaps as lime was grazed out of pasture-woodlands; hornbeam is much less palatable.

Hornbeam is a strongly gregarious species, making dense groves which often exclude other trees, and unless they are coppiced the deep shade suppresses the ground plants. It forms stands with pedunculate oak; either on strongly acid soils where the poor flora is mainly bracken or bramble, with early-flowerers like bluebell and anemone, and the subsidiary trees are birch and hazel (as in Mad Bess Wood in Ruislip). Or else on heavy, wet clays where ash and maple can be found too, along with spindle and aspen. In the latter type, the flora is richer with yellow archangel, pendulous sedge, bramble, wood sanicle and primrose. Wormley Wood in Hertfordshire, which belongs to the Woodland Trust, is typical of another type where hornbeam grows with sessile oak on strongly acid soils, and the small western stands at Chaddesley Wood in Worcestershire and Lords Grove in the Wye Valley are similar. Hornbeam makes a superb firewood, and supplied much of London's firewood for years, but is otherwise extremely hard to work (its name means hardwood), being used for a few precision parts like pulley sheaves and the teeth of mill machinery.

SUCKERING ELM WOODS (GROUP 10)

The history of ecology of suckering elms is very complicated. The simplest place to start is with the idea that whereas wych elm (Group 1 woods, p. 106) is a true woodland tree which coppices when felled, almost all other British elms are invasive in woods; when felled they die back, and the roots put out a forest of suckers, forming a clone of genetically-identical trees, which could in theory live for ever unless the roots were killed.

The suckering elms are hard to identify, because there are endless clones of smooth-leaved elms (*Ulmus carpinifolia*) and English elm (*Ulmus procera*), and the two species also hybridise extensively. In ancient times woods of suckering elms may have grown on fertile valley alluvium, from which they were soon cleared by neolithic farmers; though Richens believes most were introduced by various incoming peoples in prehistoric times. Fragments of valley elmwood still survive in Bedford Purlieus in Cambridgeshire, and in Kent and East Sussex, where Francis Rose believes they may be primary survivals. What seems to have happened is that when the valley elmwoods were cleared for farming some elms were planted, or left, around the villages, perhaps to give fodder for cattle. In later centuries these may have been used as a source of hedging material. Suckering elms are of course ideal for hedges as they keep sprouting from the base; and sometimes form clones hundreds of yards long or even more.

It is from those ancient hedges that the suckering elms have invaded ancient woodlands. Elm strongly prefers moist, nutrient-rich soils, so that the stands most often invaded tend to be ash/maple or ash/hazel woods. Sometimes invasive elm stands are extensive and uneven-aged, as at Short Wood In Northamptonshire; in most suckering elm woods, though, the elm stands are very well-defined, growing outwards from a hedge. In East Anglia, where elm genetics are exceptionally complicated, different clones of separate origin can be found in one wood. Invasive elms are exceptionally prone to Dutch elm disease, but although individual English elms in hedgerows and villages have been decimated, woodland elms usually die back and put out new suckers; there is little likelihood of these elms dying out altogether. Invasive suckering elm stands can still be found throughout much of Britain; they have a flora characteristic of phosphate-rich sites; nettles and cleavers predominate. A stand of Wyck Wood in Hampshire has a consistent flora of ivy, early purple orchid, dog's mercury and ground ivy.

A Scottish birchwood, Ben Eighe National Nature Reserve, north west Scotland. Birch still dominates the upper parts of many mountainside woods in northern Britain, which are leached and acidified by high rainfall. Beneath the trees the boulder-strewn slope is thick with heather and bilberry.

PINE, BIRCH AND ROWAN WOODS (GROUPS 11 AND 12)
Pine and birch were amongst the earliest trees to colonise Britain as the ice retreated, but both soon lost their early dominance as longer-lived, more competitive, trees filled out the wildwood picture. Pine retreated to Scotland, but birch remained widespread as a subsidiary tree of lowland woods. Even so, true native ancient birchwoods are confined to upland sites, mainly in Scotland, on sites too poor to support other tree species, except juniper, rowan or aspen. There are birch stands at the upper more acidified edges of many a west Highland oakwood, and superb birchwoods at Morrone, near Braemar, and Craigellachie on Speyside. Birch is a beautiful tree, especially in autumn Scottish sunlight, when the brilliant golden leaves and silver bark stand out against the dark moors and mountains.

There are actually two native tree birches: silver birch (*Betula pendula*) with doubly-toothed leaves, whose maximum width comes near the leaf-base, and cylindrical trunk with brilliant white bark breaking into black diamond-shaped fissures in old age; and the downy birch (*Betula pubescens*) which has hairy twigs, singly-toothed leaves, broadest midway along the blade, and a fluted trunk with reddish or greyish bark. they are both woodland trees, and in fact difficult to separate ecologically; there is a suggestion that *B. pendula* is commoner in pasture-woodlands. Both, though, are invasive either in disturbed ancient woods, where they would not last long, or in heathland where they are difficult to control.

Pine, too, colonises heathlands in southern Britain, but if you find a pine stand in England, however craggy and impressive, it must certainly be younger than 200 years, because pine was not brought back to the south until about 1776, since when it has been planted or invaded on many acid heathland sites. These are similar in some ways to the coarse acidic soils where the famous 'native pinewoods' of Scotland can be found (see p. 118). Again birch is common, and rowan and juniper can be found in these old woods, the finest of which are those of Glentanar and Ballochbuie, Deeside: Rothiemurchus and Abernethy of Speyside, and the progressively more north-westerly examples at Rannoch, Glen Affric and Glen Strathfarrar, and in the Loch Maree area.

WOODLANDS OF THE NATIONAL TRUST

The National Trust manages a portfolio which includes about 35,000 acres (14,000 hectares) of ancient woods, many of which are Sites of Special Scientific Interest. As the Trust's team of biologists, based at Cirencester, discovers more and more about the historical management of the woods, and about the birds, flowers, mosses and lichens, insects which live in them now, management is increasingly guided by the special conservation requirements of each wood.

For example, old trees are being re-pollarded at Hatfield Forest (p. 93), and careful selective management at Horner Vale woods, Exmoor, or Great Wood, Keswick, is specifically aimed at conserving populations of 'old forest' lichens. Although such special management may look odd or drastic at the time, it is carefully designed to recreate the conditions which allowed the colonisation of the wood by wild plants and animals.

The Trust's woods can be thought of in four groups;

Western Oakwoods. These are typical sessile oak/birch, or oak/hazel stands of the mild, damp Atlantic parts of England and Wales. Many were probably high forest until coppiced extensively in the eighteenth and nineteenth centuries for charcoal and tanbark, and they can be found from Cornwall to Cumbria. Particularly notable examples are:

Cornwall   The Dizzard, near Bude, Helford estuary – oakwoods meeting saltmarsh.
Devon   Teign Valley, near Castle Drogo and Bridge Steps, Heddon Valley woods, Lydford Gorge, near Okehampton.
Somerset   Exmoor – Horner Valley, Holnicote Estate. Quantocks – Shervage Wood.
Wales   Gwynedd, Coedydd Maentwrog, National Nature Reserve. Powys – Graigllech Woods, Neath.
Cumbria   Borrowdale – Johnny's Wood, Seatoller Woods, Great Wood, Keswick, Ashness Woods.
   Coniston – Park-a-Moor, Park Coppice, Nibthwaite.

Limestone Woodlands. These include several famous ash or lime woods, such as:
Somerset   Ebbor Gorge, National Nature Reserve, Avon. Leigh Woods, Bristol, Avon.
Derbyshire   Dovedale – several sites.
Cumbria   Arnside Knott and Heathwaite.
Shropshire   Wenlock Edge woodlands.

Beechwoods. Mainly in the Cotswolds and Chilterns; they include:
Buckinghamshire   Bradenham Woods and Cliveden estate, and Pulpit Wood, Princes Risborough.
Oxfordshire   Aston Wood.
Gloucestershire   Blackstable, and Lords & Lady Woods, Ebworth, Frocester Hill.

Other Woodlands. These include many typical coppice and coppice-with-standards woods, such as Selsdon Wood in London. Blake's Wood in Essex and Nap Wood in East Sussex, and more distinctive woodlands, for example Selborne Common, Hampshire, and Hatfield Broadoak Forest in Essex (p.93).

4 · Grasslands

E HAVE SEEN IN earlier chapters that the natural vegetation of most of Britain would be woodland, if man had not taken a hand in altering things. Since the peak of post-ice-age woodland cover, about 7–8,000 years ago, man has gradually cleared away woodland to make way for cultivation, grazing or hay, or because he needed the timber, or because the woodlands were perceived to hold the threat of wolves, highwaymen or something else. Some of these cleared areas have never returned to woodland; others have gone in and out of woodland according to local circumstances; and some have returned to woodland and remained woodland.

Before the days of mechanised farming and chemicals from a bag, these cleared areas, despite the fact that they were man-made in a way, reflected the natural combination of soil, drainage, climate and so on, and the vegetation that developed in cleared areas varied enormously according to the situation and management; it is from these clearings that our heaths, moors and grasslands (in all their forms, from tiny enclosed meadows to wide open

A panorama of largely unimproved grasslands on the south slopes of the Purbeck hills, Dorset. The steep slopes of these limestone hills have not been intensively-farmed in recent centuries, and the downland still supports a fascinating range of plants except where it has been fertilised. However, the abundance of lynchets visible on all the slopes testifies to the more intensive agriculture of the past, dating from the time when the slopes were ploughed in the medieval period. The National Trust protects thousands of acres on Purbeck, including this area.

downlands) have developed, influenced by man but always reflecting the underlying natural conditions and acquiring different species accordingly. This and the following chapter is the story of how these semi-natural open habitats came about, when they arose, how they have developed, and what has colonised them. The sad part is that, in the lowlands at least, most of this historic and varied legacy has gone under the modern plough or development, and nothing of its original vegetation remains. There *are* places where you can still feel and see these direct links with the past, and appreciate the beauty of the hundreds of species that this historic stability has nurtured, but they are precious few.

The way in which a cleared area develops depends on the physical conditions and on the management; it is impossible to generalise wholly, as we will see, but as a rule the more inherently fertile soils, especially if rich in lime, have remained as grasslands; acidic, infertile areas have developed into heaths in the lowlands; and many parts of the uplands with a high rainfall have become moorlands over blanketing peat. For convenience, at least, we can look at each separately, beginning with grasslands.

Grasslands are amongst the most attractive and nostalgic of our wilder habitats, with images of springy downland turf alive with flowers and butterflies, or lush hay meadows bright with a hundred different species, yet they are amongst the least natural of our ancient habitats. If you think in terms of *historic* grasslands with their rich tapestry of species (as we are in this book) in contrast to the sterile monocultures of rye grass or timothy leys or silage crops, then they are also one of our most threatened habitats, of which only the tiniest fraction still remains. The folk memory of flowery meadows, which still appears in almost every children's book on the countryside, is almost a thing of the past, despite the historic origins and rich natural history of so many of our grasslands.

Grasses have the great ability, thanks to their particular structure, to grow and thrive despite grazing or mowing, and indeed many grasses disappear if they are not grazed or cut, as taller, coarser species take over and oust them. In entirely natural situations, in our climate, grasslands of any extent are a rarity, since there have never been enough grazing animals to maintain grasslands against the constant invasion of shrubs and trees. It is difficult to say exactly what natural grasslands there were in the wooded Britain of Stone Age times, but we do know that grasses and grassland plants occurred, and we can be pretty certain that the areas least suited to tree-growth had more open grassy woodlands; upland woods, freely-draining acid soils, perhaps some exposed coastal areas, and oddities like 'sugar limestone' or limestone pavement where, as we have seen, many of our ice-age plants have survived. Some semblance of what the country looked like may be seen in northern

Scandinavia, parts of the Himalayas, or even in scattered places in Britain like some highland woods, or the New Forest, but nowhere is quite like Britain was, and we have to imagine and guess much of the picture.

EARLY CLEARANCES

In many cases, it was probably these more lightly-wooded areas that early agricultural man selected; the pre-existence of at least some pasture, the attraction of sunny clearings, and the easier task of clearance and burning would inevitably make such areas more attractive than the densely-wooded areas that covered most of the country. There is a considerable difficulty with grasslands in accurately tracing their history over a very long period: we can work out when some grasslands were first formed from forest clearings, but it is very rare to be able to accurately follow the fate of such grasslands on through the centuries, and be sure, for example, whether or not they subsequently became arable land, or became wooded again. In many upland situations, especially if stony, it is highly likely that grassland once created would have remained as such, though even here there are constant new discoveries or suggestions of the great altitude at which ploughing has occurred in times of land shortage or better climate. Here and there, a few generalisations and educated guesses are necessary in the earliest stages, though as we move towards the present day there are meadows or other grasslands whose history is tolerably well documented over hundreds of years.

Mesolithic times (up until 5,500 years ago) saw virtually no clearance to grassland that has persisted to the present day – as far as we know. Evidence is beginning to accumulate that Mesolithic man may have cleared more than we had suspected, sometimes with the aid of fire, especially on the upper margins of hill country woods, where the trees thinned out naturally and the vegetation was more combustible. Much of this has probably remained clear ever since, though most of it as heathland or moorland. A few grasslands in limestone upland areas, such as in Wharfedale or Ribblesdale, may date from Mesolithic times, but it is difficult to be sure.

The coming of Neolithic people with their more advanced capabilities undoubtedly saw some greater changes, though we cannot always pin down precisely where they occurred. One of the best-known of these early major changes took place in the strange and unique Breckland area of north-west Suffolk and south-west Norfolk. Godwin investigated the layered sediments deposited in Holkham Mere, and he was one of the first to demonstrate conclusively that considerable clearance had taken place in the area during the Neolithic period, though once ecologists had believed that the Breck was natural. In the sediment record preserved in this mere, close to the Breckland, tree pollen was substantially replaced by plants of open land, such as heather, grasses and plantains. This pollen record, and the archaeological remains of the area (including the famous prehistoric flint mines at Grimes Graves) indicate a populous past, and in late Neolithic times the Breckland was probably the most densely-settled part of Britain.

The Breckland has a peculiar geology and hydrology, some of which is still not fully explained (see Chapter 6), but in essence it consists of fine rather acidic sand over chalk. Where the sand is deeper, typical heathland soils and vegetation occur (see p. 156), but where it is shallower the sand and chalk mix or the chalk may be exposed, to give a richer more calcareous soil which supports open grassland. It is likely (though rather difficult to prove) that much of the Breck has remained open ever since; the poor, friable soil which may have made the area so attractive a target for early clearances soon loses its fertility when exposed to the climate without the benefit of tree cover, and cultivation and grazing probably simply made matters worse.

It is likely that many cropped areas would soon have been abandoned, and the sandy soil was readily transported by the wind; so much so, in fact, that inland sand dunes have formed (though many have been destroyed in more recent times) which is quite exceptional in Britain. One local landowner, when asked in which county his property lay, is credited with saying, 'Sometimes in Norfolk, sometimes in Suffolk – it blows backwards and forwards!'

The last serious sand blow was in 1668, when the village of Stanton Downham was buried by sand and the remnants of this are preserved in Wangford Glebe nature reserve. As cultivated areas were abandoned, they gradually developed a grassland or heathland vegetation, which has been kept open ever since by a combination of grazing and the inherently difficult situation. Other areas were, perhaps, cleared but not cultivated, though now they are normally indistinguishable, and the open area would have probably been extended at times by domestic stock browsing and grazing through the surrounding woods, preventing regeneration and encouraging the spread of grasses. It is surprising how quickly grassland can form in woodlands exposed to intensive grazing pressure, especially on inherently thinly-wooded soils. If man takes a hand by ring-barking or felling trees, the process is very rapid, but even without this help heavy grazing and browsing can reduce an old woodland to grassland within the life-span of the individual trees.

The grassland of the Breck country, such as Lakenheath Warren, or parts of Wangford Warren, are the closest British equivalent to some of the grasslands of central Europe; the dry climate (a mere 24 inches [60 cm] per year

East Wretham heath and Ringmere, Norfolk. The grassy heaths of the Breckland area are known to be amongst the earliest areas cleared by prehistoric man from the Wildwood. The meres are natural lakes, that fluctuate strongly according to water table levels.

of rain), the cold winters, and the strange soil, coupled, perhaps, with their position nearest to the main post-ice-age land-bridge to Europe, has left them with a compliment of unusual plants and animals such as the beautiful blue spiked speedwell, maiden pink, Spanish catchfly, perennial knawel, and shepherd's cress. Many of these are plants with a known occurrence in the post-ice-age 'tundra' flora, and they have probably survived through the forested periods in glades and open areas or in open areas on the coast, finding their way back as man colonised.

In the twelfth century, parts of Breckland, around the villages, are known to have been cultivated on the traditional open-field system with a rotation of crops, and some of these areas are still in cultivation today. Later, barley was grown extensively in the middle ages, on more suitable soils, though some parts have probably always remained in pasture.

By the thirteenth century the Breck was becoming extensively used for rabbit warrens (a favourite land use for less fertile areas in late medieval times), which undoubtedly helped to maintain the open character and increase soil

Wangford Glebe, Suffolk. In the Breckland area of Suffolk and Norfolk there are still a few remnants of the once-extensive inland sand dunes that formed in this peculiar area. The best remaining dunes are at Wangford Glebe, shown here, now a Suffolk trust nature reserve.

erosion. Rabbits are often worse than larger herbivores for causing erosion, and their tight but selective grazing produces a characteristic mixture of species, with very short turf interspersed with clumps of less palatable plants. As the use of rabbit warrens faded away, the Breck was used for sheep-grazing by a particularly hardy breed known as the Norfolk Horn. Before mutton became popular in the sixteenth to seventeenth centuries, sheep were mainly kept for their milk (especially to make cheese) and their wool, and thin hardy sheep like the Norfolk Horn, with their ability to eke out an existence on the poor pasture (and even lichens) of places like the Breck, were ideal. As more productive, meatier, sheep were demanded, the Norfolk Horn faded into obscurity, and it is now just a museum rarity.

DOWNLANDS

At about the time that man had made the Breckland into 'Britain's first industrial landscape', the high chalk and

FINDING OLD GRASSLANDS

Unlike ancient woodlands, it is not easy to identify ancient grasslands, with a few exceptions, from maps. Equally, it is not practical to scour the countryside looking in detail at the species in every meadow to see how many of them might indicate an old meadow! Ancient field patterns and boundaries are not a lot of help, because it is so easy to plough, fertilise or reseed a grassland within its old boundaries, that the turf may be completely 'modern' (and therefore of little interest to the naturalist or the historian) despite the ancient boundaries. So, you have to develop an eye for the visible field characteristics of old grassland, and once you do you can often spot them from the train, across the valley, in photographs ... anywhere, in fact, though there are less and less of them in our intensively-used countryside.

Look out for:

1) *Colour differences.* Old grassland is often brownish-green in winter, and dull green in summer, whereas modern grasslands are a bright green for much of the year; patchy colours indicate a lack of agricultural improvement.

2) *A lack of uniformity.* All modern treatments of grassland make for dull uniformity. Grasslands with variation in sward height, wetness, topography, colour, vegetation and so on are more likely to be of interest.

3) *The presence of anthills.* Distinctive hummocks of 1–2 ft (30–60 cm) high and about the same across are a sure sign that a grassland has not been ploughed or fertilised (except perhaps from the air) for a long time. The anthills are made by huge colonies of the yellow meadow ant, usually, and they build up very slowly over decades or even centuries. The ants die out if the vegetation becomes so long that it overshades the hills, and ploughing, or even driving a tractor over the field, soon destroys them. They also get larger and larger as time goes on, so you can be pretty sure that a grassland is very old if there are lots of large anthills. It is also a clear sign that the pasture is grazed and not cut for hay.

4) *Lots of colourful flowers in spring and summer.* Old grasslands invariably have a

richer and more exciting flora than modern ones, and this may show up, if conditions are right, as masses of colour, especially with pink and yellow flowers apparent. Some more modern meadows may look flowery with just one or two species, while some old meadows may look dull if they are heavily grazed, or just cut for hay, but a colourful sward is a good starting point. You can make use of the list of indicator species (see pp. 134–5) to find out more.

5) *Ridge-and-furrow in fields.* Paradoxically, this indicates that the field has been ploughed, probably in medieval times, but it also often indicates old grassland; because such meadows may not have been ploughed since, they are difficult to work

A meadow in the Itchen valley showing many of the features to look out for in an old meadow; the variable colour, lacking bright green grass, the uneven terrain, the variable vegetation height reflecting the underlying soil and drainage differences, and the lack of straight edges.

agriculturally, and they are often on heavy clay which has been traditionally kept as pasture. Many of the most exciting and species-rich old meadows are on ridge-and-furrow grassland, but you have to be prepared for disappointments as many have been sprayed or ploughed despite their appearance.

Old pasture that has not been ploughed or mown, nor allowed to grow tall, develops a dense 'landscape' of anthills built by the yellow meadow ant. The larger the hills, the older they are, and therefore the longer it has been since ploughing took place. As the anthills grow older, they come to support a different flora and fauna to the rest of the pasture.

You can also use maps to look for old commons, which, if you are lucky, may still support the original vegetation. Riverside commons, which occur all over the country, are fascinating and worth looking at if you have any near you.

THE DIFFERENT SORTS OF GRASSLANDS IN BRITAIN

Ancient grasslands, of ecological or historical interest, can be of various different types. All share the common feature of having a sward or turf that has not been disturbed by ploughing for many decades, or even centuries (and some have *never* been ploughed), and which have not been reduced to a uniformity of two or three grass species by modern treatment with fast-acting fertilisers.

Hay meadows are meadows which are cut regularly for a hay crop, most usually once a year in June or July. Ancient unimproved hay meadows, with their wealth of wild flowers, tend to grow more slowly than modern re-seeded swards, and so they are cut later, often well into July, by which time they may be a riot of colourful flowers. Hay

meadows are usually on good soil, which may often be wet or even flooded in winter, but not too wet in summer. They are usually reasonably flat, have very few hummocks and hollows, or anthills in them, and they are surrounded by good stockproof hedges or walls. Most of the surviving interesting ones are in river valleys, though here and there a farm has been managed in a traditional way to retain these bright colourful gems of the ancient countryside. Hay meadows may be opened up to stock after the hay crop has been taken, and they may graze through to late autumn or early winter, before the sward starts to grow again. This is known as *aftermath* grazing.

Pastures are managed simply by grazing. They may be enclosed land, or open common land. In some parts of the country,

where there is much dairy farming or sheep-farming, most fields may be used as pasture. In other areas of the country, it is often the less accessible or less productive areas that are used as pasture; the steep hillsides, the areas that are too wet through the year to allow a tractor in, or the areas that are simply too infertile to be worth doing anything else with.

Downland is pasture on steep chalk or limestone hillsides, usually rich in special flowers and butterflies, and often very open in character. It has developed from the great open sheepwalks of the sixteenth to nineteenth centuries, and few hedges have been planted since, even though the wide expanses of downland have been broken up. Most farmers control their stock, if any, on downland with permanent fences and temporary electrified enclosures.

Broughton Down, Hampshire. A typical piece of chalk downland, rich in plants and animals, with a long history as grazed pasture. This example, which is grazed mainly by rabbits, shows signs of scrub invasion. Note the characteristic dry valleys running down the slope.

limestone hills of England were being cleared and opened up for settlement. It has been known, or suspected, for a long time that the chalk hills were amongst the earliest permanent clearance and settlement sites, but as is so often the case evidence is gradually accumulating for earlier and earlier clearances.

There is a general lack of preserved pollen remains on or close to chalk sites, though here and there evidence has been found of late Neolithic or early Bronze-Age clearances on the chalk. Analysis of soil profiles *below* monuments of this period has sometimes indicated that open conditions had prevailed for several hundred years before they were built; and the increasing number of Neolithic monuments discovered on the chalk, often masked by later Bronze-Age or Iron-Age structures, suggests the presence of an extensive settled population. The dramatic Iron-Age fort on Hambledon Hill in Dorset conceals an extensive Neolithic fortress and funeral site, and careful analysis of the soil indicated that ploughing had taken place in Neolithic times as well as later, up until Roman times.

The precise extent of these Stone-Age clearances on the chalk is not really known, and probably never will be now that so much evidence is lost, but it is certain that there were, at least, a number of Neolithic 'centres' along the chalk, perhaps as mere islands in the sea of forest. By Bronze-Age times, however, say 3,500 years ago, it is virtually certain that most of the chalk hills had been cleared of their tree cover, and there is little to suggest that it ever returned in anything but small amounts. It is probable that similar clearances had also taken place over the light limestone soils of the Cotswolds, the Mendips, and probably the Carboniferous limestone areas of north-west England such as in Wharfedale or near Arnside, during this period, or a little later.

These early clearances were not, of course, made primarily to create grassland; they were used as arable land and were probably very productive. Yet we know that by medieval times, and certainly by the sixteenth century, virtually all suitable chalk and limestone soils were covered by downland, the remnants of which we still see today. The exact process of how ploughed arable land became the incredibly-rich chalk turf of today's downlands (with 40, or even more, species in a single square metre!) is not entirely clear, though the rough pattern can be deduced. A few parts may have become grassland very soon after their clearance;

the ramparts, barrows, boundary banks, and the other archaeological remains that litter the chalk and limestone soils (especially in Dorset and Wiltshire) seem never to have been ploughed in many cases (though modern ploughing has destroyed many), and these probably form the oldest undisturbed downland vegetation. Besides their steeper slopes, these sites may also have escaped ploughing in earlier times by the mystical associations which so often surrounded primitive burial sites. They may even have been accepted, agriculturally, as more suitable for pasture than ploughing. Whatever the reason, many undoubtedly have very fine ancient chalk turf on them now.

The question arises as to whether these very ancient grasslands, and others like them but less readily apparent, have a richer or different flora to similar grasslands of more recent origin. It would be fascinating to discover that a particular plant, or group of plants, represented, say, grassland from Bronze-Age times, or Roman times, and so on, and that others perhaps indicated a history of recent ploughing; indeed such theories have been advanced in the past, with varying degrees of precision in the dates that are

Burnt-tip orchids (Orchis ustulata) in chalk downland. The beautiful burnt-tip or dwarf orchid is one of the best indicators of ancient turf, and it most frequently grows on old, undisturbed, earthworks such as hillfort ramparts, boundary banks, and barrows, though it does occasionally invade more recent turf where conditions are right.

represented. Unfortunately, nothing this clear has emerged, though there are some useful guidelines and indications. Ancient earthworks are undoubtedly very rich in the special plants of downland turf: for example, the beautiful blue-purple spring pasque flower is only known in Britain from about 25 sites, and eight of these are on ancient earthworks, while a number of the others are ancient quarry workings, such as at Barnack Hills and Hollows National Nature Reserve in Cambridgeshire (see p. 139). Most of the other sites are on ancient-looking grassland, with steep slopes, and absence of plough marks, and a rich flora, such as Rodborough Common, or Barnsley Warren, both in the Cotswolds. Despite its wind-blown bearded seeds, and ability to travel, the pasque flower is probably one of the best indicators of ancient chalk or limestone turf.

In Hampshire and Wiltshire, the burnt-tip (or dwarf) orchid is virtually confined to old earthworks, especially hill-fort sites, but also early defensive or territorial earthworks like the Romano-British Bokerley Dyke. The odd thing is, though, that on Martin Down on the Hampshire-Wiltshire-Dorset borders, the burnt-tip orchid has spread

out from the earthworks to colonise wartime ploughed areas in some abundance, with healthy, exceptionally large plants. This may be the 'exception that proves the rule', and circumstances just happened to favour colonisation here, but it is a mystery nonetheless when elsewhere burnt-tip orchid seems to be so closely confined to ancient turf.

In general, what evidence there is (and there is a great danger of circular arguments in the use of 'indicator' species by deciding that they indicate antiquity and then using them to prove that some downland is therefore old!) suggests that there are no species to indicate certainly very ancient grasslands. Coombe, for example, suggested that a dwarf sedge (*Carex humilis*) did not occur on earthworks built after Norman times, but careful work on sites of known age in Wiltshire by Wells showed that this was not so, and indeed there are a number of examples known now where this sedge has colonised quite recently-created grasslands. For more recent times, though, the idea is much more useful, and it really does seem that the presence of groups of particular plants, if occuring in sufficient abundance, can indicate the minimum time since a grassland was last ploughed. Plants like chalk milkwort, bastard toadflax (a strange little plant, which is the only British representative of the tropical sandalwood family), rockrose, and others, usually indicate a grassland which has not been ploughed for at least 130–150 years; conversely, the presence of plants like wild parsnip, tufted vetch, agrimony and weld suggests recently disturbed or ploughed grassland since they do not persist for long in closed turf (see p. 135).

Much depends on what the 'new' habitats are like; in general, it is not that downland plants are unable to spread at all nowadays (in contrast to the situation for some old woodland indicator plants which seem to have actually lost the capacity to spread), but rather that the habitats being created are unsuitable for them, almost certainly because they are too fertile. Some nineteenth-century railway spoil heaps at Micheldever in Hampshire, still consisting of partially bare chalk, are alive with many of the exacting downland plants, and there are many examples from elsewhere of bare chalk and limestone being colonised by the rarer species, even in recent quarries or wartime rifle ranges. Such habitats with their low fertility and lack of competition are open to colonisation by the downland specialities, whereas ploughed grassland is too fertile and they are out-competed by the 'coarser' species. In time, the

WATERMEADOWS

The chalk and limestone valleys of England are studded with meadows that look, at first sight, like the traditional ridge-and-furrow meadows of medieval times; but these have a quite different origin – they are the true 'water meadows'.

At some time in the late sixteenth century, it was discovered that the productivity of damp valley pastures could be greatly improved by a carefully-designed method of controlled flooding. The idea involved taking the warm, nutrient-rich river waters and allowing them to flow gently over the grassland from late winter onwards, releasing their nutrients and warming up the soil. The waters of these chalk and limestone streams come almost entirely from springs, and they emerge from the ground at a more or less constant 13°C (55°F) – much warmer than the air or soil would have been in late winter. To achieve this, a complex system of channels was constructed; water was led from the river at an appropriate level and fed into a main 'carrier' across the meadow; a series of ridges and furrows radiated away from this carrier, carefully levelled to take the water along the tops of the ridges, and down their sides in a continuous sheet, which was then led back to the river via the furrows. This was known as 'drowning' the meadows, and it was performed by men known as drowners, who were skilled in the art of water management, but also spent much of their time looking after the sward, by removing weeds, cutting back rank areas and so on. In areas where the valleys were steeper-sided without a broad floodplain (such as Devon, Herefordshire, or the Wey Valley in Surrey) a simpler system making more use of the natural contours was adopted, but the net result was much the same.

In a way, these were the first examples of really intensive pasture management, and they were incredibly productive, with results similar to that produced by regular applications of fertiliser today. Drowning ceased by March, and ewes and lambs were put out to graze, controlled by hurdle enclosures (cut from hazel coppice, see Chapter 3), and 1 acre (0.4 hectare) of watermeadow was said to support 400 ewes *and* their lambs for a day. The sheep were taken off in April, and irrigation began again to encourage the grass for the first hay harvest in June; two or even three hay crops were taken, and then cattle were put out onto the meadows after the last hay crop until November, or when the meadows were bare, and then the drowning began again. The watermeadows were closely bound to the prevailing sheep and corn system, in which the sheep were grazed on the downland and meadows, and folded at night on the arable, thus transferring nutrients from the watermeadows to the arable.

This incredibly intensive management was not, however, quite as devastating to the flora as modern applications of fertilisers would be. Fream, in a study of some river Avon meadows in 1888, recorded 85 species of flowering plant, of which 26 were grasses, and he refers back to an earlier study in 1798 when a similar flora was recorded – far richer than an intensively-used fertilised pasture would be today. Nevertheless, this form of management probably did impoverish the flora; in the very few such meadows that have been continuously used, at Lower Woodford and Britford in the Avon Valley, the flora is dominated by grasses with relatively few herbs, whereas in the many examples of abandoned water meadows that exist, such as at Winchester, the flora is much richer with over 100 species regularly recorded, including many of particular interest. The 100 or so years since the system was abandoned, during which the meadows have simply been grazed or occasionally cut for hay, have allowed new species to come back in, perhaps from the surviving riverside commons (see p. 144) and the flora is richer as a result.

Look out for regular ridges and furrows in meadows on the valley floor, especially, though not entirely, in chalk and limestone country. The rivers are divided up into masses of channels feeding the meadows, and often a few old mills besides, and there is often a channel along each side of the valley (in addition to the central main river), where the floodplain meets the slope. Often the old engineering works are visible in the form of sluices and bridges constructed of brick surrounds, with wooden boards. If the wooden boards are still visible, the water-meadow was probably one of the later ones to be abandoned, or it may be one of the few still in use.

Part of a working watermeadow at Lower Woodford, Wiltshire. The watermeadow system has declined almost to the point of extinction, except for one or two working examples. The main carrier in the foreground feeds the secondary channels seen in the background behind the sluice, and the water trickles down the sides of each raised ridge, collecting in the furrows and flowing back off the meadows, leaving warmth and nutrients in its wake.

INDICATOR PLANTS OF OLD CHALK GRASSLAND

There is a group of plants that, if several of them are growing together on some downland, tend to indicate that the downland is ancient. The method is not foolproof, because most of these plants will colonise new land quite readily if conditions are right for them (such as where the soil is scraped away and left as bare chalk, then abandoned), but generally they are pretty reliable indicators.

Some plants that tend to indicate downland undisturbed for at least 100–150 years, if several of them occur in reasonable amounts, include:

squinancywort	chalk milkwort
dropwort	early spider orchid
rock-rose	burnt-tip (dwarf)
horseshoe vetch	orchid

| dwarf sedge | field fleawort |
| bastard toadflax | clustered bellflower |

You would be very lucky to find all of these in one site, but if you did you could be very sure that the downland was old.

Another group of plants, if several of them are found together reasonably commonly, tends to indicate that, conversely, the downland *has* been ploughed, or at least disturbed, reasonably recently. These include:

kidney vetch	tufted vetch
wild parsnip	common vetch
creeping cinquefoil	hairy tare
bladder campion	yellow oat grass

These tend to occur commonly in grasslands *less than* about 50 years old.

Look out also for the presence of anthills (the larger they are, the older the grassland is), ridge-and-furrow indicating former, probably medieval, ploughing, and ancient earthworks, which usually have undisturbed turf on them. All will give clues to the age of the turf.

THE HISTORY OF ONE DOWNLAND: FONTMELL AND MELBURY DOWNS, DORSET

On the western edge of Cranborne Chase, south of Shaftesbury, there is a long indented steep chalk scarp. Once, this was almost entirely covered in open, flowery, sheep-grazed downland; now, despite the slower pace of change in this part of Dorset, much has been converted to more intensive use. The National Trust owns almost 500 acres (200 hectares) of this beautiful area, centred around Fontmell Down, Compton Down, and Melbury Hill, much of which has been declared a Site of Special Scientific Interest.

It is known with reasonable certainty that these downs were cleared of woodland early on in our agricultural history. There is a wealth of early prehistoric remains in this area, and many others close by. On the downs themselves, there are various remains dating from the early Bronze Age, and not far away there are Neolithic long barrows and a hill-fort, indicating very early settlement and clearance. There are also later Iron-Age structures, Roman remains, and medieval lynchets, indicating a moderately continuous use, though not necessarily wholly as downland.

The history of the land becomes somewhat better documented in historic times.

We know that King Alfred gave the whole area to Shaftesbury Abbey in AD 880, and it remained under the jurisdiction of the abbey until the dissolution of the monasteries in 1539. There is an entry describing the agricultural land in the parish in the Domesday survey of 1086. The pattern of farming became settled in Saxon times, and continued broadly unchanged through until the period of enclosure, which came late to this area. The parish boundaries remain now more or less as they were established in Saxon times – typically elongated, to include both vale and downland within each parish.

The parishes here were managed on the communal open-field system, like so many others in central and southern England. The downs, however, remained largely unploughed and were documented as the

The ancient downland at Fontmell Magna is species-rich, partly deriving directly from its long history of sheep-grazing. Pyramidal orchids, lady's bedstraw, ox-eye daisies and other flowers are visible in the foreground, and many other species occur. In the background, the more heavily-grazed far slopes of the valley are visible. There are also many traces of man's early occupation here.

waste of the parish, available for common grazing. Extension of ploughing onto the down took place during the land-hungry period before the Black Death, and the present-day evidence of lynchets indicates the areas that were ploughed regularly. These reverted to grazing land at the Black Death, from 1348 onwards, and have apparently remained as downland ever since. Various records indicate the importance of sheep in these downland parishes throughout the last thousand years, and the downs above the villages have clearly played an important part in the downland-arable system throughout this period. There have been brief periods of change, such as in the inter-war years (1920s and 1930s), when sheep no longer grazed the downs, and rabbits took their place. To an extent, these were managed in warrens, though often they were uncontrolled.

Nowadays, sheep graze the downs in good numbers, though cattle are also put out in places, and the combination retains the downs in good condition, as has been the situation for hundreds, or even thousands, of years, even though the agricultural system is quite different today. The flowers, butterflies and other plants and animals are still exceptionally rich, with masses of orchids, thyme, cowslips and many other plants, and good numbers of rare insects such as the Adonis blue butterfly. We are left with an age-structure that reflects the history – a few pieces of turf on earthworks and banks that probably date back to prehistoric times, together with some of the steeper slopes; areas that were ploughed in medieval times but have probably been downland for some 600 years; and a mix of other ages, reflecting waxing and waning of scrub, minor attempts at clearance, and other factors.

ploughed sites lose their fertility, and they too become suitable for being colonised by rarities, but clearly it takes a long time. Modern agriculture is totally unsuitable for downland plants, with its deep ploughing, applications of herbicides and fertilisers, and re-seeding of competitive nutritious species; even the application of fertiliser alone onto old downland rapidly kills off the 'downland' species (the cowslips, bee orchids, bellflowers and all the colour and variety) by promoting the rapid growth of a few species.

WHERE DOWNLAND PLANTS CAME FROM

A knowledge of the different floras of different-aged grasslands gives a few clues to the gradual colonisation of abandoned arable by downland plants, but it fails to explain where they all came from, and how they survived when the downs were forested, as we are now certain that they were once. It was formerly thought that the rich and varied flora of downlands, so totally different from that of woodlands, proved that they had remained open since the ice age, but most evidence is against this, and we have to look elsewhere for an explanation. The most accepted theory (and it is difficult to prove that it is right or wrong), developed by Francis Rose, invokes the idea of 'refuges' again, that we have already encountered (see Chapter 1). He believes, with good reason, that certain areas have always remained as open habitats on the chalk and limestone soils, and the rich flora (which includes many plants now well-recorded from the post-glacial 'tundra' period) has gradually colonised the downs in the wake of man's clearance, moving outwards from these 'centres' of distribution.

For the chalk, the main such areas proposed on the North Downs are the Medway Gap in Kent, the sea-cliffs from Folkestone to near Deal, and the big chalk cliff above the River Mole at Box Hill in Surrey; on the South Downs, similar situations exist where the River Arun breaches the downs in west Sussex, and the extensive chalk cliffs between Seaford and Eastbourne. The Carboniferous limestones of west and north Britain have many obvious sites, from the sea-cliffs at Berry Head in Devon, through the great Mendip gorges at Cheddar, Ebbor, Burrington and Bristol, to the scars, 'coves' and pavements of Cumbria and Yorkshire. In addition to these major sites, there were probably always smaller clearings caused by grazing and natural disturbance that may have kept small populations of species going.

The evidence for the refuge idea is quite strong. Dr Rose has analysed the flora of many possible refuges in detail, and shown that not only do many of the specialised chalk plants occur on such sites today (e.g. man orchid, dwarf orchid, both spider orchids, box, chalk milkwort, field fleawort, horseshoe vetch and many others) but that the refuges appear to act as centres for their pattern of distribution. In other words, for many of the less widespread species, it can be shown that they are tolerably common (or, at least, have been within historical times) around the refuges, but tail off in abundance away from them. Colonisation of sites more remote from the original refuge only takes place with the aid of man or by natural long-distance dispersal, which is less likely than local dispersal.

No doubt other factors came into the picture, too, and a few species have probably colonised from the continent since the downs were deforested, but it provides a convincing mechanism to explain why our downland flora is so incredibly rich despite its apparently recent origins.

Although parts of the early history of downland may be obscure, especially in terms of how often individual places were ploughed and when, and whether they had interludes as woodland or scrub, as we come towards the present day, the picture becomes clearer. By Roman times, many of the steeper hills were almost certainly under downland pasture, part of the Roman sheep ranches, and some downland may have survived unploughed since then (e.g. some of the steep limestone downland in the Cotswold hills around Cleeve Hill and elsewhere). Many areas succumbed to the later medieval land hunger in the twelfth and thirteenth centuries, when ploughing of marginal land on steep slopes gave rise to the familiar 'staircases' of 'lynchets' (see pp. 62 and 72) in places like the Purbeck Hills, Wiltshire, Wharfedale and elsewhere. The absence of lynchets on a steep slope does not completely guarantee lack of medieval ploughing, but it makes it highly likely that the site has not been ploughed since Romano-British times. Once formed, on steep slopes, lynchets are unlikely to disappear naturally, so you can be fairly sure that downland on steep slopes with a rich flora and an absence of lynchets is at least 800 years old and possibly 2,000 years old. It is no wonder that the flora is rich! The only fly in this particular ointment comes from the possibility of more recent steam ploughing, or aerial spraying, which has occurred in some areas.

The Domesday book, produced almost exactly 900 years ago after twenty years of Norman rule, gives the first written records of downland, though it is by no means always clear what was being referred to. In Hampshire, for example, the Domesday Book records 31 places in the county in 1086 that had pasture dues to pay. These sites were distinct from 'meadow', but are not necessarily clearly defined as downland.

For Dorset, Rackham has roughly analysed the Domesday Book entries, and shown that pasture in the county adds up to about 177,000 acres (70,800 hectares), which equates to about 28 per cent of the land area; incidentally, he also shows, from the same source, that there were about 274,000 acres (109,600 hectares) of ploughlands (44 per cent), 81,000 acres of woodland (13 per cent), and 7,000 acres (2,800 hectares) of (hay) meadow (1 per cent) – an interesting insight into the balance of agricultural land 900 years ago. About one-quarter of this pasture refers to the heathlands of south-east Dorset, but most of the remainder represents chalk downlands spread throughout the centre and south of the county. In other words, there was a great deal of downland in chalk country by the eleventh century in Dorset, and the same has been shown for Salisbury Plain and elsewhere.

The evidence suggests, however, that this area of downland declined through the succeeding 2–300 years as populations increased and more marginal land was clawed into arable production from downland. Grassland of all types became increasingly scarce through this period, and highly valued since it was an essential part of the agricultural system. The bubonic plague episode (the 'Black Death') in the fourteenth century, however, undoubtedly brought about the abandonment of much of the cultivated land on former downland sites (as well as many other far-reaching changes in the countryside; see Chapter 2), and these reverted readily to downland, and, in some cases, woodland. It is highly likely that many downland sites, and especially those with medieval lynchets on, date from this period and have been unploughed since. Places like the incredible hillsides of lynchets on the Purbeck limestones around Worth Matravers in Dorset, or the valley-side grassland over lynchets in Nidderdale, or the gentler ridge-and-furrow slopes at Martin Down on the Wiltshire-Dorset-Hampshire borders, probably support grassland unploughed since the Black Death, over 600 years ago.

These downland grasslands, whether on chalk or limestone, reached their peak in extent round about the middle of the sixteenth century. The increasing value of sheep as a source of wool as well as meat and milk, had brought about a gradual increase in the numbers of sheep kept through the late Middle Ages. Despite the rising population in the eleventh and twelfth centuries, many landowners and monasteries were increasing their acreage of downland or upland grassland because sheep were so profitable. Arable cultivation was extending in areas close to villages and towns, but many upland areas, especially in the north of England where the Cistercian monasteries were concentrated, became grassy sheep walks. Many steeper and more remote sites have remained grasslands to this day.

By the sixteenth century, sheep (and downlands) were so extensive, at a time when the population was at last beginning to recover from the plagues and difficulties of the previous 200 years, that many writers of the period bemoaned the fact that sheep were driving people from the countryside, since they are relatively undemanding of labour, but nothing like as productive, per acre, as arable land. From the peak of such downland grasslands, probably in the middle of the sixteenth century, the decline set in.

Though there have been recurring episodes of high sheep numbers and grassland extent, there has probably never been so much downland before or since. The enclosure movement (see Chapter 2), whether privately or by Act of Parliament, fuelled by the increasing pressure on land from a growing population, nibbled away at the downland from then on. Yet the extent of downland at its height was so great that, even by the mid-eighteenth century, Daniel Defoe on his tour through Britain observed that 'the vast flocks of sheep, which one every where sees upon these downs, and the great number of these flocks, is a sight truly worth observation', referring to the extensive Wessex Downs between Salisbury and Winchester. Gilbert White, writing at the end of the eighteenth century whilst staying at Ringmer, said: 'There are bustards on the wide downs near Brighthelmstone (Brighton). No doubt you are acquainted with the Sussex-downs: the prospects and rides around Lewes are most lovely!'

In a detailed study of the changing downland area in Dorset, Carys Jones refers to an agricultural report of 1793 indicating that there were 290,000 acres (116,000 hectares) of downland in the county at the time (though much was overgrown with bushes) which is about 64 per cent more than in the eleventh century. The Napoleonic wars of 1790–1815, and the consequent grain shortage, gave rise to increased ploughing of downland, and other marginal land, often still recognisable by its close, straight, ridges-and-furrows. Nevertheless, downland continued to play an important part in the agricultural economy; Cobbett, during his 'rural rides', wrote in 1830: 'I like to look at the winding side of a great down with two or three numerous flocks of sheep on it, belonging to different farms, and to see, lower down, the folds in the fields ready to receive them for the night . . . The sheep principally manure the land. This is to be done by folding, and to fold you must have a flock. Every farm has its portion of down, arable and meadow.' So sheep were used, in effect, to transfer fertilising nutrients from the downs to the arable land lower down, for they graze during the day and dung at night. A complex regular shepherding pattern developed to achieve this end. Coincidentally, of course, it gradually reduced the fertility of the downs by constantly removing nutrients without replacing any, and this is one of the contributing factors to the rich flora of downlands today; the lack of the major nutrients prevents any one species from growing strongly and dominating the others, so that all comers are able to survive. This can be convincingly demonstrated (all too readily) anywhere on the downs of southern England, by comparing an untreated down with downland treated only with fertiliser: in the old, untreated downland ('unimproved' agriculturally!) there may be 40 or more species in a square metre, while after regular fertilising you would be lucky to find five or ten in the same area.

Chalk downland on Salisbury Plain, Wiltshire. This shows the tremendous flowery richness of an old downland turf, with spotted orchids, pyramid orchids, plantains, bulbous buttercups, salad burnet and numerous grasses visible in the foreground. The great steepness of slope is clearly visible in the background, accounting for the lack of ploughing or fertiliser applications in the recent past.

Burnet rose in Cressbrookdale, Peak District. The Carboniferous limestone grasslands of parts of the Peak District are beautiful examples of species-rich turf, a sort of upland example of downland! The grassland visible here has burnet rose, rock rose, bloody crane's-bill and many other species, and most such grasslands in this area are believed to be of very ancient, possibly prehistoric, origin.

Barring some reversion of arable to rough grassland in periods of agricultural depression, such as the 1870s (when cheap grain began to be imported from the United States) and the 1930s, the pattern since those halcyon days of downland, when you could walk from Reading to Salisbury barely leaving the springy intoxicating downland turf, has been one of decline, and now only the tiniest fraction of this formerly-vast, incredibly rich habitat remains.

We have looked mainly at chalk downlands, stretching from Dorset to the Yorkshire Wolds, since most is known about them, but other hilly grasslands on dry lime-rich soils have a similar history. The wide, open grasslands of Crook Peak, Cheddar, and Dolebury Warren in the Mendip Hills have a broadly similar, if less intensive, history. In the Cotswolds, on Oolitic limestone, there are many beautiful grasslands of the 'downland' type, of which many are ancient common lands (see page 144) though their history of clearance and use is similar to that of the chalk. Some may have remained as grassland, periodically invaded by scrub, since Roman times, and there is less evidence of medieval ploughing on most of them.

In the uplands of the Yorkshire Craven area, and the limestone parts of the Peak District, such as in Cressbrookdale, Lathkilldale or Millers Dale, there are extensive ancient grasslands on the slopes, sharing many plants with the chalk downs, but adding a few northern specialities of

Barnack Hills and Hollows National Nature Reserve, from the air. The ancient limestone quarries at Barnack show up most clearly from the air, and it can be readily appreciated why they have remained free from cultivation. All the flat, readily-ploughed land around has been converted from species-rich grassland to arable fields, leaving the hills and hollows as an island of habitat.

Pasque flowers (Pulsatilla vulgaris) at Barnack Hills and Hollows. The pasque flower seems to be one of the best indicators of ancient chalk or limestone grassland. It frequently grows on ancient earthworks, such as hill-forts or old workings, and is seen here growing in the turf that covers medieval limestone quarries.

their own, such as globe flower, alpine cinquefoil, mountain everlasting, blue moor grass, bird's-eye primrose, and the limestone bedstraw. There is field evidence from the undisturbed presence of Iron-Age relicts, and the absence of later plough marks, that many of these sites have been grassland for 2,000 years or more.

DOWNLAND ON THE EARLIEST 'INDUSTRIAL' SITES

There are, however, a few other interesting grassland sites on similar soils that have a rather different early origin, though the net result has produced something very similar. One of the most interesting, and best documented, is the extraordinary area of hollows and hummocks near Stamford, known as Barnack Hills and Hollows, now a National Nature Reserve. Here the Lower Oolitic limestone outcrops, in a particularly fine form for building known as ragstone. There is reasonably good evidence that this stone was first quarried as far back as Roman times, and it was widely used in many Norman buildings such as Ely Cathedral and Ramsey Abbey. By about the fifteenth century, the supply of ragstone began to run out, and the workings were finally abandoned some time in the mid- to late fifteenth century. The 'industrial' landscape produced by this extensive hand-extraction over such a long period is one of an almost lunar quality, pitted and pockmarked over a wide area. Naturally enough, in the fifteenth century, the abandoned workings were turned over to sheep-grazing, and later (as the surrounding limestone pastures all began to be enclosed for arable) the hills and hollows were enclosed by a huge stone wall (now dismantled) to keep the sheep in.

The abandoned workings provided perfect colonisation sites for the plants of the surrounding 'downland', including the rare pasque flower, man orchid, horseshoe vetch and purple milk vetch, as well as the essential grasses. Now they are the prime site in the area for all these plants, since the old grassland all around has long since submerged into the sea of arable that floods over most of eastern England.

BUTTERFLIES ON OLD DOWNLAND

Old chalk or limestone downland, rich in flowers, is often rich in butterflies too. A good downland site, with shelter, warmth, scrub, and different aspects can easily support 30 different butterfly species. Because butterflies are totally dependent on particular flowers, much of this richness can relate to the age of the grassland.

Butterflies, like most insects, are complex creatures needing different conditions at different times of their lives. The adult insect ('the butterfly') requires good sources of nectar as food from the right type of plant, flowering at the right time; many need a particular height of vegetation for courtship, or roosting, while others need the presence of bushes for shelter from the wind; but most important of all, they need the right *foodplant* to lay their eggs on. Butterflies are surprisingly demanding, in the wild at least, in terms of which species are suitable for the growing caterpillar (or larva) to eat: for instance, the larvae of the Duke of Burgundy fritillary butterfly only survive on cowslips, or occasionally primroses, and these have to be in the right conditions; the rather rare adonis blue butterfly only survives on horseshoe vetch; which is also used by chalkhill blues, and sometimes the common blue. The tiny, smokey-blue-coloured small blue needs kidney vetch for its larvae, while the brown argus (actually another of the 'blue' family) usually uses the leaves of common rock-rose for its larvae to develop on.

The much larger, and very beautiful, dark green fritillary lays its eggs on violets, usually the hairy violet on downland, while the marsh fritillary, which quite often occurs on downland in more western parts of the country, has larvae which feed on the autumn-flowering devil's-bit scabious. The larvae are unusual amongst downland species because they overwinter visibly above the ground in 'nests' of black, bristly caterpillars.

Some species are known to have close associations with particular species of ant. The story of the now-extinct large blue, which tragically disappeared from its last British sites just as its ecology and strange life-cycle was becoming fully known, is well-documented. It is now known that the adonis blue, too, shares a similar dependence on ants. In spring, when the overwintered adonis blue larvae emerge to begin feeding, they secrete a sweet sugary liquid all over their body, and particularly from two glands on their tail. This honeydew is highly attractive to ants, especially in spring when food is scarce, which gather around the caterpillar, agitatedly feeding on the sugary liquid. Normally, one particular species of red ant adopts the caterpillar, defending it against other ants coming for the honeydew, and against

potential predators. At night, the ants may even construct a special underground chamber for the larva to spend the dark hours in. When the larva eventually grows large enough to pupate, i.e. to turn into a chrysalis, it does so but continues to secrete honeydew, and is still guarded by the ants. The pupa sits in the ant's nest, guarded by the ants, until the time for emergence, when the skin of the chrysalis splits, and the beautiful iridescent blue butterfly emerges, to crawl its way to the surface, where it will expand and dry its wings, and eventually fly away. Strange things happen in the world of the downland!

It can readily be appreciated why old downland is often particularly good for butterflies; some of the essential larval foodplants, like horseshoe vetch or rock-rose, are plants of old downland (see p. 133); older downland has a better variety of flowers to ensure the availability of nectar sources for different species at different times of year; and ants do better in old, undisturbed downland turf. Other factors come into play, too, particularly management and aspect (e.g. some species only occur on south or south-east facing slopes), but it is interesting to realise that the history and antiquity of a patch of downland affects the butterflies that we see on it today.

Marsh fritillary butterfly on butterfly orchid. The marsh fritillary may occur on chalk downland, but only if its larval foodplant, devil's-bit scabious, occurs. Like many other downland butterflies, therefore, it does not occur on agriculturally-improved downlands which have lost the range of food-plants.

'LAMMAS LANDS'

There is another form of grassland common, with a rather different form of traditional management, known as 'Lammas lands', though there are very few such areas left. They have a highly-organised form of traditional management dating in general principles from medieval times or even earlier, and such meadows seem to have been managed in the same way for hundreds of years. The best-known, and perhaps the most interesting, example

Snake's-head fritillaries (Fritillaria meleagris) in alluvial floodplan meadow. These beautiful, but declining, plants, shown here in both normal and white forms, are characteristic of a few floodplain meadows in the upper Thames valley and East Anglia. They are a particular feature of the ancient Lammas hay meadows such as North Meadow, Wiltshire. The National Trust owns two of the few remaining meadows with fritillaries, in Oxfordshire.

survives at Cricklade in Wiltshire, on the floodplains of the rivers Churn and Thames. About 100 acres (40 hectares) of land, known as North Meadow and now a National Nature Reserve (though still managed in the same way), is subject to clauses stating that grazing may take place, as a result of rights granted in perpetuity, by the stock of certain inhabitants of the village of Cricklade, between 12 August and 12 February. From then on, the meadow is 'shut up' to allow the hay to grow on, and later the hay is cut by anyone prepared to buy the 'hay doles' annually. These can be bought and sold rather like any other land transaction, and interestingly enough some have been sold in recent years to seed merchants to produce wildflower meadow mixtures.

The flora produced by this regular predictable management is exceptionally rich throughout the meadow. It is best known for its thousands and thousands of beautiful snake's-head fritillaries, in both white and normal purple forms, estimated at about 80 per cent of the *British* population; it is a plant that thrives on hay-cutting, and dislikes summer grazing, and this particular form of traditional management clearly suits it perfectly. Nevertheless, it is by no means the only flower of interest in a site with adder's-tongue fern, meadow-rue, marsh orchids, greater burnet, and a host of others.

There are similar such 'Lammas lands' in Norfolk, at Port Holme in Cambridgeshire, and elsewhere. Port Holme, by the river Ouse, has a rather similar history to North Meadow, and a similar flora, though the few snake's-head fritillaries there seem to have been declining for many years.

The ancient 'Lammas lands' common at North Meadow lies on the floodplains of the rivers Thames and Churn, close to where they meet. Its historic land use as a hay meadow has been maintained and it is now managed as a National Nature Reserve. It is noticeable how much larger the meadow is than the surrounding enclosed fields. 6-inch map, 2nd Edition, Ordnance Survey.

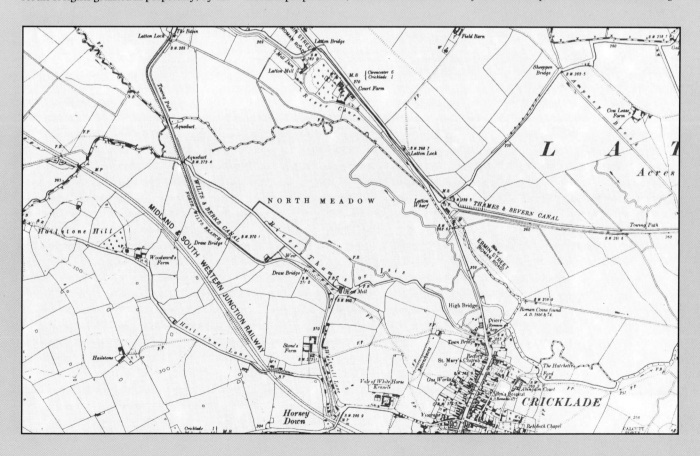

Cowslips in turf over medieval chalk workings. These ancient chalk extraction quarries on Noar Hill now support a wonderfully rich downland turf, despite their artificial origins, but the more natural downland from which their plants originally came has all but disappeared in the area.

The hills and hollows escaped ploughing by their impossibly unploughable terrain, although they nearly succumbed to another threat to old grassland, that of the growth of rank grasses and the colonisation by trees and scrub in the absence of grazing. Fortunately the danger was recognised just in time, and averted, and now sheep once again graze where pasque flowers flourish.

There are other sites with a similar history, too. High Common, at Noar Hill near Selborne, is not quite such a jumble of hills and hollows, but rather a series of larger shallow quarries on the top of a chalk hill. They seem to derive from the medieval exercise of common rights of extraction of chalk, and perhaps some later quarrying too, and now they contain a rich blend of downland flowers, such as musk orchid and fragrant orchid, early gentian, hairy rock cress, cowslips, horseshoe vetch and many others, with downland insects to match. Again, the downland has disappeared almost all around.

In Lincolnshire, Holywell Mound is similar to Barnack in origins and flora, as are Hornsleasow Roughs on old Oolitic limestone workings in Gloucestershire, and grassland over Roman workings in the Forest of Dean and Wye Valley

area. All these areas have escaped the dreaded plough by their rough uncultivable terrain, and today they give us some of the best glimpses of what the ancient downland turf was like.

COMMON LANDS

Even today, almost everyone has a 'common' near where they live. So many still exist in towns and cities, often under public ownership, like Wimbledon Common, Hampstead Heath, Southampton Common, or Town Moor, Newcastle, that the name has come to mean a rough public open space. Many have become so, for various reasons, but their origins are quite different. We owe many of our oldest and most interesting grasslands (as well as other habitats) to the ancient custom of commoning. Even now, there are well over 1 million acres (400,000 hectares) of common land in England and Wales, much of it with a rich flora and fauna, and many other places of interest, such as Otmoor in Oxfordshire, owe their survival as wildlife habitats to their former common-land status even though that status no longer exists.

All common land is owned, not by the 'common people' as is so often supposed, but by a private owner. Frequently enough nowadays, that owner is a body with some public accountability, such as a Borough Council, the National Trust, or the Nature Conservancy Council, but it need not be, and most rural commons are owned by private individuals. Similarly, common-land status does not confer public access, though usually there is a *de facto* right since the land is used for little else. Common lands are actually land over which people other than the owner hold (or once held) certain rights; most commonly, this is a right of grazing held by local people, or certain people, but there are many other rights, such as peat-cutting ('turbary'), marl extraction ('marl') and wood-collection ('estovers') that may exist.

The origins of common land are lost in the mists of time, an indication of just how old the custom is, though we can guess at how they evolved and know more about how they became formalised into 'rights'. In the early days of clearance, nobody owned rough grazing land, and it was probably open to all who could reach it, in settled times. Gradually, though, wherever pressure on land increased, such rights were more jealously guarded; on Dartmoor, for instance, known to have been substantially cleared and grazed from the Bronze Age and even Neolithic times, we find that in the earliest written records regarding use of the moor in the early thirteenth century, it was an agreed custom that all the people of Devon could use the moor 'except the people of Totnes and Barnstaple'! These were both 'new' boroughs, established in the tenth century, *after* Devon became a county in the eighth century, and it is likely that, when rights were being agreed, such new or future boroughs were excluded. In lowland England, pressure on land was increasing very rapidly, and there was a clear need to formalise the use of common grazing land into 'rights', such that by the seventh or eighth century there was defined common use of grassland, heath and marshes in most of the lowlands. In the uplands there was still much more space, for rough grazing at least, and many less written records, and there was no need for 'rights' when there was ample space for all.

Gradually rights became narrowed down to specific villages, earlier where the pressure was most, and later where it was less. In Wales, for example, where the eleventh-century population is reckoned at no more than 100,000, and agricultural land was mainly pasture, common rights were not narrowed down to specific villages until the twelfth century and later, whereas in England by this time, the practice of 'stinting', i.e. limiting the use of common to certain numbers of animals, was already widespread. It is believed that virtually all records in Domesday to 'pasture' represent common pasture, and such pasture was clearly a widespread and vital part of the Saxon-Norman way of life.

Whilst the commons may all have once been unowned, or owned in common, at various stages through history they were quietly appropriated by lords of the manor, ecclesiastical bodies and others, usually at periods when the peasants' voice was at its weakest, so that today none are owned in common in the original way, though perhaps ownership by the local council comes back close to that.

The vegetation of commons varies enormously, as widely as the vegetation of Britain can. Besides grassland commons, which we are interested in here, there are heaths, woods, marshes, wetlands, mountainside moorland and so on. Most are now on poorer soils, because those on better soils have been prime targets for enclosure over the centuries, but this was not always the case. Grassland commons, which are amongst the oldest unploughed grasslands of all in the lowlands (see below), vary enormously too, occurring in river valleys, on chalk downs, on high hills, on coastal sand and on acidic grassland, and though most are used for grazing a few are used for common hay crops. Although so many have been lost over the years, many others have survived unploughed and unimproved because the peculiar nature of the rights to the land, shared between a number of interests, tends to preclude agreement on expenditure for agricultural improvement, and few commons that still have rights attached to them have been 'improved'. In contrast, many are now neglected and ungrazed, out of keeping with present agricultural systems and rapidly reverting to woodland. The problem of road

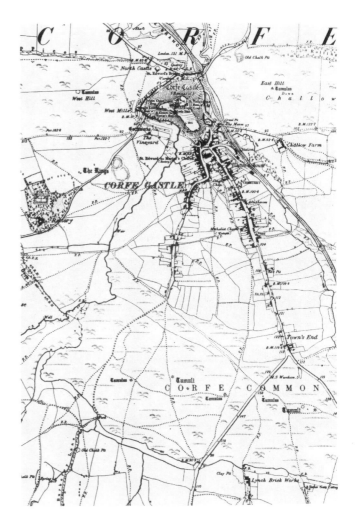

Corfe Common, Dorset, as shown on the first edition 6-inch map. The common lies south of the village of Corfe Castle, as delineated by the rough grass symbols, and the way in which the adjacent fields have been enclosed from the common – thus coming to form its boundary – is very characteristic. The common remains in virtually the same state today, now owned by the National Trust, as a haven for many uncommon plants and animals.

traffic where animals can stray has exacerbated the problem, since commons cannot normally be fenced.

Throughout the country, many high-quality grassland sites have survived as commons, rich in wildlife. Huge areas of the uplands are still common land, most of it as moorland (see page 162), but some as grassland where the soil is lime-rich, or where management has favoured grassland. The Craven area, such as around Ingleborough, supports wide areas of common upland grazings, many of them rich in the special flowers of Carboniferous limestone; the Lake District, Dartmoor, the Quantocks, the Cheviots and many of the Welsh Hills all have vast areas of common land, still as rough grazing of grass, heath or moor.

The Oolitic limestone of the Cotswold Hills, mainly in Gloucestershire, supports a beautiful series of ancient grassland (and other) commons, especially along its western scarp: Minchinhampton Common and Rodborough Common near Stroud, both National Trust land now; Stinchcombe Hill Common, and Cleeve Hill Common, a huge mixed area of almost 1,000 acres (400 hectares), and several others. The best are lovely places, rich in the commoner chalk downland flowers, but with special 'extra' species, related to the Oolitic limestone subsoil and the westerly climate, like pasque flower, meadow clary, or angular Solomon's seal.

A few chalk downlands are commons too, like Martin Down (now a National Nature Reserve) on the Dorset-Wiltshire-Hampshire borders, where the gentler chalk slopes still support rich downland turf, despite the ease with which they could be ploughed, because of their historic status.

There are still interesting grassland commons that have survived, by quirks of history, for one reason or another on better soils, but nowadays they are depressingly few. Throughout South Norfolk, there are a series of commons, mostly very small, on boulder clay, such as Fritton Common. Many have the characteristic indented, 'spiky' outlines of an ancient common, with patches of common land funnelling outwards along the access routes. They are turning out to be a rich resource of rare grassland plants, collectively, with rarities such as the bright yellow sulphur clover, confined to the grassland of eastern England. On the Isle of Purbeck, where there is one of the highest concentrations of rare or endangered habitats and species in the country, there is still a fragment of the fertile Wealden Beds left unploughed at the ancient and beautiful Corfe Common, now National Trust land. Its damp base-rich grassland flora, with marsh orchids, the strange little adder's-tongue fern, green-winged orchids, cowslips and numerous others (in addition to some acid, boggy areas) form a counterpoint to the heathlands and downlands of most of the Isle, and they owe their survival to their old common status preventing ploughing and agricultural improvement.

In the chalk stream valleys of Wessex, with their beautiful clear unpolluted rivers, there are several series of fascinating riverside commons, some of which have an extraordinarily rich flora and fauna, and the finest series of all is in the Test Valley. Most of the grasslands of these valleys have been converted to watermeadows from the sixteenth century onwards (see p. 134) but the commons largely escaped this treatment and now have a rather different flora and fauna to the abandoned watermeadows, which may themselves be of great interest if they have

escaped later ploughing. Bransbury Common is a huge flat area in the valley bottom, run virtually as an open cattle ranch. It is no longer a true common, since the rights were all bought up by the owner, but there is no doubt that it owes its survival through the last few hundred years to its former common status. Now, its flora is quite exceptional with over 300 species recorded, including many rarities not known elsewhere locally. Just downstream lies the attractive and historic Chilbolton Common peacefully grazed by cows, ringed with ancient cottages and bisected by the beautiful river Test. In this case, ownership has passed to the local Parish Council, and the villagers, and the public in general, have the benefit of access to this delightful place, which is also home to some 250 different plants and many breeding birds and mammals. A little further downstream still lies Stockbridge Common Marsh, part of a dual system of commons (the marsh and the down) pertaining to the little town of Stockbridge, which still have their own commons court, presided over by the Lord of the Manor, though the land is now actually owned by the National Trust.

The Avon Valley has a similar series of commons, amongst which one oddity is the common marsh in the Saxon village of Breamore, still grazed by a flock of geese, aided by a few cattle – a historic and medieval scene if ever there was one, with the old pollard willows, the Saxon church, and a backdrop of ancient cottages! This form of management has maintained the ponds on the common with muddy margins, and has allowed several rarities, now virtually extinct elsewhere, to survive, such as penny royal, brown cyperus, and mudwort.

In the heart of Oxfordshire lies a strange, rather wild and forgotten area, known as Otmoor, which came into prominence recently as it lay on the route of a proposed motorway. It can be worked out from the Domesday Book that it was common summer grazing pasture (for it was too wet to be used in winter) in the eleventh century, and there is an even earlier reference to its use in the Red Book of Thorney (1005–12). Its 4,000 or so acres (1,600 hectares) were shared between the seven ancient villages ringing the moor, originally as free-for-all summer grazing, then latterly as formal common land with rights apportioned between the villages. Its status passed through many acrimonious disputes, but eventually it became private land, and ultimately lost its common-land status, though its remaining patches of rich marsh and meadow vegetation probably owe their survival, at least in part, to its former status.

Perhaps the most famous ancient common meadow of all is Port Meadow at Oxford. There is an apocryphal story that an Oxford professor of history, when asked by an American visitor to show him the most ancient monument in the city, took him out to see Port Meadow! The American's reaction

Breamore Common Marsh, Avon Valley. This is a beautiful survival from medieval England, ringed with ancient thatched cottages, grazed by geese and cattle, and dotted with huge old pollards, like the willows shown here. It is also rich in plants, by virtue of its unusual management and long history.

to this is not recorded. Port Meadow and the adjacent Wolvercote Common form an area of about 400 acres (160 hectares) of open grazing land on the banks of the Thames just above Oxford. There is direct historical evidence that the pastures have been used as common grazing by the 'Freemen' of Oxford and the Wolvercote Commoners since, at least, early medieval times. Before this there is archaeological evidence of occupation of the site from Bronze-Age times, 3–4,000 years ago. By the Iron Age, there was a small group of farms on the land, and analysis of contemporary remains has shown that the predominant vegetation was open pasture, with a very similar flora to the meadow of today, except for immediately around the farmsteads. The archaeological evidence also suggests a high water table in those days, and we can picture an Iron-Age family group using the site for summer grazing, perhaps moving elsewhere for the winter.

At some later time, perhaps in the post-Roman Dark Ages, it became common land and is known to have been managed as such for many hundreds of years, and the Freemen still meet annually, as a body known as 'Common Hall'. The grassland itself provides a marvellous example of what a very ancient pasture, perhaps thousands of years

old, looks like, undisturbed by modern agricultural practices in the main. The flora is best described as 'interesting' rather than exceptional and perhaps this reflects the constant drain of nutrients through grazing, and the present over-grazing of the site. It provides a fascinating comparison with the nearby Pixey and Yarnton Meads which are cut annually for hay and only the 'aftermath' is grazed in late summer and autumn. Many plants thrive on the 'rest' that hay-cropping gives, allowing uninterrupted growth and flowering while the hay matures, and (for earlier species, or where the hay is taken late) some may even seed annually, allowing a dense population to develop. Plants like hay rattle, greater burnet, meadow-rue and meadowsweet are present in Pixey and Yarnton but not in the continuously-grazed Port Meadow.

HART'S FARM, ISLE OF WIGHT

Parts of the Isle of Wight seem to have let time pass them by, and one of the most historic and interesting landscapes lies around the tiny village of Newtown, close to Newtown Harbour. The whole of this area is of enormous nature conservation value, with many habitats represented, almost all of it within the ownership of the National Trust. One particular area, known as Hart's Farm, is of especial interest for its ancient pastures.

Newtown was founded in 1256 as the last of six boroughs or freetowns established by the Bishops of Winchester on their enormous land holdings (Many towns

Part of the 1768 map of the Borough of Newtown, showing the intriguing layout of plots in the borough. The present Hart's Farm lies to the south and west of Gold Street and Broad Street, and the present field boundaries have not changed greatly.

called 'Newtown' have a very long history!). The intention of such developments was to encourage settlement in otherwise unproductive areas, and the settlers in such places were usually freed from the normal manorial dues, and allowed to pay a money rent instead. This allowed them to develop a more enterprising and varied culture.

The economic basis of the new town lay with the harbour, which offered trade, an oyster fishery and saltworks. However, this prosperity was short-lived, as other ports increased in importance, and Newtown suffered severely from raids from the French. By the end of the fourteenth century, the venture can be seen to have failed, and Newtown was virtually depopulated.

However, for various reasons, successive monarchs were anxious to maintain or restore the town, and it was granted a series of Royal Charters. Up until the Reform Act of 1832, the Borough was entitled to send two MPs to parliament; since the voting

A meadow at Hart's Farm, Newtown, showing the unspoilt situation, and the species-rich turf.

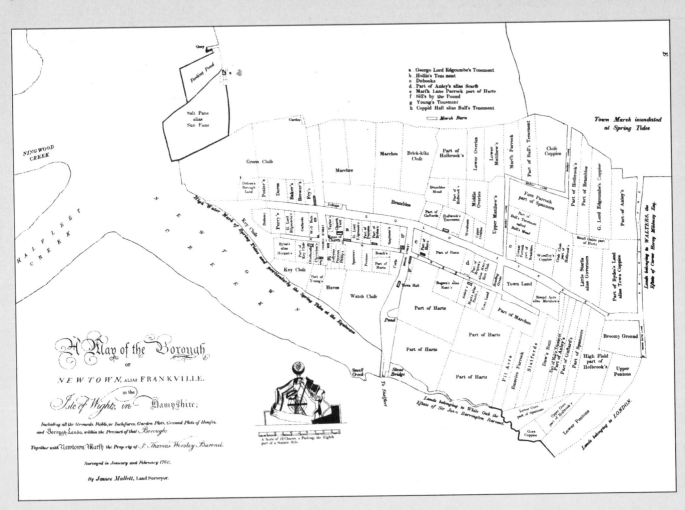

a. George Lord Edgcumbe's Tenement
b. Hollis's Tenement
c. Dubooks
d. Part of Anley's alias Scarfs
e. Marsh Lane Parrock part of Harts
f. Sill's by the Pound
g. Young's Tenement
h. Coppid Hall alias Bull's Tenement

rights were confined to those who held land in the borough, the value of the poor-quality land as a political tool far outweighed its value agriculturally. The resident population virtually disappeared, and the only building of any significance to remain was the old Town Hall, where political meetings could take place. The significant point, though, is that this strange situation allowed the layout of the original 'Newtown' to survive.

In medieval times, it is known that the town area was divided into 73 plots, most of them held singly. These were managed as furlongs, within the traditional open-field system. An estate map of 1630 shows that some enclosure had taken place by then, whilst the 1768 map indicates a much greater degree of enclosure. However, although many of the original strip, and subsequent enclosure, boundaries have been lost, there is still a fascinating pattern of narrow rectangular fields, interlocked with the ancient layout of the borough and its old streets.

Thanks to the unproductive clay soil, and some sympathetic management in recent historic times, much of the old pasture vegetation has survived as species-rich sward, which dates back 300 or 400 years, since enclosure from open-field arable. It now contains a beautiful mixture of flowers, many of them typical of old pastures, as distinct from old hay meadows. Species present include Dyer's greenweed, stone parsley, pepper saxifrage, burnet rose, devil's bit scabious, saw-wort, strawberry clover, corky-fruited water dropwort, ox-eye daisies and cowslips. The present light-grazing regime, mainly in winter, allows the flora to be seen at its best. The associated fauna of insects and other invertebrates is also rich, with many butterflies and some fine anthills.

Altogether, the site is a marvellous mixture of historic species-rich vegetation, set in an ancient landscape, wholly owned by the National Trust.

MONEWDEN MEADOWS

A contrast in historical development is provided by a group of meadows near Monewden in Suffolk, now managed as nature reserves by the Suffolk Trust. These beautiful and incredibly species-rich meadows. lying on sandy clay loam of the boulder series, are believed never to have been ploughed. Their existing boundaries go back at least to the seventeenth century, and some of the hedges are believed to be 600 years old. There is no evidence at all of ridge-and-furrow, or other form of ploughing, and certainly no effects of recent agricultural improvement, and it seems likely that this is what might be termed an ancient *primary* meadow, i.e. one that has been meadowland ever since it was cleared from woodland in Saxon times or before. It is still managed by shutting up for hay, which is cut in mid-July, late by modern standards but right for these sorts of mea-

Early purple orchids (Orchis mascula), *cowslips* (Primula veris) *and other plants in the turf of Martin's meadow, Monewden. The vegetation of this very ancient hay meadow is a dense concentration of herbaceous plants, with many uncommon species, through rather surprisingly there has been space for an exotic daffodil, the Van Syon, to invade the turf, and its tall leaves can be seen on the left, and behind the orchids.*

dow. The net results is an unbelievably rich flora. With a pageant of colour from spring to autumn, as fritillaries, cowslips and early purple orchids are succeeded by one group of flowers after another, through to the pink of the autumn-flowering meadow saffron. It is a salutary reminder of what we once had, but have almost wholly lost, but it is also of interest in having had such a different history to the almost equally rich meadows in Oxfordshire.

INDICATOR PLANTS OF OLD MEADOWLAND

Just as with downland, there are a group of flowers (and one fern) that, if several of them occur in reasonable abundance, are likely to indicate old meadow grassland that has not been ploughed or fertilised for a long time. It is impossible to put an exact date on the grassland, though if you find ten or more such 'indicators', you could be reasonably certain that the grassland was 100 years old or more. Grasslands over 150–200 years could contain any of these species, according to the part of the country and the soil, and there seem to be no reliable indicators of even older grasslands.

Experience has shown that the following are all reasonable indicators of old grassland, though the presence of just one or two of them, especially if in small numbers, is unlikely to mean much:

Dyer's greenweed
devil's bit scabious
green-winged orchid
cowslip

saw-wort
adder's tongue
    fern
lousewort

butterfly orchids
    (either species)
burnet water dropwort
heath spotted orchid
globe flower
common milkwort
mmeadow barley
yellow pimpernel
pepper saxifrage
melancholy thistle
bog pimpernel

betony
great burnet
spiny restharrow
marsh orchid
meadow saffron
meadow thistle
dropwort
hoary ragwort
wood crane's-bill
pignut
bitter vetch

Meadow saffron (or autumn crocus) (Colchicum autumnale), in a hay meadow in Worcestershire. The autumn crocus is a local and declining plant of meadows and open woods, mainly in the west, usually indicating a stable, long-established habitat. Its life cycle differs from most meadow plants in that it flowers in autumn, without leaves, and puts up its leaves, together with the fruit from the previous year's flower, in spring.

ENCLOSED MEADOWS

Commons and downlands are both open grasslands – wide open spaces without hedges. The enclosed hedged meadows of the Midlands, the Yorkshire Dales, the West Country, parts of Wales and Scotland, and elsewhere, have quite a different feel to them. Their character is as varied as the British countryside itself, and there is not enough space to look at more than a few examples here.

Hay meadows (see p. 131) probably date from Anglo-Saxon times, though the areas involved may well have been grassland for much longer than that. It seems that the Anglo-Saxons were the first farmers to appreciate the need for adequate grazing in summer *and* an adequate supply of hay for winter fodder. Prior to this, any surplus beasts for which there was not going to be enough food during the winter were slaughtered and salted for later consumption to avoid the need to keep them over the winter. Hay rapidly assumed an important part of the mixed economy of the time; for although the crops from the arable land were essential as the staple foods, they could not be produced without a good team of oxen for ploughing, and the oxen could not survive the winter without a good supply of hay. On average, an eight-ox team could plough about 60 acres (24 hectares) per year, and they needed some 8 tons of hay

Hay meadow flora, New Forest. Meadows on more acid soils, such as this New Forest-edge meadow, tend to have less species than the calcareous ones, but the proportion of herbs is still very high, and they may be even more colourful. The main flowering species visible here are self-heal, ox-eye daisy, yellow rattle, red clover and hawkbit.

Lake district meadow. Upland or northern unimproved hay meadows are almost invariably highly colourful, and frequently rich in plant species. This lake district meadow is dominated by bistort and buttercups. The National Trust owns huge areas of land in the Lake District.

to keep them going through the winter season, Thus, the system of arable, hay meadow, and pasture (usually common pasture, coupled with grazing of the arable land and many fields after the crops were harvested) evolved.

Records from the time of Domesday (1086) onwards through medieval times constantly underline the scarcity, and the high monetary value, of good hay meadows. In many documents of the period, hay meadow can be seen to be worth three to four times as much as arable land, with enclosed pasture worth less again. As part of the cooperative approach of these Saxon settlements, a system of drawing lots annually for different parts of meadows arose, to try to ensure that all had a chance of using the most productive sections at times. These were known as 'lots' or 'doles', occurring in Dole Meadows.

Hay meadows of this period were undoubtedly rich in a

great variety of different flowers, and, with a few exceptions, this variety was appreciated and used. From the seventeenth century onwards, however, things began to change, and the 'heyday' of the meadow was over. Enclosure encouraged, and gave more opportunity for, new ideas and crops; root crops began to be widely used for maintaining stock through the winter, and new seeds and artificial fertilisers of one sort or another began to be used. The old form of hay meadow declined in area. Most hay meadows of today consist of highly-improved, ploughed swards, with a very high proportion of grasses and clovers, but very few flowers. Yet there *are* traditional hay meadows to be found, bright with summer flowers like crane's-bill, knapweed, marsh orchid, meadow-rue, globe flower and others, or spring flowers like cowslips and green-winged orchids. In the uplands, many of these probably link directly with those early medieval meadows, and some have probably not been used for anything else, and the same probably applies to the ancient Lammas lands (see pp. 140–1).

We know, though, that other meadows, still with a rich flora, have not linked directly with these. Many of the finest, for example, lie over ridge-and-furrow, so they almost certainly became meadows after enclosure, probably in the seventeenth, eighteenth or nineteenth centuries. Other species-rich meadows have unequivocal records showing their use for arable crops at some stage or other in the past, though usually at least 100 years ago if they are of much interest now. When creating hay meadow from arable, or merely patching up muddy areas, farmers would regularly scatter the sweepings from the barns thus re-introducing all the old meadow plants into the sward, plus any from elsewhere if their hay had been bought in. This would not have been an instant process, and some species probably only established after constant accidental introductions, but gradually the richness of the flora increased.

The hay meadows of the northern dales, like Teesdale, and of parts of Scotland, are still marvellous places for the naturalist. Their uneven terrain, or the low incomes of their farmers, or their difficulty of access, have kept many in their traditional form, with no more than an annual application of farmyard manure. Somehow these northern meadows seem even more colourful than their southern counterparts – there are flowers everywhere, with barely a blade of grass to be seen! A good Teesdale meadow, for example, has meadow crane's-bill, wood crane's-bill, globe flower, several species of lady's mantle, bistort, marsh orchids, spotted orchids and frog orchids, meadowsweet, great burnet, melancholy thistle, ragged robin, betony, and many others according to the characteristics of the site. The National Trust now owns some fine hay meadows in Upper Wharfedale, North Yorkshire.

GRASSLANDS OF THE NATIONAL TRUST

Afton Down, Brook Down, Compton Down etc., Isle of Wight. Remarkable suite of chalk grasslands, strongly affected by the sea at the western end, with a rich flora and fauna.

Arnside Knott, Cumbria. Limestone grassland, with many rare plants.

Brean Down, Cheddar, Crook Peak, etc. Somerset. A remarkable series of Carboniferous limestone grasslands on the Mendips. Many rare plants in open stony grass sward.

Cotswold Commons, Gloucs. A group of ancient and attractive commons on Jurassic limestone, including Minchinhampton and Rodborough, still grazed as they have been for centuries.

Eggardon Hill, Dorset. Chalk grassland on steep slopes around an Iron-Age hill-fort.

Golden Cap, Dorset. A mixture of meadows, pastures and coastal grassland in an ancient landscape.

Peak District grasslands, Derbyshire. Many fine old grasslands on Carboniferous limestone, including Dovedale, Milldale and Thorpe pastures. Mixture of northern and southern species.

Purbeck grasslands, Dorset. Numerous beautiful sites on chalk, limestone and clay; e.g. Ballard Down, Corfe Common and Seacombe.

Stockbridge Commons, Hants. A pair of commons, the marsh and the down, still managed under a traditional 'lord-of-the manor' system.

5 · Heathlands and Moorlands

EATHLANDS AND moorlands have such a natural, ancient look about them that it is difficult to imagine their being created by man. Yet, in most respects, they were, for there is indisputable evidence that virtually all of the heaths and most of the moors were once fully wooded, not necessarily so very long ago. At the same time, though, they are amongst the most natural of man-made habitats (if that does not sound too contradictory!) in that their vegetation closely reflects the character of the under-lying soil, and is almost always open, wild and unploughed.

To understand heath and moors (and, for our purpose, we can treat the two in a similar way as wide open spaces dominated by heather or similar dwarf shrubs despite some ecological differences), we have to go back a long way in time. It is well known that many heaths have numerous Bronze-Age remains on them, indicating that they were open habitats then, if not necessarily heathland, but arch-aeological research has indicated even earlier origins for some heaths.

At Iping Common, near Midhurst in West Sussex, a

Moorland on Haytor, Dartmoor. The moorlands of Dartmoor are intermediate between lowland heaths and upland moorlands, in many respects. The area shown here is dominated by bell heather, western gorse, and bristle-bent grass, over granite soil, with granite tors visible in the background. Dartmoor was one of the earliest upland areas to be cleared of its tree cover, and there are abundant relics of early man all over the moor.

Marsh gentian (Gentiana pneumonanthe). One of the most striking plants of wet heathland is the autumn-flowering marsh gentian, which tends to grow on the junction between wet heath and bog, though nowadays it is a rather rare plant.

number of Mesolithic sites are known. Careful examination has revealed a buried land surface, under blown sand, with abundant hazel pollen in it, but evidence of heather spreading and becoming dominant *before* the sand was blown over the surface. Putting the various pieces of archaeological and botanical evidence together, reveals the probability that Mesolithic man created heath from hazel scrub and woodland *over 8,000 years ago*, probably with the aid of fire, and almost certainly for the purposes of herding wild or semi-domestic animals. The heath still exists at Iping today. At another Mesolithic site on heathland near Winfrith in Dorset there is abundant ivy pollen dating from this time, and this is almost certainly associated with Mesolithic man collecting ivy in autumn (when it would be

in flower, thus shedding pollen) as fodder for animals. Ivy is insect-pollinated, so its pollen would not have blown in from the surroundings in these quantities. Similarly, Middlebere Heath, in Dorset, is probably late Mesolithic in origin.

We have already seen that the Breckland area was substantially cleared by Neolithic times (see pp. 128–9) and much of this cleared land became heathland. In pollen diagrams from many sources, there are indications everywhere of an increase in heather pollen in Neolithic times, and this pattern gathered momentum through the Bronze Age and into the Iron Age.

So the picture is clear enough of a gradual clearance of woodland throughout prehistoric times, some reverting to woodland, and some going to grassland, but much of it going to heathland. Today there are heaths and moors over most parts of Britain, or recent historical knowledge of them, and the main factor that links them all is that they are almost invariably on poor, usually acid soil. Lowland heaths are on dry acid sands and gravels, and upland moorland is usually on peat (though actually the position is much more complex, and there are many types of heath in Britain). Even today, with deep ploughing, fertilisers, subsidies and so on, they are rarely considered to be worth doing much with, so why was early man spending so much time there, and what did he live on? Why do some clearances go to heathland, while others have become grassland? The answer lies in the soil.

One of the most interesting techniques developed for investigating the conditions that early man lived under involves the study of soil profiles, and their pollen, buried *under* ancient monuments. From these, given a few *caveats* and assumptions, a great deal can be discovered about what was going on at the time that the monuments were erected. Soil development goes on continuously as a result of the interaction of rainfall, vegetation and subsoil, but when a soil surface is buried by a large heap of earth, this process virtually (though not entirely) ceases, giving a fossilised soil profile. Now, the soil under most heathlands today is a strongly layered, leached soil (see p. 156), well developed but very poor in nutrients. Examination of these ancient soils in a range of sites, especially by Professor Dimbleby and others, has shown not only that they are frequently rather different to the heathland soils of today but that they may even be akin to woodland soils. In other situations, there are part-formed heathland soils, and in some cases (e.g. under medieval earthworks), there are fully-formed heathland soils, similar to those of today. In some soils, there is evidence of earthworm activity (which you will not find on most heathland soils today) and signs of much more calcium and nutrients in the soil.

From all this evidence, from different sites and periods, quite a clear picture can be constructed of early man clearing woodlands on moderately deep well-formed soils to

The plants of wet heathland. Marsh clubmoss (Lycopodiella inundata) is growing on bare damp peat in the foreground, together with the pink-flowered cross-leaved heath, and a few small insectivorous sundew plants.

Breckland lichen heath. The poor sandy soils of the Breckland area often support little except a mixture of dwarfed heather with an abundance of lichens, especially Cladonia spp., such as at Wangford Warren, Suffolk.

make clearings for various purposes; the soil was fertile and made good pasture or arable at first, but where the underlying rock was acidic then changes began to take place, leading gradually to the development of the poor acid soils under heathland that we know today. This is a complex relationship between rainfall level, vegetation and soil type, but in all lowland or reasonably dry areas the bedrock under heathland is always acidic, such as the Folkestone Sands, the Reading Beds, or glacial gravels. If trees are allowed to grow, as they did after the ice age, their deep roots constantly bring nutrients up from deep in the soil and deposit them as leaf litter on the surface, as well as providing shelter and humidity for micro-organisms to get to work on the organic matter. On acid soils, if the woodland is cleared, the cycle soon breaks down and almost all the nutrients are leached downwards. On less acid soils, or where there is regular flooding, or where a fluctuating water table keeps bringing nutrients back to the surface, the problem does not arise. This leached soil most readily supports heathland, and regular grazing or burning readily maintains it as heath.

So we can see what has been happening: on most acid soils, clearance of woodlands (which *may* have been rather less dense in the first place than on better soils, but probably were not) gave rise to briefly fertile soil, used for pasture or cultivation according to the people involved; this gradually lost its fertility to become fit only for pasture, and then ultimately became more acid and less fertile, and supported only heathland. The higher the rainfall, the quicker this process happened. By this stage, the original colonisers had moved elsewhere, probably, to find more fertile land, though in many cases the heathland will have continued under grazing, as many domestic animals, especially more primitive ones, survive well on heath grazing.

UPLANDS

In the uplands, the position may be slightly different. Vast areas of the Pennines, Wales and Scotland carry a heathy moorland vegetation, but much of it is over peat. The pollen record shows that most such areas were covered by woodland, but that about 7,000 years ago, during the Mesolithic period, peat began to form over much of the uplands, blanketing vast areas and apparently swamping existing forest of pine, birch or oak. The remains of quite large trees, embedded in peat, and dateable to about this period, represent graphic evidence of the changes that took place. It has always traditionally been associated with the changing climate, as the drier 'Boreal' slid into the wetter 'Atlantic', but there is increasing evidence that man, yet again, may be at the root of at least some of these changes.

Firstly, we are seeing over and over again that Mesolithic

ARE THERE ANY NATURAL HEATHS?

At first, it is difficult to imagine heaths and moorlands as anything but natural – they all look so wild, and so much part of the countryside that they could hardly be anything else, it seems. Yet the great weight of evidence now shows that they *are* products of man's efforts at clearance and cultivation. So, are any of them natural, and where did all the heathland plants and animals come from?

It seems now that the extent of natural heaths, or heath-like vegetation, must have been minimal. The Breck area was once thought to be naturally-open heath and grassland, but that was shown to be erroneous; coastal areas were believed to support natural heaths, but it has been shown that even somewhere like the Scilly Isles, over 20 miles (32 km) off Land's End (and it is difficult to get much more maritime than that), were once well-wooded some 6–7,000 years ago with mixed deciduous forest. It seems now that the most likely places for natural heathland are just along the cliff-edge; work in Brittany has suggested that the very edges of cliff-tops may always have remained open, despite the development of forest immediately inland, but it is very difficult to reconstruct the vegetation of 8,000 years ago on such a tiny scale with any precision, and we may never be sure. Heather, and its associates, occurs throughout the pollen record from soon after the ice age, so it must also have survived inland, perhaps in clearings, especially on the poorest soil, here and there.

Many of the plants and animals of southern heathlands are south-European species at the northern edge of their range; further south, they often occur in different environments, frequently with much more shade. One possibility is that some, at least, could have withstood the forested period better than they would have done today because the climate remained warmer just long enough, until Mesolithic man helped them to blossom into their present abundance. It is also true that many heathland species would occur in other habitats if there were more of them; they have only become confined to heathland because of the demise of alternative habitats. Whatever happened exactly, there is little doubt that the exciting flora and fauna of heathlands, from Dartford warblers and hobby falcons to spider-hunting wasps or sand lizards, has benefited enormously from man's creation of heaths. Tragically, many are threatened by just the reverse process, as more and more heathland is converted to plantation or poor pasture.

HOW HEATHLAND SOILS FORM

When the first trees colonised after the last ice age, almost all soil conditions were rich in nutrients, from the glacial deposits or the churning action of frequent frosts. As we have seen, woodland established virtually everywhere. Trees have long, deep, extensive root systems and, as fast as percolating rainfall carries nutrients down through the soil, the trees bring them back up again, depositing them back at the top in the form of leaf litter. In this way, to put it very simply, the brown earth soils formed, and it was these rich deep soils that were available to the early farmers who cleared the forests.

Nevertheless, robbed of the tree cover that gives sheltered humid conditions, and the deep tree root-systems, some soils have developed quite differently. If the base rock, and so the soil that derives from it, is inherently *acid*, then the flow of nutrients downwards, and out of the soil, is greater than the speed at which shallow-rooting plants and the natural upward process of evaporation can replace them. Under these circumstances, a quite different soil develops which most readily supports heathland. These soils, when well-developed, are known as *podsols*, from a Russian word meaning 'ash'. The upper layers, immediately below the fibrous peaty surface of the soil, become bleached and acid, and take on the appearance of light

Most dry heathlands occur over strongly leached soils known as podsols in their more extreme form. In this picture, the unaltered bedrock of gravelly material is yellow-orange, while the leached and ash-coloured layers of the podsol can be clearly seen above. These have been formed under heathland, by acidic water moving downwards through the soil, only in the last few thousand years.

wood ash; indeed, it was once thought that it *was* ash. Below this, the iron and the alkaline compounds that have drained out collect in a red-stained layer, and they may often form a hard impervious layer known as an *iron pan*. Not surprisingly, such soils are not very fertile, and if they are grazed or burnt regularly, they continue to support heathland more or less indefinitely. Some sites have been heathland for about 4–5,000 years without much apparent change, so they obviously remain stable as long as the management does. Almost all heathlands, though, will revert to woodland if grazing and burning ceases, with birch and pine, followed by oak, soon colonising.

The whole process of *podsol* formation speeds up in wetter conditions, as the leaching speed exceeds the evaporation speed by much more, so leached podsols are much commoner in the west, and the uplands of Britain. They can occur in the drier areas, though, as there are heaths in the driest parts of East Anglia with podsols below.

THE LIZARD HEATHS, CORNWALL

The most southerly part of mainland Britain is a broad peninsula in Cornwall known as The Lizard. It has a warm, mild climate, with winters not much different from the south coast of France, and an extraordinarily-rich flora with many rare species. The plateau of the peninsula is mainly heathland, apart from the areas of agricultural land and small villages, and the edges tumble away in steep cliffs at evocative places like Kynance Cove, Mullion, and Asparagus Island. Altogether there are seven higher plants (six flowering plants and one fern-ally, the quillwort) that occur nowhere else in the country, and numerous others that are rare or local, like Cornish heath which dominates these heathlands, yet barely occurs anywhere else in the country. Why should the Lizard have all these rare plants?

As usual, the answer is far from simple. The climate plays some part, obviously, allowing many tender species to survive; but there are other areas with just as mild a climate; the rocks and soils are unusual, too; much of the peninsula is composed of serpentine which weathers easily, and is high in magnesium, and elsewhere in the country it supports areas with rare plants such as the Coils of Muick in the Dee Valley. The remainder is composed of schists and granitic rocks, less exceptional geologically, but still supporting some of the rare plants. The other ingredient to add is the history of the Lizard.

Like most heathlands, the evidence shows that the Lizard peninsula was forested up until the Neolithic period, with oak woodland or hazel scrub, when man began to clear and cultivate the soils, eventually producing heathland as we have seen elsewhere. The difference lies, probably, in the fact that the cliff-tops were always open, and the hazel woods may not have developed so densely on the crumbly, serpentine-derived soils with their heavy load of metals like magnesium. So, before the land-bridge with France finally breached, plants were able to colonise up from the continent, across the 'English Channel' reaching these bare cliff-edges and clearings, and surviving there through the most densely forested period. When Neolithic, or possibly even Mesolithic, man came along, he produced conditions that just suited these warmth-loving heathland plants – the twin-flowered clover, the upright clover, the long-headed clover, the pygmy rush, the spring sandwort, hairy greenweed, and the pale heath violet, to name but a few – and they spread throughout the peninsula. Today, the National Trust owns and protects huge areas of the Lizard peninsula.

Cornish heath (Erica vagans) at Mullion Cove, the Lizard Peninsula. The striking coastal scenery of the Lizard, Cornwall, with its ancient heaths over Serpentine and other rocks, is home to numerous rare plants, including Cornish heath, many of which occur nowhere else in the country.

Tumuli on Fylingdales moor, North Yorkshire moors. The upland moorlands of the North Yorkshire moors are known to have been created from a predominantly wooded and surprisingly fertile countryside by the efforts of early man, and the tumuli are striking evidence of the former presence of prehistoric man.

man, though he may not have been a settled hunter, could and did directly influence the environment to his own benefit. Secondly, many of the deposits of peat, if analysed carefully, have a tiny band of the pollen and remains of weeds and grassland plants at their base, in some places there is also charcoal, indicating widespread fire. Thirdly, peat formation seems to have begun in different places at different times, which makes the changing climate less likely. Finally, there is the indirect evidence that there are many parts of the world with a climate similar to that of our uplands in Mesolithic times where forests flourish without any sign of peat formation. So we may never know for sure, but in view of what we know of the capabilities of Mesolithic people, their regular transhumance to higher slopes in the summer, and the accumulating evidence, we can at least say that man influenced the beginnings of peat formation and the spread of moorland some 7,000 years ago. There are places, however, where all the evidence suggests that peat formation and the demise of the forest, or even the complete absence of woodland, are quite unrelated to man. These occur in the harsh cool damp climate of North Scotland, such as in Caithness.

In some areas, especially as we come closer to the present day, the evidence becomes more definite. On the North York Moors, there is a clear picture of the clearance of woodland by fire to produce, ultimately, heathland. At Great Ayton Moor, on the north-east boundary of the Moors, lying at about 1,000 ft (300 m), a detailed record exists showing how Neolithic man started, and Bronze-Age man greatly extended, the clearance of forest, producing, at first, a grassland and arable landscape. By Iron-Age times the site was as open as today, and was well-cultivated, but there was little sign of heather. It was only later, after the Iron Age, that the soil deteriorated and heather colonised to produce heathland.

In Perthshire and coastal Aberdeenshire, a major expansion of heathland (or moorland, for lowland Scottish heaths lie somewhere in between) took place about 2,500 years ago, associated with the efforts of a Bronze-Age culture (which lasted until several hundred years later than in England), though further inland and further north it took place later. The *first* known clearances for settlement in Scotland took place some 5,000 years ago in Galloway and up the west coast, and some heathland formation derives from this period.

Elsewhere in Britain, there are clear signs that Exmoor, parts of upland Wales such as at Carneddau Hengwm, and Dartmoor, were significantly cleared by Neolithic times, or at the latest by the early Bronze Age. The Lake District Hills seem to have suffered early on, but in general the hills of the north were cleared and occupied later than those of the south, no doubt largely for climatic reasons.

It is not always clear what happened to the cleared areas, or precisely how they became heathland. In many cases, they were probably cultivated first, then used for pasture, before becoming heathland as the nutrients drained away; but in the uplands, grazing only, except in favourable sites, is much more likely. In the New Forest, a number of Bronze-Age barrows were clearly built over abandoned arable land, and the picture of cereal cultivation is confirmed by cereal pollen from the time; nevertheless we do not really know the exact extent of cultivation of these prehistoric heaths, and it is likely that many areas were never cultivated at all.

By Roman times, we can picture considerable areas of heathery moorland in existence, and a scattered heathland vegetation over those sites that had been cleared earliest, with many others going through a phase as rather acidic, unproductive grassland on their way to becoming heathland. There was much less heathland then than, say 200 years ago, for not only were many eventual heaths still going through grassland phases but also many known heathland sites date from later clearances, particularly in the eleventh to thirteenth centuries.

HEATH AND MOOR IN SAXON AND MEDIEVAL BRITAIN

By Saxon times, in England at least, the heathland had become part of the agricultural and social system where it occurred, and, although it may not have been highly productive or fertile, what it could produce was used efficiently. In the seventh century in Wessex, land was divided into five categories: arable, meadow, pasture, forest and waste. Wastes were not viewed in the same way that we think of 'wastes', but rather as valuable supplementary areas, usually unenclosed. Depending on the parish or manor, there could be marsh, woodland, fen or heathland, and they provided supplementary food and grazing for livestock, bedding, fuel and so on, shared amongst the community. Thus evolved the right of common, already discussed, originally from common ownership and usage; but between the sixth and thirteenth centuries, most commons or wastes became privately owned by the lords of the manor, leaving just the rights to the people. Thus most heathlands were common land, and still are today.

The Domesday Book gives us an interesting, if rather patchy, view of heathland in the eleventh century, near the start of Norman times, but really reflecting the Saxon system. In Suffolk, for example, Domesday records that 'in the hundred of Colneis, there is a certain pasture (which includes heathland in Domesday) common to all the men of the hundred'; in other words, the common was used freely by men from several parishes. 'Colneis' occupies the land between the estuaries of the rivers Orwell and Deben (i.e. between Ipswich and Felixstowe) and there is still some heathland there now. At some stage, the old Saxon common became divided up between the adjacent parishes (a frequent story for larger commons) and became represented

by Nacton, Bucklesham and Levington heaths, but there is precious little of these left now. In Norwich, the 'Mousehold Heath' mentioned in Domesday still exists, in a greatly reduced state, and its story is an interesting one. Its early origins are obscure, since there are no prehistoric archaeological remains, but by Domesday it was a huge area of heathland, covering thousands of acres with woodland only at the south-western end, closest to Norwich. Clearly the woodland was not protected from grazing, and despite attempts by the owners (the Bishops of Norwich) to protect it the wood pasture gradually contracted under heavy grazing pressure. Allusions to the heath and wood in 1156 and 1236 indicate a gradual increase in heathland, while by the sixteenth century the heath had spread all over the flatter areas, leaving woodland only around the edges, on the steeper slopes. The heath survived in this form until about 1800, when a series of Enclosure Acts for the eight parishes that each contained parts of it spelt its demise, and

Purbeck hills looking west, towards West Lulworth. The strong relationship between historic land uses and geology or topography can be clearly seen in the photograph, with heathland (used for military training now) on the acid soils (extreme right); arable land on the fertile soils at the base of the hills; old woodland on the north-facing chalk scarp, downland on the south-facing scarp, and arable or rich pasture in the fertile valley beyond.

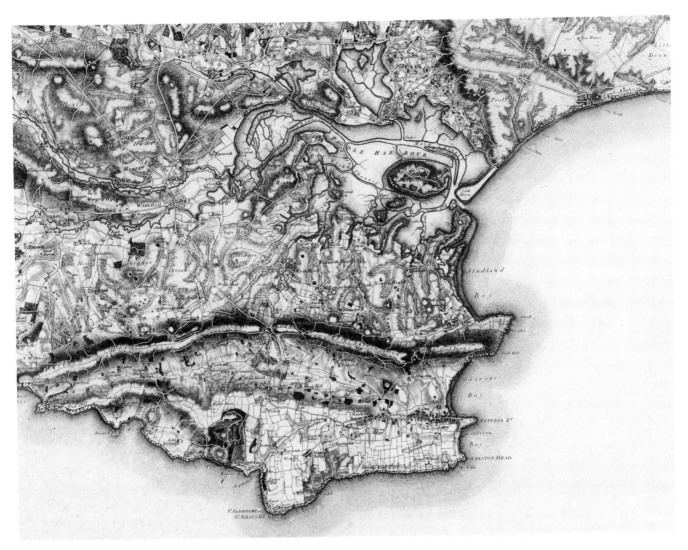

The Isle of Purbeck, Dorset. 1st Edition Ordnance Survey map dating from the early nineteenth century. It would be almost possible to write this book around this map alone, as it shows so many features of interest. North of the chalk ridge running across the 'Isle', most of the countryside is heathland vegetation; the section south of the harbour has remained virtually untouched, and is now mostly within nature reserves, whilst the whole of the north-east corner is now under Bournemouth, which did not exist 160 years ago!

by the time of the O.S. Map of 1838 only the portion within the city boundaries remained. The 180 or so acres (72 hectares) of city heath is still unenclosed, though it has suffered the fate of so many heaths as invasion by birches and oaks has ousted the ancient heath vegetation.

An area like the beautiful Isle of Purbeck, in south Dorset, has retained much of its historic pattern of land use. Its geological features are stamped so strongly on the land that the ancient division of land use between soil types has remained broadly unchanged. It comes as no surprise that this mass of ancient sites are all of immense nature conservation importance, and there is a string of nature reserves and sites of special scientific interest (SSSI) across the 'Isle'. North of the Purbeck hills, the heath was once almost continuous (now admittedly much less so) and it is possible to reconstruct the eleventh-century land use from the Domesday Book; at Povington Heath, the pattern of heath to the north, then arable along the base of the hills with common pasture next to it and open common downland on the chalk hills, mirrors so closely the soils and the present-day situation. The heath lies on the extremely acid Bagshot Beds, the Wealden Beds give rise to the more fertile soils, and the steep scarp is open downland.

Throughout the early medieval period, the population was increasing, and this was a period when many rich wildlife habitats on marginal land were claimed for more intensive use, and in many cases they never recovered. The 'waste' was being brought into cultivation. In the uplands,

CHALK HEATH

There is a strange and intriguing form of heath (or is it a grassland?) known as chalk heath. Although most lowland heaths, as we have seen, occur in areas of acidic soils, there are a dwindling few that occur in areas of *apparently* lime-rich soils, especially chalk. Some of these are simply areas of heath on patches of more acid soils, such as clay-with-flints, over the chalk, and where the area of acid soil is large enough quite extensive areas of pure heath can develop, and once did. Elsewhere the mixture of soils is more complex, and here we get the true chalk heath: an intimate and unexpected mixture of downland plants like salad burnet, rock-rose or dropwort, with heath plants like ling and bracken.

There seem to be three main types of chalk heath: 1) on plateau chalk areas where there are remnants of acidic Eocene or clay-with-flints soils which have become mixed with the chalk to give a patchy soil with an average pH (acidity) of about 6; 2) in chalk valleys, where similar material has slumped down, probably during the immediate post-glacial period before vegetation had become well-established, and

mixed to form similar soils; and 3) the commonest type, where wind-blown (loessic), sandy, acid material partially covers the chalk and becomes mixed with it. The largest area of this type of chalk heath occurs at Lullington Heath National Nature Reserve, and there are interesting examples elsewhere, such as at Martin Down where heathy vegetation sits on top of the ridges of medieval broad-rig ploughing, while chalk grassland fills the troughs.

It is an unexpected experience to find such chalk downland specialities as squinancy wort, dropwort, rock-rose, flax, salad burnet, burnet saxifrage and others growing within inches of heather, gorse and bracken, but it does occur. Nowadays, it is thought to be due to the creation of a soil intermediate between heath and chalk grassland providing conditions suitable for plants from both habitats. In some circumstances, the complexity of mixing is such that you can find really demanding calcicoles like dwarf orchid or dwarf sedge growing next to heather, obviously in different soils despite being so close.

A rather similar, though perhaps more obvious, phenomenon is the extraordinary

heathland stripes that occur in some areas. Looked at from a distance, or seen from the air, these show as regular alternating stripes of heathland and grassland, with 30–40 ft (9–12 m) between each repetition, and it is hard to believe that they are not man-made. They are best seen in eastern England, of which the most accessible place is at the flint mines, Grimes Graves. Despite their appearance, they are wholly natural, the result of periglacial sorting of different parts of the soil under a regular freeze-thaw regime. The stripes are actually polygons that have become indefinitely elongated down a slope, and the heathy parts cover troughs filled with sand, while the chalk downland flora sits directly on the chalk.

Moorland on Long Mynd, Shropshire. The vegetation of the Long Mynd, though created by man after clearance of trees, is now semi-natural moorland managed as grouse country. It still clearly exhibits the effects of arctic conditions, from just after the ice age, in the heathland/grassland stripes running down the slope. The National Trust owns 4,530 acres (1,830 hectares) of moorland at Long Mynd.

hamlets (or more often a single farm) appear for the first time at this period, often with names like 'Brackenthwaite', indicating clearance of the land from bracken-covered moorland. All over the country, much heath and moor was lost at this time to a land-hungry, expanding population. The existence of extensive Royal Forests (see p. 94) which almost invariably contained large areas of heath in addition to woodland, gave some protection to heathland, but even here there are endless records of fines for breaking the laws, or fees paid for licences to cultivate. The power of the Norman Kings was by no means absolute, and by the thirteenth century new cultivation within the Royal Forest was widespread.

Paradoxically, the reclamation of wastelands did not cease with the Black Death. Despite the decimation of the population, and the consequent reduction in land-hunger, the plague brought many social changes too, and the death of whole families and even villages allowed the lords of the manor to appropriate the waste for their own use. Then, as now, the large landowner usually looked to the most profitable use rather than that most beneficial to the community, and much waste land (including heath and moor) became more intensively used.

Yet, at the same time, heaths were still being created. Many areas of the Pennines that are now heather moorland were cleared from forest at the beginning of the twelfth century, and the thirteenth century saw considerable clearance and reversion to moorland in Wales and elsewhere in northern England. Many Scottish heaths are believed to date from much later than this; the first iron works were established in about 1600, on the west coast, and after the Jacobite Rebellions the highlands were opened up and iron-smelting became more widespread. The predominant forest tree of the area, Scots pine, does not regrow from cut stumps, so it is little surprise that the landscape rapidly became more open, and heathland developed. Destruction of the highland forest continued through the eighteenth and nineteenth centuries for various purposes, and the increasing populations of sheep and cattle, together with the native red deer, finished off the job. Most of the great moorlands of eastern Scotland date from this period.

Apart from these instances of heath or moorland creation or expansion in historical times, however, the process has generally been one of steady attrition since medieval times, at least in the lowlands. The heaths have been a consistent target for enclosure, whether privately, illegally, or by Act of Parliament. It is an indication of how much waste there once was that Gregory King, in a survey of the land use of England and Wales in 1688, indicated that about a quarter of the land was still waste (and this included a high proportion of heath and moorland). The process has gone on inexorably, however, as heathland has steadily lost its place in the local economy, and still goes on today. The

Northern moorland has a rather different mixture of species from southern heathland, though many species are the same. In this example, on the Muir of Dinnet, in the Dee valley, the heath is dominated by bearberry, bilberry, crowberry, petty whin and heath milkwort, together with more heather in places.

early 1st edition Ordnance Survey maps, dating from 1810–1820, give a fascinating picture of the extent of heathland at that time, since it is usually clearly enough defined. From these maps, the position of heaths in relation to villages can be more easily appreciated but they have also allowed a calculation of the extent of heathland 175 years ago (though the exact condition of the heath is not always known). In Dorset, for example, there were an estimated 100,000 acres (40,000 hectares) of heath in 1759 (it is little wonder that Hardy refers to them so much), reduced to 76,000 acres (30,400 hectares) by 1811, whereas by 1960 there were only 25,000 acres (10,000 hectares). The depressing thing is that the 1960 figure has already halved again in the face of agricultural 'reclamation' and housing development. Today, heathland holds no place in the

This photograph clearly demonstrates the way in which management affects vegetation. The foreground area of wet heath vegetation is regularly grazed by cattle, maintaining a varied heathery sward; the background, behind the fence, has simply been abandoned (not planted) and has rapidly become covered by pine and birch saplings.

agricultural economy of the lowlands, and it only gains protection from common-land status or special protection by virtue of high conservation importance. Upland moors have survived more extensively partly because there are fewer alternative uses, but also because they have remained part of the system, especially for sheep-grazing, and later grouse-shooting in deer areas. Many moorlands are managed quite intensively with a programme of moor-burning, aiming at a rotation of ten years, to maintain their condition and productivity, which neither sheep nor grouse will do unaided.

In contrast, in the lowlands, even heathland that is protected by its status as a nature reserve, common or public open space is steadily losing ground. Because heathland is not the original natural vegetation, on most soils it is

readily re-invaded, in the absence of grazing, by birches, pines and ultimately oaks. Very few heaths are now grazed, partly because many modern breeds do not thrive on heathland vegetation, partly because many heaths are too small to work as viable units, and because of the danger of unfenced busy roads crossing heathlands. In Dorset, the soils are acid enough, and woodland is sparse enough, to have slowed the rate of invasion; but elsewhere, such as in Surrey, Berkshire, or north Hampshire, many 'heaths' are now wholly woodland despite their name. Fires, almost invariably accidental, provoke mixed responses; in some circumstances, they can genuinely help to maintain heathland, but in others they merely hasten the process by 'coppicing' the birches and providing fertile seed-beds for birch, gorse and other colonisers.

THE NEW FOREST

By far the largest and best example of a lowland heath that *is* still grazed, though, is the New Forest, in south-west Hampshire. Here the system works, just like it used to in so many other places throughout the country, thanks to a

Heathland after fire. The effects of fire on heathland vary enormously, depending on the soil, the strength and timing of the fire, and the existing vegetation. In this example, on Ludshott Common, the rapid regeneration of birches from their burnt stumps ('coppicing' by fire), and the reappearance of flowering gorse can be clearly seen, though, over much of the common, heather-dominated vegetation has re-established. The National Trust manages the site through an active local committee.

fortunate combination of circumstances. The New Forest is a direct descendant of a former Royal Forest, still owned by the Crown, with a total of some 45,000 acres of 'Open Forest' open to grazing by commoners' stock. The Forest is large enough to be buffered against the changes that have gone on around it, and apart from two major A-roads, all other traffic travels on roads open to the grazing ponies, cattle and deer of the heaths, grasslands and bogs.

The New Forest gives the clearest insights into the ways in which many heaths must once have worked, ecologically and economically speaking. What we see today elsewhere are the tiny relics of a once greatly more extensive system, and our view of heaths is often coloured by the fact that only the most infertile, intractable fragments are left, and their boundaries are hardened up by encroaching roads, fields, plantations, playing fields and houses, to say nothing of the fact that they are no longer managed by grazing and cutting. In the New Forest, though, the whole spectrum of common-land habitats is represented, and you begin to gain an understanding of what has happened elsewhere.

Throughout most of the Forest, except for the forestry enclosures, there are no hard edges or straight boundaries,

A beautiful piece of Dartmoor heathland, showing intimate juxtaposition of species – bell heather, ling, cross-leaved heath, western gorse and bracken, in this example.

only natural blurred changes. Dry mixed heathland grades downwards into wet heathland, and then into bog; hollows with damper, more fertile soil support dense bracken growth which fades away, turning yellow from its poor diet, as it becomes out-competed by heather on the drier surrounding soils. In another direction, the heath may give way to acid bent-grass dominated grassland with scattered heather and gorse bushes; while in another direction, often up the hill, the heath may give way to woodland with birch at the transition and oak or beech beyond. For plants and animals, this is how things should be: adders, or even the rare smooth snakes, can move from warm heath in spring to cool damp bog in summer, or they can escape the effects of a heath fire by moving to the damper safety of the bog. Dragonflies breed in the bogs, but hunt over the heathlands and woodland margins, and it is the same for many other

species; the Forest provides opportunities that are denied them in much of the rest of the planned, straight-line countryside.

Investigations of the age-structure of the woodlands of the Forest (see p. 94) has not only revealed much of how the woods regenerate, but has also shown how the extent of heath or woodland waxes and wanes according to grazing pressure. In times of high grazing pressure, there is little or

New Forest heathland. Heaths may sometimes appear to be uniform, and
even monotonous, but they very rarely are, even in small areas. If you look
closely at this heath, you begin to see the variations: the bracken in the
foreground, low heather beyond, and taller gorse beyond that; while down in
the valley behind, the dry heath grades through wet heath into the pale
yellow-green of valley bog, and on the far slopes the dominance of bracken in
the fertile hollows can be clearly seen, with the fringe of yellowed leaves
visible where it fails to colonise the poorer soil dominated by heathers.
Different species use different parts of this matrix, or move between different
parts utilising aspects of each.

no regeneration, and the margins of the woods retreat
giving way to advancing heathland; in times of lower
grazing, such as during depressions or at times of stock-
disease outbreaks, the woodlands advance again behind
their frontal line of birches, or sometimes Scots pines. Those
habitat divisions are not stable, and the same applies to the
thin dividing line between acid grassland and heath, as we
know from the progression that takes place in the formation
of heaths, though the evidence of change is less readily
visible in the vegetation on the ground.

Rackham has shown that there is considerable evidence,
perhaps not surprisingly, for the same process having gone
on since at least Roman times. He suggests that many
Anglo-Saxon heaths were found adjacent to pasture woodland (see p. 89) because the wood pasture had developed
from Roman heathland in the absence of adequate grazing,
after the Romans left, to maintain the larger area of
heathland. This implies some deliberate policy, perhaps by
keeping one part of the heath free of trees and encouraging
stock to graze on it rather than in the woodland; similarly,
there were attempts to maintain the woodland area *against*
heathland in times of higher grazing by the construction of
wood banks. The example of Mousehold Heath, already
cited, is one where the attempts to keep heathland back
failed. An interesting case of the reverse effect having taken
place over the last century or so is at Ludshott Common, on
the Hampshire-Surrey border, where mature sessile oak
woodland is gently spilling over its boundaries from the
adjacent Waggoner's Wells Valley onto the heath; the
contrast between these mature trees and the usual invading pines and birches suggests that grazing has been low
here for at least a century.

HEATHLAND AND MOORLAND SITES OF THE NATIONAL TRUST

Dartmoor moorlands, The National Trust owns a relatively
small acreage of Dartmoor moorlands. The main estate is that
which includes Hentor and Trowlesworthy Warren, on the
south-west flank of the moor. It includes numerous sites of
archaeological interest.

Dunwich Heath, Suffolk. A good example of an eastern coastal
heath, of which few now remain.

Exmoor moorlands, The National Trust owns some large
estates on or close to Exmoor, including the coastal moors at
Heddon's Mouth, Woody Bay and Lynmouth in Devon; and
some beautiful examples of high moorland in Somerset,
especially within the Holnicote Estate (which includes Dun-
kery Beacon, Exmoor's highest point), and at Winsford Hill.
Both include prehistoric features such as barrows.

Kinver Edge, Staffordshire. High-quality lowland heath, with
interesting archaeological features.

The Lizard heaths, Cornwall. The National Trust owns a
number of examples of these unique heaths, with their
exceptionally rich flora and interesting history (see p. 157),
particularly around Kynance and Mullion Cove and at
Predannack.

New Forest heaths. Although the Forestry Commission owns
the bulk of the New Forest, the National Trust owns and
manages a number of interesting commons and manorial
wastes around the north side. These include Bramshaw,
Plaitford and Half Moon Commons, some of the finest grazed
dry heaths in the forest.

North York Moors moorlands, Yorkshire. Bridestones' moor is a
large and important area of moorland, managed as a nature
reserve. There are many archaeological remains, including
barrows and linear earthworks. The moors in general are
known to have been cleared early in the Bronze-Age period.

Peak District moorlands, Derbyshire. The National Trust owns
enormous areas in the dark peak moorland area, including
Kinder Scout, Mam Tor, the Winnats and the Longshaw
estate, on the east side. Characteristic northern moorland
flora and fauna, together with many archaeological remains.

Purbeck Heaths, Dorset. The Isle of Purbeck has some of the
finest lowland heaths in Britain, and the National Trust owns
many examples, including Middlebere, Studland and Godl-
ingston. Much of it is managed within National Nature
Reserves and the flora and fauna is exceptionally rich.

St David's commons, Dyfed. The National Trust owns a series
of commons between St David's and Fishguard that include
some very fine examples of lowland heath, not dissimilar to
Purbeck and the New Forest. The Ddowrog is particularly
fine.

Surrey Heaths. The National Trust owns numerous heaths
and commons in the Surrey area. Many are now wooded, or
partially so, though some fine open heath still remains, such
as at Frensham Common, Headley Heath, Hindhead commons, etc. Bramshott and Ludshott commons, just into
Hampshire, are very similar.

Thustaston Common, Wirral, Merseyside. An interesting area
of damp heathland, in an area where heathland is now rare.

6 · Wetlands

THERE IS NO DOUBT that the landscape of Britain, as the ice retreated, was a wet one. The vast power of ice-sheets to move material around and redeposit it, the changed courses of rivers and the lakes created by dams of ice, and great quantities of water from the melting ice, all contributed to the landscape studded with open waters. In the wetter uplands and western areas, almost any hollow with an impermeable base (and there were huge numbers of these left by the retreating ice) would support a water body, large or small. In other places, lakes were formed by huge blocks of ice melting later than the main ice-sheet; their presence alone caused uneven deposition of the glacial 'till', so that when they melted the waters ran into their own ready-made depression, which could often be very deep. Many such lakes still exist today, north of the line defining the limit of the last lot of ice, and they are known as 'kettle-holes'.

In much of the uplands, the deposit of till was small or non-existent, except for in the valleys, but the form of the land scraped bare and eroded by the advancing or retreating ice left ample hollows for water to fill, and the much higher precipitation and lower evaporation (because it is

Elterwater, Lake District. Upland lakes are almost invariably of natural glacial origin, and most of them are acidic and rather poor in life, due to the poor climate and acidic bedrock. Elterwater is richer than most, with more of the character of a lowland lake, and a rich aquatic flora. Its northern edge is owned by the National Trust.

Valley bog, with cotton grass. Many bogs and bog pools form in valleys, especially where the catchment produces acidic water and the drainage from the valley is impeded in some way. If left alone, they tend eventually to polarise into a central channel with drier fringing woodland, though peat-cutting, grazing, burning or raising of the water levels all contribute to maintaining their structure. This example shows a cushion of bog moss in the foreground, with narrow-leaved cotton grass, and some plants of the great sundew.

of the landscape, and no redistributed glacial till. Lakes undoubtedly did form, however, for a permafrost layer below the ground surface is highly impermeable to water, and evaporation rates were lower in those cold, early days. As we have seen, the sea has risen over 300 feet (90 m) since the ice retreated, and the uneven advancing tide gave numerous opportunities for the creation of wetlands, especially where the sea advanced and then retreated again for a while. As we shall see, the results of some of these invasions and retreats are still visible as the wetlands of today.

So, leaving rivers aside, there were still a great many wholly natural water bodies over the surface of Britain, and especially north of the last glacial limit line running roughly (in a very convoluted way) from the Bristol Channel across to the Wash, after the ice retreated. Many of these still exist today, but many more do not, and many of our lowland water bodies, in particular, have a more recent origin, often with the aid of man.

THE NATURAL DECLINE OF OPEN WATER

In any reasonably warm, productive environment, such as pertains over most of Britain through the summer, the natural fate of a still-water body is, ultimately, to disappear. The process is straightforward enough, though it varies from place to place. Firstly, if the rate at which water evaporates exceeds that at which it enters the water body (whether by rainfall or from springs or rivers), then the water body will gradually dry out, perhaps disappearing for the summer and reappearing in the winter as some groundwater-fed 'winter pools' in the Cotswolds do, or the rain-fed 'temporary pools' of the New Forest. This has happened over most of southern England. Nevertheless, even if the water supply exceeds the evaporation rate, there is still an inexorable loss. First, wetland plants colonise from the shallow edges of the water, and at the same time floating or deep-rooted aquatics establish out on the water surface. The floating aquatics die, and their remains sink to the bottom, starting the process of building up the bottom layers of silt and organic matter. They are joined by the remains of any other living organisms (plankton, invertebrates, or whatever) together with any silt brought in by streams, or direct run-off from the catchment area. Any trees near the site will cast their leaves and a proportion will fall into the water body; a high proportion if the trees are upwind from the place. So, the water body gradually fills up from the base.

At the same time, however, vegetation begins to colonise the shallower margins all around the water. There are many plants which will grow perfectly well with parts of them submerged, whether permanently or occasionally,

cooler) means that such hollows remain as water throughout the year. There were hollows, too, from earlier events such as the line of lochs along the great Highland fault from Inverness to Fort William (including the famous Loch Ness), but even in places like this the last ice-sheet aided the formation of lakes as moraines were deposited and new 'dams' raised up to hold water back.

South of the maximum limits of the ice, in south and east England particularly, the effects were undoubtedly less because there were no melting ice-blocks, no scraping bare

Insh marshes, Spey Valley. The Insh marshes are a vast collection of pools, lochs, reed-beds, sedge beds and wet pastures, strung along the Spey valley where it passes below the Cairngorms. They are largely natural in origin, and have survived attempts at drainage, though man's hand is always in evidence. Current management, mainly under the RSPB, is aimed at maintaining and restoring their wetland character.

and growing conditions in warm shallow water are exceptionally good, so this vegetation grows vigorously and fast. As it does so, it rapidly produces large quantities of dead and dying organic material, and readily traps any silt or detritus from the water. So the edges build up, and become drier, raised a little above the water level. As they do so, they become suitable for colonisation by other plants, such as willows and alders. It is an interesting fact that vegetation, especially if trees and shrubs are present, evaporates more water through it than a bare water surface would on its own; so, the rate of drying out begins to increase as the vegetation establishes. The colonising zone of wetland plants moves one stage further out into the lake, followed eventually by the trees and shrubs. In the wake of the alders and willows, eventually the drier land species will come in, usually led by the pioneer tree, birch. So the process continues, producing in time, in classic sites, a clear zonation of different vegetation types around a central, diminishing water body. Eventually, the water body may disappear and simply become woodland.

Yet this does not always happen, or at least has not yet happened, and we still have many of our natural post-

Yellow water-lilies in an unspoilt stream. Many lowland rivers have lost their natural character through drainage works and canalisation. The richness of life in a river depends heavily on the natural variation of depth, flow etc provided by a varied, meandering course, such as on the River Oberwater shown here.

Great bladderwort (Utricularia australis). True aquatic plants tend to be very specialised; bladderwort, in addition to its ability to grow freely in deep water, also has the ability to supplement its diet by catching aquatic invertebrates in its underwater bladder traps.

glacial waters, for one reason or another. In the highland zone of Britain, many open waters have persisted with very little change from their original shape, apart from some changes in level. The higher rainfall ensures that the waters never dry out, but, more importantly, the acidic nature of the water, almost invariably poor in nutrients for plant growth, coupled with the cold climate and very short growing season, means that many such lakes are almost sterile and the filling-up process simply does not take place. Many highland lakes are also incredibly deep (for instance, Loch Morar is about 1,000 ft, 300 m deep) and the process would, in any case, take an inordinate amount of time.

Further south, though, the process becomes more interesting, and more complicated. It can be seen at its best in an area of the West Midlands where there are a whole series of lakes in all states of transition from open water to dry land, with the added complication of new lakes being formed as well! The meres and mosses of Cheshire and Shropshire (extending into Staffordshire, too) are a fascinating and very species-rich series of wetlands, many of which are now protected as nature reserves. The Cheshire Plain and the area to the south was glaciated during the last ice age, and much of it is covered by glacial drift of up to 300 ft (90 m) deep. Some of the drift is unlayered boulder clay, and some of it is layered sands and gravels, and the wetlands tend to

Cheshire Rock Salt beds, or, to be more precise, Saliferous Beds of the Upper and Lower Keuper Series. Salt is soluble in water, and it seems that in areas where the beds come sufficiently close to the surface they have indeed dissolved, giving rise to local subsidence and slumping. It is virtually certain that lakes such as Pickmere, Redesmere, Great Budworth Mere and others, and now-colonised former lakes such as Holford Moss and Masseys Moss, are at least partly a result of this natural subsidence giving rise to huge depressions. The picture is complicated further by the fact that extraction of salt in recent times is known to have given rise to considerable subsidence, and some such areas are now water bodies of no mean size, such as the Flashes around Sandbach in Cheshire. This type of extraction has now ceased, so this form of subsidence is reduced.

In other words, the origins of all the lakes are very varied, and so are the physical conditions within them. What we are particularly interested in here are the processes that have gone on since. Some, such as Rostherne Mere and Great Budworth Mere, and a number of the Shropshire meres, show relatively little signs of disappearing. This may relate in some cases to their more recent origins by subsidence, and in other cases to their shape. Most of these meres are very productive, and the climate is quite good, so their non-colonisation must relate to other factors. Some of the kettle-holes have steep sides and very deep waters, and this naturally slows down their colonisation. Lakes like Quoisley Meres have survived, though many have deep deposits of peat, 15 or more feet (4.5 m) in depth, on their bottoms, which shows the way they would have gone if they had been shallower, and their margins are often extensively colonised.

Some of these former lakes have reached a fascinating state, known as a Schwingmoor (from the German). In the more acid lakes, a carpet of bog moss (*Sphagnum*) may creep over the surface of the water, forming a floating carpet or lawn. In deep ancient sites, the peaty material that continually breaks off from the base of these lawns gradually fills up the water below, tending to end up as a layer of peat at the bottom and 'lenses' of peat suspended elsewhere in the murky water. You can actually walk, or at least bounce, your way over these wet lawns, and will usually find a more or less central patch of open water where the *Sphagnum* has not quite covered, often supporting a patch of the floating insectivorous plant, lesser bladderwort. There are good examples of these Schwingmoors at Abbot's Moss and Black Lake, Delamere Forest, and Wybunbury Moss further south. At Wybunbury, you can gain a strong impression of the power of subsidence as you stand on the quaking moss surface and look across at the adjacent parish church tower, which leans considerably! These Schwingmoors are stages in the creation of eventual dry land, but in these acid, steep-sided deep lakes, it takes a long time, and,

Yellow flag iris (Iris pseudacorus) *by the river Test. The bankside vegetation is an integral part of the ecology of a river, providing nesting cover, nectar for insects, and emergence sites for invertebrates.*

be more concentrated over these latter areas. The actual origins of the wetlands, whatever their state now, are varied. The ice clearly stayed put in this area during its retreat for a considerable while, leaving a hummocky landscape with abundant hollows, and the whole area was the site of a large lake for a while, dammed by ice and encircling hills. Ice-blocks probably fell from the ice margin, and formed kettle-holes on melting, and many of the lakes can be traced to this origin. Some wetlands, such as Danes Moss, which is now merely a cut-over former peat bog, represent the remains of former lakes, in this case developed by the ponding up of the headwaters of the River Bollin on the edge of the ice. The whole business is complicated, though, by the fact that much of the area is underlain by the

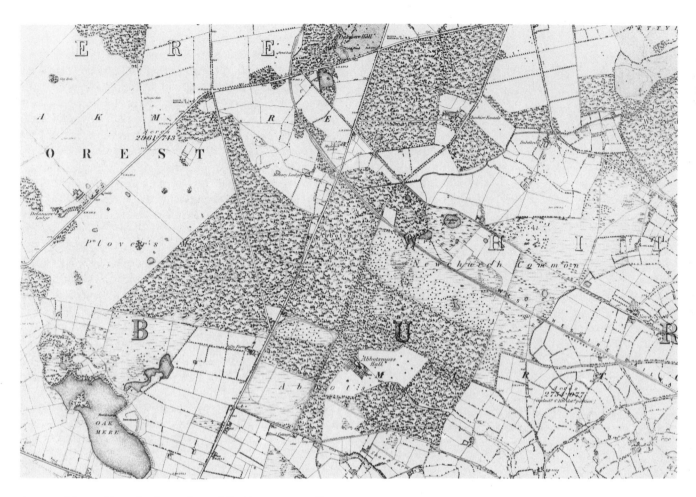

A section of the 1st Edition 6-inch map of central Cheshire, an area notable for its natural meres and mosses. This small area exhibits all stages of wetlands: the large lake, Oakmere, is a natural mere that has survived by virtue of its size and depth, though it is clear from the marshy surroundings how much it has contracted. Newchurch Common has small areas of open water to the north, a moss that is well on the way to becoming dry land in Shemmy Moss, and several 'Schwingmoors' with floating carpets of moss like Plover's Moss to the west that are now purely agricutural land. What this map does not show is the creation of new wetlands since then: for example, Abbotsmoss Wood is now a lake with the new name of Nunsmere, on the site of a sand extraction quarry, and the whole process of moss formation and drying out can begin again.

incidentally, produces some fascinating wetland sites in the process, with sundews, cranberries, bog rosemary (*Andromeda*) and a fine insect fauna with rarities like the white-faced dragonfly.

Elsewhere in the area, there are many sites where the process has gone further, and there is no open water at all. Some may have been Schwingmoors on the way, others have gone a different way.

There are similar lakes elsewhere in the country, though nowhere else is there quite such diversity in one area. Llangorse Lake, or Llyn Syfaddan, within the Brecon Beacons National Park, is a large shallow lake formed in an old glacial kettle-hole, with a naturally-rich water chemistry supporting a varied flora and fauna, including many attractive floating aquatics, such as white, yellow, and fringed water lilies, though it is in no danger of filling in at the moment. Hawes Water, on glacial deposits overlying Carboniferous limestone in north Lancashire, is now a small, though very rich, lake surrounded by calcareous fen. It is clear, though, that it extended much more widely once, in post-glacial times, and its basin has gradually filled in with vegetation.

In East Anglia, there are many series of small lakes or ponds, all with a rather similar regular, artificial appearance, on old common land or in the Breckland valleys. Their origins lie in glacial or immediate post-glacial times, and they delight in originating from natural periglacial structures known as 'pingos'. These are domes of soil pushed up by a growing lens of ice, constantly enlarged under freeze-thaw conditions, by groundwater from below from a spring or seepage. When a more permanent thaw arrives, the lens of ice collapses, and the bulk of the

Budworth mere, Cheshire. Most of the Cheshire and Shropshire meres are of natural origin, in various ways. Budworth mere, which is probably the result of natural subsidence over salt beds, coupled with glacial redeposition of soil material, is one of the largest. The natural process by which it gradually converts to dry land, as other shallower meres have already done, is clearly visible in the fringe of reed beds colonised by alder and willows.

overburden is deposited around a more or less circular hollow in the form of an encircling bank. They tend to occur in groups, wherever the right combination of springs, overburden and climate prevailed, and can still be seen clearly at places like Thompson Common in Norfolk, or Chippenham Fen in Cambridgeshire, though many have been destroyed by ploughing. Pingos themselves can be found elsewhere in the world in their frozen state, especially in the North American arctic, though they are not common, and the word is of Eskimo origin. Apart from the knowledge of equivalent structures elsewhere, the idea that they are artificial is belied by the ancient periglacial sediments at the base of some, and by asking the question 'Why should anybody have constructed such ponds?'

FORMATION OF NEW WETLANDS

Not all wetlands date from the days of the receding ice. We have already mentioned that some Cheshire meres are believed to have come from natural subsidence over dissolved salt deposits, and there is an old contemporary account of this happening at Bickley, in south Cheshire, where in 1657 'A parcel of land belonging to the Earl of Cholmley did sink into the earth ... the chasm formed by this singular phenomenon is still to be seen occupying about the eighth of an acre, the centre of which is covered with water now 33 feet deep.'

Subsidence is not a particularly common event naturally, however, at least not on a scale large enough to produce significant water bodies, since soluble deposits like the salt beds are themselves rare outside Cheshire and Worcestershire.

The great majority of the wetland around our coast (and we are only considering the genuinely freshwater ones

Central pool of Abbot's Moss Schwingmoor, Cheshire. As the glacial lakes became colonised by a floating carpet of bog moss to form Schwingmoor, a central clear area usually remains as a pool, often colonised by white water lilies, lesser bladderwort and bog pondweed. The water below this pool is usually very deep, grading downwards into liquid peat.

here, not the brackish or saline ones, that are reviewed in Chapter 7), have been formed by the activity of the sea, since the ice age. Many are entirely natural, while others, like the Norfolk Broads, are a combination of nature with man's activities.

The sea, as we will see, is constantly moving material around, throwing up shingle banks, sand bars, and so on (see Chapter 7). There are many instances, throughout recorded history, and others that pre-date recorded history, of the sea creating completely new freshwater wetlands by this means, gradually cutting off a portion of seawater or river water from the sea itself; in some cases, especially where coarse shingle forms the barrier, the lagoon may remain saline, but in other cases it eventu-

ally becomes pure freshwater, just as any other inland lake, apart perhaps from a little extra sea-spray. As far as succession to swamp and dry land goes, such lakes behave no differently to any other lake, according to their chemistry and climate, but the difference from many of the lakes that originated after the ice retreated is that they are *newer*, and the processes have not had so long to work. Many older coastal lakes have gone the same way as the Cheshire 'mosses' we have already seen, but the more recent ones survive.

A good example, with complete documentation of its history (see p. 179) lies at Studland in Dorset. Here the sea has gradually pushed sand dunes northwards over several hundred years, eventually enclosing and isolating a considerable lake known as Little Sea. Although saline at first, and therefore deserving the epithet 'Sea', it is now completely fresh, and has the feel of an inland lake in virtually all respects. Its waters are on the acid side of neutral, thanks to the acidic sands underlying and surrounding it (which derived from Bagshot Sands, the same sands that underlie many an acid Dorset heath), and its flora and fauna has developed accordingly. Newly-created lakes quite readily acquire a new flora and fauna, partly because many water

Wybunbury Moss, Cheshire. One of the most dramatic of Schwingmoor bogs lies at Wybunbury, on the Staffordshire-Cheshire border. Its probable origins from salt subsidence are graphically reinforced by the strongly-leaning (and rather dangerous) church tower in the background! The floating nature of the bog carpet is illustrated by the numerous dead pines, which germinate and begin to grow on the relatively dry surface, but die as soon as their roots break through the crust and penetrate the acid water below.

An aerial view of Thompson common, Norfolk. The hummocky nature of the ground caused by pingos in the glacial till can be clearly seen from the air and several hollows still visibly exist as ponds.

plants and animals are also widespread in wet places, and find their way readily to nearby new waters, and partly because many aquatic denizens are quite mobile. Birds, naturally, can soon find a new site, but most dragonflies are surprisingly mobile, as are water beetles, bugs, and other insects. The groups that are likely to be most poorly represented in a newish lake are the specialist large lake species like some of the bigger freshwater mussels, which are not generally mobile, and many of the fishes. Little Sea, for example, after existing for a hundred years, still only has three resident naturally-occurring fish species, the eel and two species of sticklebacks.

On the south coast of Pembrokeshire (Dyfed), close to St Govan's Head, there is a most unusual lake, formed within an old drowned river valley which has become blocked at its exit to the sea by sand dunes. The valley was first dammed 200 years ago by the Cawdors, and subsequently the sand has built up. Behind it, a large lake, known as Bosherston Lake or Llyn Bosier, has formed, fed by streams and by a series of calcareous springs, many below the water. Since virtually all of its water supply comes through, or flows off,

the Carboniferous limestone, the lake is very rich in lime, and is one of the very few such 'marl' lakes formed on the coast. Marl lakes are exceptional in having such a high proportion of calcium carbonate (lime) in them that it precipitates out, usually taking some of the water nutrients with it, as a white layer over the bottom or over any plants growing in it. Marl lakes, not surprisingly, have an unusual specialised flora and fauna, and they are often very clear because the conditions are unsuited to the excessive growth of phytoplankton and much silt precipitates with the lime deposit. Bosherston Lake now has no entry from the sea at all, but it does have a slightly higher than usual salt content, simply from exposure to the wind-driven spray from the nearby exposed coastline. Its flora and fauna is rich, much of which probably colonised in from the streams flowing into it, and it includes many molluscs, freshwater sponges (together with a species of caddis fly that lives only in sponges), and many fishes, plus an underwater 'lawn' of aquatic plants, like stoneworts, that can tolerate the lime and thrive in the clear water. The whole area is owned by the National Trust.

There are also pools that actually form within sand-dune systems as they build up, as the lower levels of sand dunes are surprisingly impervious. Alternatively, the water table

Langham Pond, Runnymede.

RUNNYMEDE LAKES, SURREY

Runnymede in Surrey is famous for its historical associations with the Magna Carta, and the National Trust owns a large area of land around this important site. Within the land, there are three ponds – Langham Pond, Lily Pond, and an unnamed one – that were once part of the course of the River Thames, though this now flows well to the north. The Thames, like most lowland rivers, used to constantly shift its course, and if the 'neck' of a sinuous meander eventually cut through, it left part of the old river-course high and dry. Where a lake, or series of lakes, remain in the old river course, these are known as oxbow lakes. Langham Pond and the others are a superb example of this form of pond, one of the few ways in which new lakes can form naturally in the lowlands, though nowadays many rivers have their courses too constrained by embankment and canalisation for this to happen.

By virtue of their situation, the ponds at Runnymede are fed not only by rainwater but also by calcareous springs, rising from the chalk, that were once in the bed of the river. This helps the waters of the lakes to remain clear and unpolluted, as well as keeping the levels high and preventing the lakes from drying out. This stable, lime-rich, unpolluted water regime has allowed the development of a very rich flora and fauna, with additional species-rich marginal fen and meadows. Altogether, it is one of the finest lowland wetland systems in the Trust's ownership.

Plants there include flowering rush in abundance, greater water-parsnip, marsh stitchwort, all four species of *Lemna* duck-weed, frogbit, fringed water-lily and many others. The insects are correspondingly rich, with many rarities, including a fly that is restricted to flowering rush, and which only occurs in one other place in Britain. It is an excellent dragonfly site, with several uncommon species breeding there, particularly those that prefer less acid waters.

Altogether, it is a superb and unusual example of a natural lowland wetland.

level may reach to beyond the surface for part of the year, and pools are formed. Many just remain as damp areas, and they have a very rich flora, especially on calcareous dunes, but others have developed as extensive pools. There are dune-slack pools (as the hollows in sand dunes are known) in most of the larger sand-dune systems, like at Kenfig in South Wales, Braunton Burrows in Devon, or Newborough Warren in Anglesey, but the most remarkable one of all is the Loch of Strathbeg in Aberdeenshire. It is far and away the largest dune-slack 'pool' in Britain, about 4 miles (6.5 km) long and over ½ mile (1 km) wide! It is caused by the presence of an extensive calcareous dune system to the seaward side of it, forming a dam about ½ mile (1 km) wide in places, ponding back the waters from a number of streams to form the lake. The flora and fauna is not dissimilar to that of the Little Sea at Studland, allowing for the great difference in latitude and the rather more calcareous nature of Strathbeg, and it has few species of fish; just the stickleback and eels again, together with brown trout, probably from the inflowing streams which Little Sea lacks.

THE FORMATION OF LITTLE SEA, STUDLAND

The southern arm of the entrance to the beautiful Poole Harbour, one of the largest natural harbours in Europe, is formed by a long sandy promontory extending northwards from the village of Studland up to Shell Bay, at the narrow entrance to the harbour. Contained within this promontory is a large freshwater lake, about 1 mile (1.5 km) long and ¼ mile (0.5 km) broad, called 'Little Sea', with a smaller lake to the east of it, and to the east of these lie a large area of sand dunes, varying from stable heath-covered older ones to young unstable bare dunes.

A series of maps from 1600 to the present day show that the lake was completely absent in 1600, and the promontory was much narrower; gradually two sand-dune systems, one coming up from the south, one coming down from the north. came towards each other and met in the late nineteenth century, cutting off a large part of the bay and turning it into a lake.

A series of historical maps showing how sand dunes have formed around an arm of the sea at Studland, in Dorset, to isolate two areas of salt water which have then become freshwater lakes.

Although at first this was a saline lagoon, gradually it became isolated from the sea and its influence, and was fed only by the small streams from the surrounding heath, turning into a stable freshwater lake.

Little Sea, Studland, and Poole harbour from the air. This large freshwater lake has formed naturally during the last few hundred years as the dunes on the right have advanced northwards, gradually enclosing an arm of the sea and eventually isolating it as a lake fed by streams.

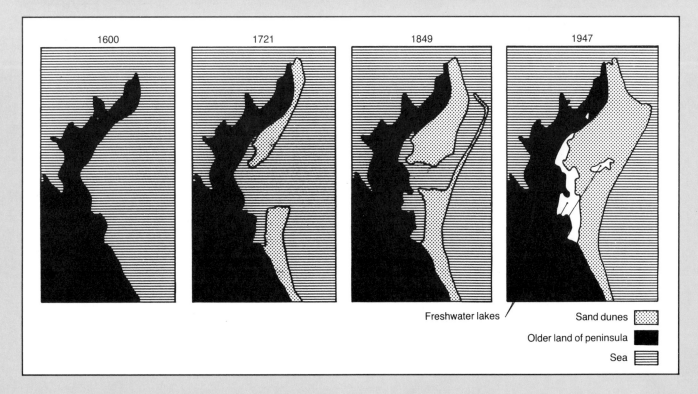

| 1600 | 1721 | 1849 | 1947 |

Freshwater lakes

Sand dunes

Older land of peninsula

Sea

Unimproved grazing marshes, Somerset Levels, near Catcott. The result of the Somerset Levels' long and complex history is a ditch-dissected landscape of meadows, marshes and woods, broken here and there by arable land or peat extraction. The ditches are vitally important to the wildlife value of the area, and they are rich in plants and animals. Some meadows, such as this one, remain unimproved and flower-filled, while others have been fertilised, reseeded, or even converted to arable land.

THE SOMERSET LEVELS

One of the most fascinating stories of any wetland system, whose history can be followed through thousands of years, is that of the Somerset Levels. It is an intriguing blend of nature and man's activities from earliest times, where we can follow the progression from open water, through several transgressions of the sea, to fen and bog, with the modifying hand of man laid over the later stages, ultimately forming the area we know today: a blend of rich pasture land, dissected by 'rhynes' (i.e. ditches, or wet hedges), partly flooded in winter, and nationally-known for its birds, flowers and insects. The story is a long one, but it is worth reciting in detail, partly because of its intrinsic fascination

to the ecologist or historian, but also because it is broadly typical of that of many other 'levels' systems around our coast today, like Pevensey levels in Sussex, the Gwent levels in South Wales, or even the fenland of eastern England.

The Somerset Levels cover a huge area, altogether of over 200 square miles (500 km²) in the area bounded by the heights of the Mendip Hills to the north, the sea (the Bristol Channel) to the west, and other hills, including the Blackdowns, to the south. They are split by a low range of limestone hills known as the Poldens, and here and there 'islands' rise out of the levels, like Glastonbury Tor, Berrow Mump, or Brent Knoll, and most of the villages are on low islands of some sort, raised above the marsh area.

At first, after the ice age, the sea was much lower than it is now, and the Somerset Levels were a terrestrial landscape of valleys and hills, far from the coast. As the sea level rose, these valleys (whose floor is some 90–100 feet, 27–30 m, below the present-day ground surface), became drowned like so many other valleys in the south by about 6000 BC, and vast quantities of silty clay were deposited on the valley floors under estuarine conditions, like, say, Morecambe Bay today. Eventually, this brought the valley floor up to

roughly the present level, so that when the sea retreated slightly, a huge expanse of mud and shallow water was exposed for colonisation. Rivers such as the Brue and Parrett (as they are known today) meandered through the area in erratic courses, changing according to circumstances, and gradually a vast marshy area developed, eventually completely losing its marine character. In the period between 4000 and 3000 BC, the Levels were a huge fenland area, still rich in nutrients from the estuarine soil and the lime-rich groundwater, with much open water scattered about. The coastal strip was slightly higher, where more clay was deposited, and this remained as dry land, but over the rest the remains of the fen vegetation was steadily building up into fen peat, or sedge peat, now the prime target of the peat-extraction companies. Some areas became dry enough to support woodland, others remained as fen, and some was open water, with the balance shifting as river courses became blocked and altered, and regular floods occurred.

In Neolithic times, by about 3000 BC, the climate is believed to have become wetter, which produced wetter conditions throughout the Levels, and hastened the leach-

Somerset Levels from the air. This view, looking roughly westwards along the Polden Hills ridge towards the sea, shows more clearly than from the ground how closely the levels relate to the sea. The ridge-top road and the settlements on higher ground (once essential to avoid the winter-flooded areas) can also be seen.

ing out of nutrients left by the marine transgressions. So the area became steadily more acid, causing a change to different vegetation. Acid wet conditions are ideal for bog-formation (the same process as occurred in some of the Shropshire and Cheshire mosses) in which bog moss (*Sphagnum*) species thrive, building up an acidic peat of partly-decayed remains below them. It is this peat which most frequently provides so much evidence for past vegetation changes, since the acid conditions favour the preservation of organic remains, including the all-revealing pollen grains.

At the same time, the first evidence of man in the area becomes apparent, in the form of some remarkable ancient trackways. Two Neolithic trackways, dated to about 4,800–4,900 years ago, have been discovered and partly excavated from the Levels. They are amazingly well-preserved, in places, and their construction has revealed much about the times that they were built in. In the Abbot's track, planks of alder, trimmed on both sides, were laid crossways and held in place by birch pegs, with thinner whips used to hold the structure together. It is estimated that some 50,000 pegs would have been used for the Abbot's track, indicating a great deal of organised work, and some importance attached to the route. The other track, the Bell track, was constructed of transverse planks of ash, over which a layer of hazel twigs up to 1 ft (30 cm) thick was laid, held in place by birch pegs. Both are known as corduroy roads, from their appearance, and they are the earliest-known examples of wooden roads in the world, though there are also later examples known from the Levels. Whether the increasing presence of man in the area relates to the changing vegetation is uncertain; it may be that Neolithic man merely crossed the levels on the trackways (for it would have been a long way round on wholly dry ground), or moved between raised areas where there were early settlements; or he may have utilised them as a source of fodder for animals, wood, and perhaps grazing in drier areas.

From this period, some 5,000 years ago, onwards for 2–3,000 years, much of the Levels area developed as a huge raised bog. Raised bogs occur widely throughout northern Europe, though there are few left in Britain that have not been modified by man; they occur in quite high rainfall conditions, and the centre of the bog continues to grow upwards, well above the surrounding land level, pulling the water table with it, but also depending on rainwater – hence their development in higher rainfall areas. Thus the bog ends up as a great domed structure, usually with a watery rim where drainage from the raised centre ends up, and it spreads outwards as far as conditions permit. In wetter times during this period, the bog filled the whole Levels from edge to edge, creeping up the lower slopes of the surrounding hills, but retreating again when rainfall was lower, edged out by the lime-rich water flowing off the Carboniferous limestone Mendip Hills, or the Liassic limestone Poldens. Towards the end of the Bronze Age, the bog began to slow down and dry out, mainly as a result of a drier climate, and much of the surface became drier peat, colonised by heather and heathland plants. Shortly afterwards, in about 500 BC at the end of the Bronze Age, the Levels were again flooded by the sea. The change in sea-level was enough to flood much of the area, but the higher parts of the raised bog and the island areas across the Levels escaped, so parts of the area had a new deposit of clay or detritus, while others remained as peat.

Excavations have shown that, by about the third century BC, 2,200–2,300 years ago, there was a large lake, over $1\frac{1}{2}$ miles (2.5 km) across, between Glastonbury and Meare,

and that here the 'lake village' people had settled. In fact, the original rather romantic idea of these Iron-Age people living in houses constructed on stilts out in the water is now seen as less likely, and it is more probable that their houses were constructed on clay and brushwood bases on more stable peat on the lake margin. They were clearly a settled and well-to-do people, with many crops and ample luxuries. There are also remains of beaver, otter, sea eagle, and pelican, indicating a generally wet environment with a much richer wild fauna than we can contemplate now!

About AD 250, well into Roman or Romano-British times, there was another episode of considerable flooding by the sea. The flooding must have been highly dramatic, because it extended tens of miles inland, and deposited a layer of brown clay over all the low-lying parts at least 3 ft (1 m) thick; it has been calculated that about 1,000 million tons of clay were deposited during this episode, so it was clearly a period under seawater rather than just a flood. The Romans were certainly in evidence in this part of Somerset, but they probably had little use for the Levels themselves, concentrating on more productive arable and mining areas nearby, leaving the Levels to such native peoples as could survive there.

THE SOMERSET LEVELS AFTER THE ROMANS

What little is known of the Levels during the Dark Ages suggests that it was simply a wild, marshy, little-used area, with a low population concentrated on the islands, with occasional connecting trackways. It is highly likely that it was subject to regular flooding of various sorts, just as before and since. By Saxon times, there is evidence that the moor was used as common summer grazing, possibly without any formal rights, by neighbouring villages, with some separation of the use of different parts. Domesday tells us relatively little, but it does refer to 15 fisheries on Sedgemoor, so it was clearly a wet place, but being used in one way or another.

In the thirteenth century, Glastonbury Abbey, one of the most powerful religious institutions in the country, and other religious houses around the Levels, began the first organised attempts at reclamation and flood-prevention. The Somerset Levels suffered then, as they do now, from being very low-lying; the tidal range in the adjacent Bristol Channel is one of the greatest in the world, and many parts of the Levels lie below high tide level, often well below. At the same time, large quantities of water pour into the Levels from surrounding higher land, through rivers, streams and direct drainage. Sea walls, which were already constructed by this period, may keep the sea out (as long as they are not breached), but at high tides and when rainfall is high there is no way that all the water can be removed in time to

West Sedgemoor, Somerset Levels, as shown on the 1st Edition Ordnance Survey 6-inch map. There is a very clear distinction between the enclosure-pattern fields of the levels, and the more varied field shapes of the surrounding higher areas. The fields on the levels with the regular symbols in are osier beds, which still exist on the levels today.

prevent flooding. So, these early attempts were largely aimed at ensuring a reasonable sea wall, and constructing internal ditches to get the water off the land as quickly as possible, though of course it could not remove the inherent likelihood of major floods. It was clearly worthwhile, though, and there are records of hay-making and grazing, and in due course the land use was formalised into 'marsh, mow, pasture and meadow', with specific common rights attached to individuals. The thirteenth century was a time of pressure and change in the English countryside, and there was much buying and exchanging of rights and appropriation of land. One land dispute, at Eddington, failed to reach a settlement because 'the tenement ... is so covered by water, that a view cannot be made'! Throughout the monastic period, attempts continued to drain and improve the Levels, and many rivers were straightened and ditches constructed during this period. From the earliest times of reclamation, these ditches (locally known as rhynes) have marked ownership, tenancy or right boundaries. Mud from the cleared ditches was spread on the fields, an early form of fertiliser which also raised and improved the enclosed land slightly, and the ditches and channels were used as fish supplies and as a means of navigation. It might stretch the analogy too far in some ways, but a visit to the Marais Poitevin on the west coast of France helps to

understand the medieval Somerset Levels, as all these historic uses still take place, in an area that is very similar to the Levels.

The situation by the late Middle Ages was clearly a complex one; there was much shared responsibility between owners, tenants and right holders, and increasing amounts of maintenance work needed to keep the system going. There is ample evidence for much of it falling into disrepair by the fifteenth century anyway; for example, the Abbot of Athelney and some of his tenants were summoned in 1443 for neglecting ditches, but the dissolution of the monasteries (between 1536 and 1540) led to much more widespread neglect. Although the pattern of drainage was broadly established, the maintenance was inadequate, and use declined. Then, in 1607, came another great flood. The sea wall near Burnham was breached, and a mixture of

Peat-digging on the Somerset Levels, from an old photograph in the Museum of English Rural Life, University of Reading. An extensive industry, now largely mechanised, has built up around the peat deposits laid down on the regularly-flooded Somerset Levels, as they evolved from estuary, through freshwater wetland, to the characteristic landscape of today.

greater effort, together with *pumped* drainage schemes, has altered the intensity of use of the Levels.

Today, the Somerset Levels are a fascinating blend of nature and man, though any naturalist or historian must long to have been able to study them 50 years ago, when so much would have been clearer! We can still see remnants of the great raised bog episode at Shapwick Heath and nearby, patches of fenland vegetation are long-established, and some of the meadow swards are undisturbed since enclosure. The eighteenth century enclosure pattern, superimposed on the medieval efforts, is still a primary feature of most of the Levels, and the pattern of settlements on higher grounds, many of them still called 'Isles' gives a feel of the way that the Levels once were. Man's efforts have failed to destroy totally the natural pattern and wildlife, and some areas, meadows and ditches are still superbly rich, yet it is still disappearing. . . .

The Somerset Levels are remarkable in their continuously documented history and the range of historic features seen today, but the same processes have been going on over much of southern Britain in a broadly similar way. Most such levels have gone further in the direction of reclamation than the Somerset Levels, partly because the natural difficulties compounded by high tidal range, and encircling hills, were less in other places. The same pattern of later drainage and reclamation has proceeded unabated in almost all the wetlands of England, and in many in Scotland and Wales, but nowhere has the process been more complete, and devastating to the natural life, than in eastern England.

seawater and freshwater flooded over 100 square miles (260 km²) submerging 30 villages, and killing 65 people. This, and the subsequent neglect, put the Levels back into the realms of real waste land. A visitor at the end of the eighteenth century wrote: 'Here we descend into the marsh or fen lands . . . On these bogs, scarce any pasturage grows . . . They are observed to rise with much wet, and sink in dry weather.' There was little sign of the medieval use of the Levels. However, the seventeenth- and eighteenth-century reclamation of the Fenlands of eastern England, aided by the Dutch engineer Vermuyden, had shown what could be done (though actually the problems were considerably greater on the Levels), and the general trend towards enclosure and intensification led to the enclosure of much of the Levels between 1770 and 1833. Interestingly enough, most of the drainage schemes were vociferously opposed by the local farmers and commoners, in sharp contrast to the reaction to the Nature Conservancy Council's attempts to prevent improvement today! Ultimately and gradually the work went ahead, however, cutting straighter river channels, and ditching all the fields, slowly bringing them into greater production. Most arable schemes failed through waterlogging or flooding, and the pattern of land use on the Levels remained broadly similar until recent times, when

THE FENLANDS

The ebb and flow of marine transgression, natural succession, and man's reclamation has been going on in eastern England around the Wash since Roman times, accelerating through the Middle Ages, and culminating in the efforts of the sixteenth to eighteenth centuries, by when virtually all these coastal areas were in intensive production.

There was a similar process going on inland, however, in the great natural fenland area around Wisbech, Cambridge and Peterborough. Today, it is a highly productive, bare open area, with scarcely a fragment of semi-natural habitat to be seen, but 400 years ago it was a vast 'wetland' covering over 1,000 square miles (2,600 km²). By the beginning of the seventeenth century, progress in agriculture and engineering was such that it became feasible to contemplate draining such areas, and there were wealthy landowners with the money, and vested interest, to achieve it. A 'Great designe' was proposed, and eventually initiated

Rich aquatic vegetation in ditch, Sussex. Although any wetland will soon fill with plants, it is generally true that older-established wetlands have a better range of plants and animals, and are likely to include more uncommon species. This old, well-managed ditch on the Sussex coastal levels supports a tremendous range of aquatic plants, including arrowhead, frog-bit and pondweeds visible here.

Ditch, Amberley Wildbrooks, West Sussex. Although now well inland, Amberley Wildbrooks have the same origins as levels such as Pevensey Levels or the Somerset Levels. Despite pressures, they have remained relatively unspoilt, and still support a very high proportion of Britain's aquatic flora and fauna in their ditches and streams.

by the fourth Duke of Bedford, who owned some 20,000 acres (8,000 hectares) around Whittlesey and Thorney. He joined forces with a number of other 'Adventurers' (as they were known, for risking their capital on such ventures) to begin drainage work, with the aid of the Dutch engineer Vermuyden, in 1630. Extensive works with undertaken, involving the construction of new cuts, and drains with complex sluices. Part of the work involved embanking areas specifically to receive floodwaters, of which the most ambitious involved the construction of the embankment to the Old Bedford river in 1636, to the west; followed, after an interruption for the Civil War, by the creation of the New Bedford River (or Hundred Foot River) to the east in 1651, together with the Forty Foot Drain, Twenty Foot River, and Sixteen Foot Drain.

Before 1812, this embanked area was also used to contain marine floodwater, for none of this area is far above the sea, but at this time work to build an adequate sea defence was commenced, and the problem soon ceased. Paradoxically, in view of the devastating effects on the natural fenlands and their wildlife, this, the most engineered part of the scheme, is now a wetland site of international importance. Every winter, the washes are again allowed to flood for the same reasons, aided and abetted by a number of conservation organisations, and they become a paradise for a multitude of wintering birds; as the washes drain in spring, they attract a wide range of breeding wetland birds, including, since 1952, the black-tailed godwit. The flora of parts of these washes is also rich, since previously flooding, and latterly their conservation status, has retained parts in an unimproved state.

Lake at Holme Fen National Nature Reserve, Cambridgeshire. Holme Fen is a degraded relict of the fenlands, spared from intensive agriculture by its poorer soil and sympathetic ownership. Recently, an artificial lake has been constructed, in conjunction with peat extraction, to re-form one of the missing natural habitats of the fens – open water.

The last major part of this wetland to survive in a relatively natural state was the famous Whittlesey Mere in Huntingdonshire, now Cambridgeshire. In 1697, there is a record indicating that the mere covered over 11,000 acres (4,400 hectares), in a shape 6 miles by 3 (10 by 5 km) but it was shallow and in the latter stages of its natural life as reeds and fen vegetation crept outwards from the margin. A hundred years later, the open water area was down to 1,570 acres (628 hectares), and shortly afterwards the water table began to fall as well, reacting to the extensive drainage of the surroundings. In 1826, in a severe drought,

it dried out completely, and was only a shallow expanse in wetter years. Nevertheless, the process of transformation to fenland, woodland and dry land was never completed, because, in 1851, with the aid of the newly-invented steam pump, the remainder of the mere was drained in just three weeks. All the teeming wildlife of this last great natural lowland lake was gone – the marsh harriers, cranes, bearded tits, large copper butterflies and all the unrecorded species. In 1890 a visitor wrote: 'All is gone – reeds, sedges, the glittering water, the butterflies, the gypsies, the bitterns, the wildfowl, and in its place . . . a dreary flat of black arable land'! It is difficult not to agree with the sentiments.

One small part of the former extent of Whittlesey survives, however, though it was not open water itself in 1697. As the mere had contracted through historical time, it had left areas of peat in its wake. One of these, at Holme Fen, proved too acid and wet to be worth cultivating, and it was used instead as an area of rough grazing, and later a game reserve. Since 1954, it has been a National Nature Reserve,

The Holme Fen posts. The cast-iron post here was erected in 1851, and at that time its flat top was flush with the ground. It gives a graphic picture of the way in which the peat has shrunk, and the ground level dropped, all over the East Anglian fens as drainage and reclamation has proceeded.

Woodwalton Fen, Cambridgeshire. This nature reserve represents a bastion against the dramatic reclamation and changes that have gone on in the fenlands all around it. It remains many feet above the arable land that surrounds it, and its value as a wetland site is maintained by pumping and considerable management work.

Wicken Fen, Cambridgeshire. This National Trust site is one of the earliest nature reserves in the country. Besides protecting an extensive area of mixed wetland habitats, it also encompasses historic land uses, such as the cutting of saw-sedge for thatching. Adjacent to the reserve, there is still an area where common rights to cut saw-sedge exist. The windmill in the background is an old drainage water pump.

one of the few remnants of the once-vast fenlands, and it now has open water again in the form of sizeable new meres from which the peat has been dug. Wicken Fen, not far away, near Cambridge, is an area of peatland left over from the days of fen and bog, when the sea controlled the levels of the area, and peat built up in continuously waterlogged conditions, just as in the Somerset Levels. The vegetation there now has an intriguing mosaic character associated with a past system of strip use in which peat was cut in some areas, saw sedge (*Cladium mariscus*) was harvested in others, and clay was dug elsewhere, mostly on a common rights basis. So, although the site is not truly natural, in that the original fen and bog surface has long since been removed, it closely mimics the natural vegetation, and peat-cutting, by taking the ground surface back to water-table level, re-starts the succession, as it has elsewhere so often. The result is a marvellous mixture of habitats and species, giving a real feel of how so much of the area might have been once.

MARLPITS

In the days before fertilisers came from a bag, the need for agricultural improvement of acid soils was well-recognised by farmers. The commonest solution to the problem, in areas where it was possible, was to dig for marl, and to spread this on the land. Marl itself is a calcareous clay, and the best material for agricultural purposes comes from below the surface of the ground, where the lime from the upper layers has added to the existing lime. In parts of the country where marl was available, such as Cheshire, Shropshire, Hampshire, Oxfordshire and Norfolk, large numbers of ponds were created by this process.

Although marl-digging is now irrelevant to modern agriculture, many of the ponds have survived intact. The moderately lime-rich waters of the ponds favour a rich flora and fauna, and where such ponds have survived in good condition they remain havens for wildlife, though many have been filled in, polluted, or otherwise lost. Some National Trust estates are particularly rich in marlpits; for example, there are over 80 such ponds at Tatton Park in Cheshire, many on the Erddig estate in Clwyd, and others on the Wirral and elsewhere. Collectively, they are an important biological resource, though individually they may not always be special.

In the southern half of the New Forest, there is an exceptional collection of marlpits. Although the forest soils are generally acid, much of the southern part is underlain by Headon Beds, which yield a rich marl. Through medieval times, marl-digging gradually became a common right for the people living in or around the New Forest, which became formalised in the seventeenth century in a unique register of claims.

In 1877, the Office of Woods ensured that rights of marl-digging and peat-cutting (turbary) were to be exercised only 'by view and allowance of the Foresters', though in fact the practice had declined considerably by then anyway. Keepers' accounts for the period 1850–80 make no mention of it and a contemporary account suggests that it had not been exercised for some while.

The legacy of this phase, though, is a series of shallow ponds and damp depressions, which ceased to be worked at least 150 years ago. The effect of such digging

New Forest marlpit in spring. The old marlpits of the southern parts of the New Forest, despite their origins from the ancient common rights to marl-digging, are exceptionally rich habitats. The dense aquatic and emergent vegetation can be clearly seen, and this includes a number of rarities as well as supporting a wide range of animal life.

was not only to begin a new open-water succession, but also to expose the most lime-rich layers of the clays, skimming off the leached upper layers. This produced a series of calcareous lakes, perhaps with many affinities to those in the early post-glacial period. They now have a marvellously rich flora and fauna, and they are kept open by the ponies and cattle that graze under existing common rights on the Forest. Collectively, they form an exceptional series of small and very species-rich wetlands.

HOW OLD IS YOUR LOCAL WATER BODY AND WHY IS IT THERE?

Water bodies have a tremendous range of origins, both natural and artificial, dating from all periods of history and prehistory. The current use and appearance may have little to do with the origins of the pond, and this is an abbreviated guide towards feeling your way towards an answer to the above question.

1) *The ageing process.* We have seen already that, in most parts of the British Isles where people live, the natural tendency is for water bodies to fill in and dry out. Thus, if your water body is *natural*, then there must be a good reason why it has not dried out. Some possible reasons include: very acid water and cold climate (mainly in the uplands); the water body is very deep; it has a naturally fluctuating water-level, like the Breckland meres; or it is of recent, natural origin (see pp. 175–8) e.g. from the sea, or from subsidence over chalk or salt deposits.

Old ponds that have been dredged or enlarged to keep them open will most probably be more detectable under (3) below.

2) *Names.* Pond is not an ancient name, and it appears first in the Middle Ages, specifically meaning a *dammed* pond such as a fishpond; *lake* is more recent, too, transferred from its meaning as part of a river system (and still used as such in some areas); *mere* is the Anglo-Saxon word for all forms of open water, and will usually indicate a much older water body, though not necessarily a *primary* one. In some areas, the term *mere* may be adopted for more recent water bodies, such as at *Nunsmere* in Cheshire, which is a gravel-pit, though no doubt there was an older lake somewhere nearby.

3) *Uses.* If the water body is artificial, what was it used for? Does it have one straight side forming a dam? Is there an access route

was dug purely to provide a sheet of water? Although there are almost as many uses for ponds as you can think of, they tend to fall into broad categories and respond to these sorts of questions.

4) *Boundaries.* How do ancient or dateable boundaries and features relate to your water body? Do boundaries cross it, suggesting that it arose later than them, or do they go round it? Do they deviate towards it, or meet at it? If there is ridge-and-furrow, does the pond cut across it, or does the ploughing relate to the pond? Not all water bodies have such boundary features, but many do, and you can make full use of them.

5) *Position.* Some artificial ponds have predictable positions, like hammer ponds in valleys, peat-cuttings in boggy areas, marlpits in the *middle* of fields, monastic fishponds close to old monastic sites, or old gravel workings amidst gravel deposits ... and so on.

Hammer ponds at Waggoner's Wells, in the western Weald (National Trust). Many ponds, especially in areas like the Weald, were originally constructed to provide power for the iron industry, though now they may be scenically attractive and important for wildlife. The ponds in this picture were known to have been constructed in 1647, since they were the subject of a court case at the time, involving the misuse of common land.

THE ANCIENT CREATION OF WETLANDS

From the story so far, it would be easy to assume that the whole picture is nothing but nature having created wetlands, and man and nature combining to destroy them. Thankfully, this is not quite the whole story, and in many areas, man has created new wetlands, or rejuvenated old ones. Because they are more recent in origin than most of the natural post-glacial waters, the natural processes of succession through fen and woodland to dry land have not run their course, and open water still remains, even in the warm climate of the south which so favours the disappearance of open waters. Many of these are still being created today, and one hopes that gravel-pit complexes like the Cotswold Water Park in the upper Thames valley will become the prime wildlife sites of the future. We are only really concerned here with the more ancient creations, however, where the effects of man and nature have had time to mingle and interact.

Why should man have created wetlands? The answer, as usual, is far from simple. Some wetlands were created deliberately, as fishponds, or water supplies for industrial use, whilst others were simply by-products of other uses,

The superb lakes at Bosherston, at peak flowering time for white water-lilies. These historic and beautiful lakes are also rich in other forms of wildlife and are managed as a native reserve by the National Trust (see p. 177).

Alresford pond from the air. This lake was known to have been constructed in the thirteenth century, as a canal reservoir, and its dam can be clearly seen. The natural silting-up and filling-in processes have reduced the lake over the years to a fraction of its former size, and the original extent, extending away to the margins in a 'Y' shape, can be visualised.

like the gravel-pits of today. The origins of the very earliest artificial wetlands are uncertain, but certainly by Roman times wetlands were being created, by peat-digging, or associated with mining and quarrying, and, no doubt, some took place before. There is evidence of prehistoric man-made ponds from near Cissbury Ring on the Sussex Downs, where some embanked ponds took the drainage from pre-Roman roadways; and Wiltshire, where one of the many Bronze-Age Grim's Ditches diverts to pass through a pond, but such definite instances are few in number.

By early medieval times, open water was being created for a range of different purposes; peat-digging, and extraction, was widespread, but so too was the construction of monastic fish ponds, or stew-ponds, many of which remain today, and many others are traceable; and the damming of water to run mills (by the time of Domesday, hundreds or even thousands of water mills were in existence). There are even some surprising early examples of engineered wet-lands; by AD 1200, the growing wool trade, centred around Alresford in Hampshire, led Bishop Godfrey de Lucy of Winchester to attempt to make the Itchen navigable as far up as Alresford by constructing a form of canal for which he made an enormous reservoir by damming the headwaters

of the river Alre, a tributary of the Itchen. The scheme was never very successful, but the lake was used later as a head for mills, and is now a Site of Special Scientific Interest. It also provides an interesting dateable progression of the colonisation of the lake, as history has seen the lake, known as Old Alresford Pond reduced in size by well over a half during its life, as reed-beds and scrub, together with the shallowing effects of silt, have filled it up.

THE NORFOLK BROADS

The most remarkable of all known examples of man-created wetlands is the Norfolk Broads. Once, it was not considered that the Broads were anything but a series of natural lakes, until in the 1950s a botanist called Joyce Lambert began to investigate their profiles in some detail. She took peat cores across marshland and open water, and began to suspect that the shape of the lakes was not quite natural; an increase in the number of cores revealed that the lakes were, in fact, straight-sided, flat-bottomed holes in peat, which immediately suggested that they were ancient peat-cuttings rather than natural lakes. Two other lines of research began to fill the picture in; medieval records from Norwich Cathedral and elsewhere indicated the extent of peat use in the area during early medieval times, and other work indicated that the land was about 13 ft (4 m) higher in those times in relation to the sea than it is now, making the pits (which are 8–10 ft, 2.5–3 m, deep) easily dry enough to work. So the medieval peat-digging theory was confirmed, and a combination of lines of investigation has shown roughly what the history has been.

The early history of the Broads area is really very like that of the Somerset Levels; alternating periods of marine inundation, the development of fen and sometimes bog left a marshy area dominated at times by reeds, over deep peat that had built up below the fen or bog. The area was probably only used very sparsely at first, as it was too wet to be settled, though no doubt some of its products, like fish, were used. The Romans were known to have used peat as fuel to assist evaporation in their fenland saltings, though there is no direct evidence that it came from the Broads. By the end of the ninth century, the Danes settled in the area, and they may well have been the first to exploit the peat, at a time when it was dry enough to work easily. If the land surface was 13 ft (4 m) higher than now, the peat probably supported a heath or wet heath vegetation on its surface, and the peat would have been readily accessible. The amount of peat that was extracted from all the Broads has been calculated at 900 million cubic feet (25.5 million m^3)(a fair amount!), and by working out an approximate annual rate from its known uses a figure for the life of the pits has been calculated at about 350 years. It is known that the

Upton Broad, Norfolk. The famous Norfolk Broads have suffered drastically from pollution and disturbance, and have lost most of their aquatic wildlife in the process. Upton Broad, by virtue of its isolation from the main system of broads, and its status as a nature reserve, has survived almost unscathed. Here, marsh fern and Norfolk reed are visible in the fringing vegetation.

open water, but others are simply too deep or large to have gone through the whole process, while others have been kept open by rivers flowing through them. The sad part is that, although the Broads have survived in appearance, at least, as a vast semi-natural wetland, they have changed dramatically at the insidious hand of man in the last 20 years. From being a pure, healthy water system, teeming with life of all sorts and as clear as a spring, the Broads have become degraded and polluted, with few traces of this life left. Once, 27 species of dragonfly were recorded from here, including several real specialities; many have gone altogether, like the Norfolk damselfly now extinct in Britain, whilst others, like the Norfolk hawker, just hang on in sites around, but not in, the Broads. The aquatic plants, the mainstay of any aquatic system, have virtually all gone, except for in a few isolated broads. The problem is still not fully clear, but at the heart of it lies the pollution of the Broads by fertiliser and chemical run-off from agricultural land, perhaps compounded by the silt and hydrocarbons from boat traffic. Efforts are, at last, being made to resolve the problem, but it has gone so far, and may be so complex, that it could be too late for the Broads

There is nowhere else quite like the Broads, but we should note in passing just how important peat-cutting has been in maintaining the natural history interest of many a wetland site, whether bog or fen. Because the natural progression of any peatland site, itself frequently a development from open water, is to dry out, the peat-cutting constantly restarts the cycle; Cothill Fen is a calcareous fen in Oxfordshire where ancient peat diggings have retained the open nature of the site, and the same goes for many mature bog areas, like Whixall Moss in Shropshire where the peat cuttings are often the richest part. It would be nice to have more totally undisturbed bogs and other peatland sites, but at least peat-cutting can maintain the species and a continuation of the habitat, as well as giving a link with an ancient management tradition. It is worth mentioning the Avalon Lakes scheme on the Somerset Levels, where lakes that are not dissimilar to the original Broads are being created; the (Somerset) Broads of the future perhaps?

Broads were abandoned after a great flood, caused basically by rising sea-level, in 1287, so this would give a starting date, assuming a constant use rate, of about AD 930.

The great flood caused most of the pits to be abandoned immediately, though some higher, or drier, ones continued to be worked and were not abandoned until rising water levels forced digging to cease in the fourteenth century.

So, the 52 or so Broadland lakes, together with some of their navigable waterways, are the product of an uneasy alliance between medieval man's great demand for peat, and the ever-prevalent rise in sea-level and water table. Since their creation as wetlands, the Broads have, of course, succumbed to the natural processes we have seen before, though their relatively late starting date has kept most of them with at least some open water. The shallowest ones, like Sutton Broad, have become fenland without natural

> ### NATIONAL TRUST WETLANDS OF INTEREST
>
> In addition to those mentioned in this chapter, the National Trust owns important wetlands at: Esthwaite North Fen, Cumbria; Horsey Mere, Norfolk; Crag Lough, Northumberland; Malham Tarn, N. Yorks; Cock Marsh, Berkshire; Marine and various highland lochans within the National Trust for Scotland's property, such as at Torridon and Glencoe.

7 · Coastlands

𝕭RITAIN HAS ONE of the longest, richest and most varied coastlines in Europe. We call ourselves the 'island race', but it is easy to forget, for example, that the British archipelago consists of several hundred islands, and even the most basic estimate gives us more than 7,000 miles (11,200 km) of coast. Yet the true figure could be much higher; one island alone, Mull, has a coastline of more than 300 miles (480 km). Add in all the Shetlands, the Scillies, the Hebrides and so on, and you could reach a much higher figure.

Our coastline also has an unparalleled range of scenery, from the spectacular 1,000 ft (300 m) cliffs of Waterstein Head, Skye, to the mile-wide sand flats of Morecambe Bay or the Wash. A varied geology gives us the red cliffs of Devonian sandstone, the brilliant white cliffs of the Seven Sisters, and the contrast between the ancient pre-Cambrian coast of north-west Scotland, with rocks more than 1,000 million years old, and the soft crumbling sediments of the Pleistocene cliffs of southern England, perhaps only 1 million years old. In between lie coasts of granite, volcanic outcrops, fossil-rich sediments spanning much of geological

This coast of the Lizard Peninsula near Mullion Cove, Cornwall. In the ice ages the coastline lay far to the south-west, but these cliffs have formed the ancient shore in previous interglacials as well as the present one. The steep cliffs with rocky clefts and ledges and the uncultivated clifftop grasslands provide one of the few really natural habitats in Britain.

195

time; and saltmarshes, wooded valleys, sand dunes, shingle beaches and coastal lagoons.

The habitats of rocky coasts have changed little over the historical period, but the soft coasts have seen perpetual changes created by the sea, and many attempts by man to gain ground for farming or industry. These changes have had a significant effect on the places for wildlife along our shores. In order to see how man has affected them, however, we must start by looking at natural changes since the ice age.

THE RISING WATERS

Watching the Atlantic waves smashing on to the rugged coastline of Cornwall's cliffs, you might well conclude that parts of our coast must have been pretty similar 10,000 years ago to what they are today. Yet only a few miles away are the drowned valleys or 'rias' of the Fal, Camel or Tamar, which show that river valleys can be invaded by the sea. The factor which links these contrasting situations is the oscillations in sea-level caused by global climatic changes over the last million years or so; when water is locked up as ice at the poles, sea-level has been some 330 ft (100 m) lower than it now is; whilst in the warm interglacials sea-level has been high, sometimes up to 100 ft (30 m) higher than it is at present.

The geological foundations of Britain are tilted downwards in the south-east, where the old hard palaeozoic rocks, which in the north-west lie at the surface, are deeply buried beneath softer sediments. With hard rocks to the north-west, and soft rocks in the south-east, it was inevitable that the erosion by ice and sea would in the end separate Britain from the Continent. We now know that this has happened repeatedly in warm climatic periods, and that in each glacial period Britain has once again been part of Europe, whatever politicians might think!

During each glacial period, the ice-sheets which covered parts of Britain were re-shaping the ground later to be re-occupied by the sea. Glaciers deepened Scottish valleys well below present sea-level; and further south ice-streams ground out the floor of the Wash. As much as 480 cubic miles (2,000 km³) of rock debris was left strewn around Britain, where much of it still forms a drift cover over the in-situ rocks below.

In the last, Devensian, glaciation, the ice-sheet covered only northern Britain (p. 12) yet its surface lay at 5,700 ft (1,700 m) over southern Scotland only 18,000 years ago. Sea-level was about 330 ft (100 m) lower than the present level, so that Scotland and Wales were joined to Ireland, and a vast silty, partly ice-covered landscape we call Doggerland linked East Anglia to Holland and Denmark.

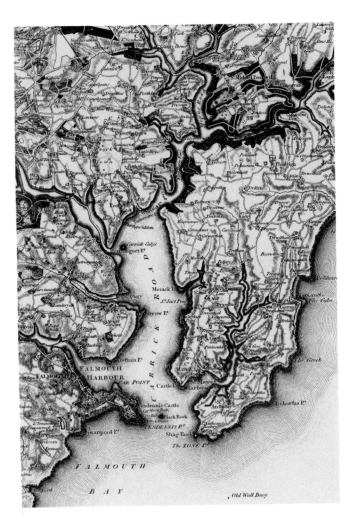

Carrick Roads and the estuary of the Fal form a striking pattern of deep inlets in Cornwall's south coast on the 1st Edition of the Ordnance Survey 1-inch map. These valleys were eroded deeply by rivers when sea-level was much lower, and have been drowned by the rising ocean during the present warm period.

Great sheets of ice and mounds of glacial debris blocked the northerly outflow of the Rhine, which was forced to turn west and south where, combining with the Thames, it escaped through the Dover Strait, deepening its channel, to join the Greater Seine in its westward journey to the Atlantic.

As the ice retreated and the present interglacial developed, sea-level rose rapidly, from minus 330 ft (100 m) 15,000 years ago to almost its present level by 4,500 years ago. Swiftly, the sea re-occupied the parts of the continental shelf from which it had retreated, re-invading the Dover Straits by about 9,600 years ago and generally reducing

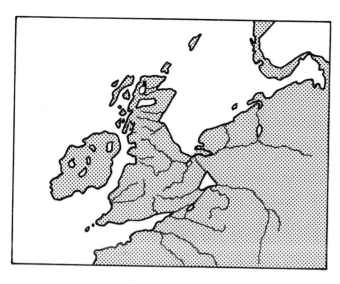

It was only 8,600 years ago that Britain was still physically connected to Europe by the great sedimentary swampland called 'Doggerland', which formed a corridor across which the last plants and animals to colonise Britain made their way. By this time, Ireland had been separated from Wales for at least a thousand years.

the Doggerland from north and south until, probably in some violent winter storm the last vestige of the link from Norfolk to Holland was destroyed around 8,600 years ago.

This re-invasion had several effects. In the hard rock coasts the sea merely re-occupied the territory it had lost, 'exhumed' (with minor modifications made by the ice) the coastline of earlier interglacials and got on with the job of slowly wearing away these hard rocks. Secondly, whilst the sea-level had been low, the rivers feeding the coastline had cut deeply down into their beds, forming narrow, steep-sided valleys. The sea now flooded these and 'drowned' the valleys, forming estuaries or 'rias' like those of Cornwall. The deep-cut river beds can still be detected as fossil channels, now buried deep beneath modern marine sediments, in places like the entrance to Portsmouth Harbour.

In the east, the sea began to create the coastline of today by re-working the prodigious volume of debris, silt, rubble and boulders left by the glaciers and the diverted rivers. It is this material which has given us the massive coastal sediment features like Orfordness, at Shingle Street in Suffolk, Dungeness in Kent, Chesil Beach in Dorset, and Dawlish Warren in Devon. Once this was begun, the sea could, once again, begin the attack on earlier soft cliffs like the Seven Sisters in Sussex. It was probably at this time that the chalk ridge between the Needles and the Isle of Purbeck was completely destroyed, isolating the Isle of Wight. It is also clear that by eroding the cliff base, the sea set the scene

for the great coastal landslips at Axmouth-Lyme Regis and Folkestone Warren (p. 221).

Around 8,000 years ago, there was a particularly rapid rise in sea-level – probably when the great North American ice-cap melted. Enormous areas of low-lying Britain were invaded, and the sea deposited great spreads of marine clays over the land west of the Wash, the coastal hinterland of Norfolk and Suffolk, and the estuary of the Parrett in Somerset. Later, when freshwater conditions returned, these places were to become the expanses of the fen peat in Whittlesey Mere, the Broads and the Somerset Levels. In Scotland the 'Carse clays' were laid down in the shallow Midland Valley from the Forth to the Clyde.

The story has not been all one of rising sea-levels, however. Although the 'eustatic oceanic rise', caused by melting ice, slowed down around 3,000 years ago, local adjustments to the relative level of sea and land have been going on all the time as the elastic crust of the earth rebounds from the crushing weight of glacial ice. This rebound has been much greater in Scotland, where the ice was far thicker, so that in effect the whole of the British Isles has been tilting about a line near Morecambe Bay, downwards in the south-east and upwards in the north-west. This explains why the coast of north-west Scotland is marked by a pronounced 'raised beach', the remains of an earlier seashore, hoisted out on to dry land around 7,000 years ago when the rising ocean could no longer keep up with the rebounding of the land. This raised beach lies at around 25 ft (7.5 m) above present sea-level; there is also a 100 ft (30 m) raised beach, but this dates from an earlier interglacial, perhaps 220,000 years ago!

On the other hand, in the south and west the land has sunk a little further; and at low tides we can still see evidence of ancient forests, overwhelmed by the waters. Fossil forests are widespread; a good example is at Borth in Cardiganshire where, protruding through the mudflats, are the stumps of trees 6,000 years old, roughly the same age as the giant fenland bog-oaks of the 'Atlantic' wildwood (pp. 79–80).

The inundation by the sea can explain many strange legends, such as 'Lyonesse', a fabled land believed to have sunk beyond trace off Land's End, or the strange boulder causeway of St Patrick which winds 20 miles (32 km) or so out from shore at Mochras, and is probably a linear deposit of glacial debris. Some parts of the coast have been destroyed entirely, historical records of the 'lost villages' of Holderness, Norfolk and Suffolk show that the land has retreated many miles.

The basic form of the coast, then, is an ever-shifting re-activation of a basic pattern of hard and soft coasts which has been with us for a million years and more. Now we must briefly look at the work of tides and currents in creating our coastal habitats of the present day.

THE RUN OF THE TIDES

The tides which bathe the coastline twice a day are caused by the moon, and to an extent the sun, pulling on the earth's great oceanic water masses. Their effect differs from place to place. For example the Bristol Channel, where the ocean funnels into a neck, has a tidal range of nearly 40 ft (12 m) at spring tides – the greatest range in Europe. In the English Channel the situation is complex, as the Channel waters oscillate about a point near Portsmouth, where the range is only about 6 ft (2 m); but have a range of about 12 ft (3.5 m) at Land's End or Dover.

Around the coast, tidal movements interact with long-range currents and the effects of wind-driven waves to give us a remarkably complex pattern of shoreline erosion and deposition. On the Atlantic coast the incredible pressure (up to 30 tons per square metre) of the oceanic rollers forces water into every minute crack, exploiting joints or bedding planes in the rock and creating a remarkable range of cliff types, whereas in the sheltered Solent wave heights are rarely over 3 ft (1 m).

Where there are soft rocks, even low waves can cause rapid erosion; in Christchurch Bay the Eocene sands and clays retreat at about 3 ft (1 m) a year, adding at least 100,000 tons to the sediment burden of the Solent, and similar rates are widespread in the Thames estuary and on the east coast. In this way more and more sediment is added to the coastal system; but of course since the sea can only carry so much at a time, for every ton eroded, another ton must be deposited somewhere. The amount the sea can carry depends on its energy, which is higher in winter than summer.

The size of the sediment particles dropped by the sea at a particular point is also determined by the wave energy at that point, so on the jutting headlands of the west coast where energy is high there is nothing except a few pebbles jammed into rock cracks. On exposed beaches we find a gradation of particle size: at the top lie big boulders or large pebbles flung up by storms and not removed, then down the beach come successively smaller shingle, grit and coarse sand. On the other hand, in sheltered estuaries where there is little energy in the water movement, sandy silts or even fine muds are dropped.

Another factor affecting the nature of the coastline is the kind of sediment available. In north-west Scotland salt-marsh is uncommon partly because there is little clay sediment available; but there are vast (and beautiful) beaches of the coarse sand derived from the old rocks, whereas on the east coast there are large saltmarshes in the Moray Firth, as in England around the Wash and the Thames estuary, because the two conditions for saltmarsh formation (fine silts and sheltered waters) are fulfilled.

On most of our coasts a variety of sediments is available,

SCOLT HEAD BLAKENEY AND THE NORTH NORFOLK COAST

The 24 miles (38 km) of coast from Hunstanton to Sheringham in Norfolk is a beautiful, windwept, outdoor laboratory where the natural and human processes which shape the complex shingle, sand and saltmarsh habitats have been studied for more than 50 years by many scientists, including the great coastal geographer Professor J. A. Steers. This is also one of the birthplaces of coastal nature conservation, with at least 12 major nature reserves managed by the National Trust, the Nature Conservancy Council, the Royal Society for the Protection of Birds, the Norfolk Naturalists' Trust and the Norfolk Ornithologists' Association.

The wild coastal habitats of north Norfolk have been evolving for several thousand years, but the landforms are so dynamic that much of the present vegetation cover is actually quite young. The raw material is the millions of tons of flint shingle, sand and mud which was slowly shoved against the low chalky coastline as the rising seas swept clean the floor of the North Sea around 8,000 years ago. These sediments have become piled into a great shingle barrier beach which runs parallel with the old shoreline and just offshore, and shelters a series of peaceful creek-dissected saltmarshes, many of which have been walled off from the sea at various times and converted into enclosed grazing marshes.

The barrier ridge is highly mobile, and broken in places by the channels of rivers flowing north from the land. Where it is best developed, the barrier is capped by high sand-dune ridges, such as those of Blakeney or Scolt. Where the barrier is absent the sand dunes are piled against the ancient shoreline itself, as at Holkham Meals (an ancient name for dunes) partly wet and partly dry and pine-planted, and now a National Nature Reserve supporting such uncommon species as red squirrel, natterjack toad, and the orchids – creeping ladies' tresses and marsh helleborine.

Blakeney Point, a shingle spit joined to the coast at Cley, has belonged to the National Trust since 1912. It is a truly wild place, an important bird migration staging post. As you trudge the 3 miles (5 km) west, under the gigantic Norfolk skies, the great bank gradually diverges from the shore, and you will notice yellow horned-poppy, saltwort and other plants which seek out the fresh water deep in the shingle. Near the Cley end relict 'lateral' shingle ridges run off south-west from the spine before curving back south-eastwards, a pattern repeated on a much larger scale when you reach the western point. In fact each of these old 'laterals' was itself once the west tip of the spit; a map of 1586 shows that 400 years ago the tip was opposite Blakeney village; now it has now grown some 2 miles (3 km) further westward.

These processes are shown even more impressively at Scolt Head Island, a great shingle ridge overlain by blown sand, which is completely separated from the mainland by Norton creek and its fringing saltmarsh. You can get to Scolt through the sloppy, clinging mud of Norton creek, or even by wading neck-deep across the mussel-beds of the Brancaster channel, but these routes are dangerous unless you know them well, and it is better to book a lift in the warden's boat from Brancaster Staithe. Scolt Head feels a world apart from everyday life, with its surprisingly high dunes covered in marram grass, its vast beach, and the sun, wind and sky. Its 4-mile (6.4-km) long spine is buried in sand, the visible shingle has mostly been piled by the

tides into ridges along the upper beach, where it has been stablised by sea beet, sea campion and the straggling oraches.

The strand line is often an extraordinary collection of flotsam swept or thrown from the world's shipping plying the busy North-Sea routes; but if you climb the dunes away from the beach and look down the inland side you are again in a completely wild world, where the sand is gradually tamed by dune plants, first sand couch, then marram, lyme grass, sea bindweed, sea holly, sea spurge and so on. These dunes have a very specialised invertebrate fauna, including insects, pseudoscorpions and salticid spiders, and it is interesting to think just how such species can have arrived here, especially because Scolt Head may be no more than about 600 years old – in fact the evidence for its rapid evolution is all around you, in the structure of the spine and its lateral recurving crests of dunes.

The sequence of lateral recurves is particularly clear. The present landing point is the south tip of the western recurve, known as the Wire Hills, and virtually all the area to the west of this, called Cockle Bight, Bight Hills and Far Point, has been added by the growth of the main spine since the first

6-inch map was surveyed in 1886. Today this part is especially important for breeding terns, which nest here in their thousands; Sandwich terns are the commonest, with up to a twelfth of the world population breeding here; there are also a few hundred common terns, and less than a hundred little terns. As you walk eastwards, each successive lateral, swinging south-west from the outer ridge, is older than its westerly neighbour, and each has a slightly different ecological character; until finally your reach the Norton Hills at the eastern end of the island. Across the Burnham channel, which some believe was formed by the sea breaking through the ridge centuries ago, lies Gun Hill, the west tip of the Holkham dunes.

What is certain is that as Scolt grows westward, its eastern part becomes weaker; in 1953 the sea did break across, spilling shingle across the ridge on to Plantago Marsh. In fact the 1824 Ordnance 1-inch map shows two gaps in the dunes. The main ridge is also slowly rolling over the landward saltmarshes; after storms you can find remains of ancient marsh exposed on the outer beach. Between the laterals lie the individual saltmarshes, Great Aster Marsh, Plantago, Plover, Hut and Missel Marshes, on whose growth and colonisation much ecological research has been done, whilst across Norton creek on the mainland there are some unenclosed marshes and then the grazing freshmarshes of Burnham Deepdale and Burnham Norton, walled off from the sea by a great sea-bank.

Scolt Head is a paradise for any naturalist, with a wealth of plants of coastal habitats, including several of the less common sea lavenders, thrift, eel grass and the shrubby seablite, a Mediterranean species at its northern limit here; as well as a host of insects and other animals. But, for its inhabitants, Scolt is a testing environment, where storms can create or destroy a habitat overnight.

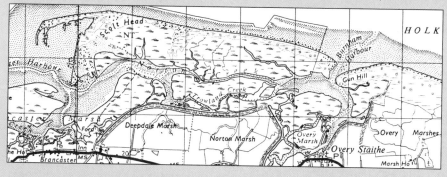

Two maps of Scolt Head, showing its development since 1886.

Sea lochs, which deeply indent the west coast of Scotland, are valleys gouged out well below present sea level by ice, and then drowned as sea level rose again when the ice melted. Many, such as Loch Sunart, are extremely sheltered, warm and clean, although they are threatened by commercial fish-farming. This is the north shore of the Sound of Mull, near Drimnin, Argyllshire.

and the sea is continually moving them around, optimising their resistance to water flow; so the exact pattern of the coastline is changing all the time. Spits and bars form, saltmarshes grow or die, and cliffs are cut back, as the sea sorts the sediment into vast inter-connected systems of shingle banks, sand flats, or intertidal mudlands.

One of the most characteristic coastal systems, particularly where sediment is moved along the coast by 'long shore drift', is the creation of shingle, or sand, bars when the sea extends a beach line across the mouth of an estuary. Inside the spit the water is sheltered and this is where the finest muds drop out of suspension and gradually form the basis of saltmarshes. There are several examples of this later in this chapter.

THE COASTAL HABITAT – AND MAN'S INFLUENCE

The coast with its rapidly shifting sediments and almost unchanging cliffs provides a remarkable range of habitats for plants, and there are relatively few of our 1,500 or so native species which cannot be found somewhere along the coast. Coastal plants are of three main types; the first, the great majority, live in other places as well, but they occur near the coast because the unfarmed coast provides an undisturbed corridor of heaths, grasslands and sometimes woodlands in the para-maritime zone, just inland from the maritime zone influenced by salt-spray.

The second group live on the coast because it gives them a special ecological bonus – some feature which they need to thrive. Vernal squill, a tiny blue-flowered bulb found abundantly all over the Welsh and Cornish cliff-tops is a

Along the south and east coasts, soft cliffs are rapidly eroded by the sea. Here the Eocene Barton Beds are being undermined by wave action and by a process of slumping, in which the wet clifftop gravels slide over the clays beneath. Here the cliffs can retreat by several feet a year.

'Lusitanian' (south-western European) species which grows on the coast because it cannot stand frost, for example. Mountain avens, moss campion and several kinds of saxifrage are part of an assemblage of mountain plants which come down to sea-level in Sutherland, or the Burren in County Clare, because here the climate is not too hot in summer but there is little overshading or grazing. Thrift, common on cliff-tops and offshore islands, can tolerate some grazing but needs an open habitat, as does sea campion which forms white-flowered cushions on many of our coasts. Sea cabbage, a rare flower of rocky cliffs is one of a group of flowers which are highly susceptible to grazing, whilst other short herbs like the fen orchid or the creeping willow, which suffer from shading out by tall herbs in their marshland abodes, do very well in the open coastal dune slacks where taller competitors cannot succeed.

The third group of coastal plants is only about 150 species in all. These are the ones specially adapted to life by the sea; and in general they have overcome the paradox of coastal life: water everywhere, but not a drop to drink! At the coast, fresh water is in short supply; in the sand dunes there is little humus to prevent rainwater soaking away, whereas in the saltmarsh the plants have to contend with the salt water which is unsuitable for their metabolic processes. In both situations the problems are compounded by the drying wind and the salt-spray.

Coastal plants have developed many fascinating ways of solving these problems. Sea holly, for example, has acquired a thick leathery cuticle and spiny leaves which reduce water losses; marram grass achieves the same objective by rolling its leaves up, with the transpiration pores or stomata enclosed within the curl, in dry weather, whilst other plants cover the leaves with long hairs to reduce drying wind currents across the leaves, or have reduced the leaves to spikes or scales, as in the glassworts.

True halophytes, or 'salt plants', go further; many of

The chalk cliffs at Lulworth, Dorset, are a riot of wild flowers in May and June. Cliffs form one of the habitats least affected by grazing or human interference in Britain, and here the tall blue spikes of viper's bugloss, white ox-eye daisies, yellow hawkweeds and, behind, yellow-flowered wild cabbage, decorate the cliff, out of reach of grazing stock or tourists' feet.

them are succulents, storing large quantities of water in their tissues, though as this is saline its purpose is not yet clear. Some, like cord grass, actually separate salt from water and secrete the salt through special glands; but this process uses a great deal of chemical energy. Some of these halophytes can withstand conditions where the water is up to half the full salinity of sea water.

Another problem for coastal plants is the instability of the sand or mud they grow in: cord grass has extremely long roots full of air spaces to anchor it deep in the de-oxygenated muds of estuaries; whereas marram grass on dunes is adapted to a life of continual upgrowth to keep above the sand which the plant itself is trapping. If dune growth stops, the marram loses vigour and is out-competed by other plants.

In addition to the natural constraints and opportunities for coastal plants, man has of course had an impact as well. Unstable sand and shingle environments do not make good farmland, and have been altered relatively little, but the salt marshes are deep deposits of mineral-rich clay particles brought in by river or sea and slowly built up, and they make good pasture if they can be protected from the sea by sea-banks. Over the years vast areas of saltmarsh have been reclaimed and form many superb examples of man's influence on wildlife habitats; see for example the panel on Farlington marshes on p. 214.

SHINGLE BEACHES, SPITS AND BARS

Britain has some of the finest developments of shingle beach features in Europe, especially on the south and east coasts. Along the Sussex coast at Brighton and Bognor there are *fringing* beaches, where the beach remains in contact with the land itself. In fact these are often a mixture of shingle and sand; the sea sorts everything out so that the largest pebbles are on the top of the beach, where the wave energy is dissipated, creating a ridge or storm crest, and the pebbles become successively smaller down the beach. The pebbles in between the tidemarks are immersed in salt water and continually grinding against each other, so there is no vegetation in this unstable, inhospitable zone.

Above the spring high tide limit, plants begin to find a

home. One of the earliest is the shrubby sea blite, which can tolerate being buried occasionally; when this happens it responds by producing new vertical shoots to reach the shingle surface. Sand grains, decaying seaweed and detritus trapped between the pebbles help other flowers to colonise the upper shingle levels; prostrate annuals like the various oraches and a coastal form of goose grass. In the least stable areas these may be the only plants present; you can tell, by looking at a shingle beach, which are the more stable areas by the other plants which come in; short-lived perennials like the yellow biting stonecrop, and the unmistakeable yellow horned-poppy with its yellow sap and curving foot-long seed pods. Further from the sea come white-flowered sea campion, and sea sandwort with its fleshy geometric leaves.

Yellow horned-poppy with its long curving seed pods, growing in the shingle at Cuckmere Haven, Sussex near the Seven Sisters. Many shingle plants are very sensitive to disturbance and grow near the beach-top where the pebbles are quite stable.

Scolt Head Island, part of the vast swirl of shingle and sand along the north Norfolk coast, looking east. Notice the recurved end of the spit in the foreground, and three older series of these 'laterals', now vegetated, beyond. Between the laterals lie saltmarshes, which drain landwards into Norton creek. To the south lies the ancient stable coastline and farmland, and a large area of saltmarsh walled off by a great curving bank. Scolt has been the subject of intensive study for many years; it has a very rich flora and fauna, and is managed as a nature reserve.

Rarer plants of shingle tend to occur in places only occasionally subjected to spray – sea pea, a purple-flowered pea of the east coast around Orfordness, and Chesil beach; and the huge sea kale with its mass of white flowers and sea-distributed seeds. Even rarer are the oysterplant, *Mertensia*, a northern species, with bluish leaves and blue flowers turning pink, known from Cumbria but only frequent in Scotland as far north as the Shetlands; and the southern little robin (*Geranium purpureum*) whose yellow anthers distinguish it from the ordinary herb robert (*Geranium robertianum*) which often grows nearby. In the south-east another rare beach-top or upper marsh plant is sea heath. The upper beach often contains some blown sand, and here stork's-bill and buck's-horn plantain grow, together with sea beet, perhaps the remote ancestor of our domestic root-crops.

The pebbles on these fringing beaches are often battered along the beach with each successive obliquely-breaking wave; a process called longshore drift. The wood or sheet steel groynes you see running down the beach profile are intended to stop the sea from sweeping the beach clean and attacking the cliff behind, and you can soon work out which way the winds and currents are moving as the sand and shingle pile against the groyne. Another, more exotic, underwater mechanism for pebble movement has been put forward. The giant brown oarweed or kelp, which lives below low-water, attaches its 'holdfast' to pebbles. In spring the increasingly buoyant kelp 'sail' lifts the anchoring pebbles from the bed, and the kelp 'forest' goes bobbing and scraping its way along the sea bottom!

Moving shingle forms three other features which create a range of conditions suitable for different plants and animals; spits, bars and 'nesses' or apposition beaches. When longshore drift carries shingle or sand on beyond a promontory on the coast (such as the corner where an estuary emerges) a spit develops out into open water. Spits have a characteristic shape; hooked at the end where the tip is recurved towards the land by seasonal currents or tidal effects. As the spit grows, earlier 'hooks' are left behind, and form lateral ridges, between which saltmarsh usually grows in the lee of the spit. The greatest development of these complex coastal landforms is in North Norfolk, at Scolt Head and Blakeney Point, in an area where conflicting currents are reshaping huge volumes of sand and shingle derived from the old Doggerland and from present-day erosion of the coast from Caister to Sheringham. Other classic spits can be seen at Hurst and Calshot in Hampshire, and at Spurn Head and Gibraltar Point.

Obviously, a spit can only grow as long as coastal erosion goes on feeding it with shingle. Groynes can upset the shingle supply and leave a spit very over-stretched and weak, as drift is still lengthening it, and in storms the sea may break through the neck and overwhelm the marsh-land in its protection, as began to happen at Hurst in 1985. The flora of a spit is richer than that of a fringing beach, because the extent of stabilised, vegetation-covered shingle is much greater. Orfordness and Gibraltar Point both have superb examples of this habitat, where the vegetation's character indicates the age of each ridge and shows how the coastal landform has changed.

If a shingle spit is built out across a bay, rather than an estuary with strong currents, it may eventually reach the other side, and form a *bar* across the bay, which becomes a lagoon. Lagoons such as that at Loe Bar in Cornwall or at Slapton in Devon are slightly brackish, though fed by streams, and provide a habitat for many special plants and animals which require these brackish conditions, such as

The great shingle bar of Chesil beach is unlike any other in Europe, and seems to have been created as the returning ocean cleared the channel floor of erosion debris. Within it lies the lagoon known as the Fleet – salty at its tidal eastern end, almost fresh in the west. Both Chesil beach and the Fleet have many remarkable plants and animals.

the strange stoneworts. By far the best shingle bar in Britain, however, is Chesil beach, stretching 18 miles (30 km) from Bridport to Portland in Dorset, protecting a lagoon known as the Fleet, which is slightly tidal at Portland, and almost fresh at its western end. In it grow all three British species of the eel grass *Zostera*, a strange plant which is the only flowering plant in Britain to be fully marine; its reproductive system is amazingly adapted to allow pollination to occur in water. The Fleet was almost the only place where *Zostera* did not suffer a devastating disease which almost eliminated most European populations in the 1930s, and is therefore an international refuge for many invertebrate animals which live in *Zostera* beds.

One strange feature of Chesil beach is that the pebbles above low-water mark are graded in size (smaller in the west and largest in the east), which is very useful for local fishermen in a fog! Oddly, this beach is also the only British site for the wingless cricket (*Mogoplistes squamiger*), and

parts of it have a rich shingle flora too with several rare species.

The last kind of shingle beach is the 'apposition' beach, formed where shingle is flung ashore against some kind of barrier at right angles to wave direction. Deposition seems to run in great cycles, new ridges being formed to seaward periodically, as at the fine shingle apposition beach of Browndown, Gosport, which shows the usual succession of increasingly stable vegetation. Ground-living lichens like the *Cladonias* help to stabilise the shingle, some of them resembling the 'reindeer moss' of the Arctic, others bearing tiny green cups or red or brown fruiting bodies. Nottingham catchfly, with its sticky upper parts, is common on the shingle here too. Another beach nearby at Gilkicker has fine stable shingle full of wet hollows where uncommon plants like pale flax, the prostrate carline thistle, and many sedges including distant, dotted, divided and long-bracted sedges provide plenty to keep the coastal botanist happy. Progression from loose shingle through low scrub of heather and blackthorn to woodland is relatively rare, though this is known from Dungeness and Bridgwater Bay in Somerset.

These coastal shingle features are better developed in Britain than almost anywhere in Europe; they originated in a period when the sea-level was rising, and sweeping much of the glacial debris of the Channel up onto the shoreline as it did so. Today they are still complex, dynamic structures with which we usually interfere at our peril; it is extremely difficult to predict the results of disturbing them.

SAND DUNES, SLACKS AND MACHAIRS

As with shingle, the sandy beach between tidemarks is no place for plants to grow, and if you are standing in one of those delightful sandy rock-encircled coves in Cornwall that is where this section will end (turn to page 217 and read about cliffs!). If on the other hand your sandy beach is not enclosed by cliffs, you may find yourself at the seaward edge of a pattern of coastal habitats which gives us some of our most exciting maritime and para-maritime vegetation.

Sand, of course, is even less stable than shingle, as it is shifted by the slightest wind as well as by the sea, as any holidaymaker munching a sandy sandwich knows only too well. Above the strandline the sand is dry and may begin to be piled up by the wind, if there is a plentiful sand supply in offshore flats for example, forming either a frontshore system to seaward such as a spit or ness, or more commonly a hindshore of dunes behind the beach. Some dunes are quite flat – vast sandy undulating plains like the well-known 'links' of eastern Scotland, covered in closely-grazed turf. A special form of these wide dune-pastures is the Hebridean 'machair' (see p. 208), a kind of shelly sand plain, full of flowers, which covers large areas of North and South Uist, especially.

The sandy strandline often supports a true maritime plant community, usually of annuals like sea rocket, with its lilac-pink flowers sprawling along the high tide-mark; the prickly saltwort and the oraches we saw on the shingle beaches. Behind the strandline, the dunes build up in a complicated way. The individual sand grains move by a

jumping process called 'saltation', and any slight reduction in wind speed may allow grains to settle and not become airborne again, so that they collect in the lee of stones, bits of dead seaweed, or strandline plants. The additional stability encourages the perennials like sea sandwort, or the various sand couch or twitch species, to gain a toehold – with their spreading rhizomes beginning to build the foredune up by a few feet, reducing the salinity and allowing the main dune-building plants to establish themselves. These are the more southerly marram grass and the lyme grass which is more northern, taller and slimmer. Young marram plants grow fast, and trap sand as they branch upwards and outwards. Marram can keep pace with 20 or even 40 inches (50–100 cm) of sand deposition during a single year, binding the swelling pile of loose sand with its tough branching rhizomes.

In the most active outer edge of the dunes, only marram or lyme grass will grow, but beyond the dune crest, where sand is spread more widely and builds more slowly, other flowers begin to come in to occupy the wide gaps between the grass tussocks. Sea holly with its beautiful spiny blue-green leaves can also grow upwards if buried, and the little sea spurge is common. One of the most attractive of these dune plants is the sea bindweed which has pink and white striped bells, and round leaves which hug the sand surface. Sea sandwort and sand sedge are also important in this area behind the dune crest.

The normal limit for the height of the marram-bound dunes is about 60 ft (18 m). Marram's capacity for trapping and stabilising sand is very useful and it is often planted, alongside brushwood windbreaks, to help restore dunes eroded by too many feet and blown out. The marram dune is often called the yellow dune. If you walk inland from the dune crest, however, down the marram-dominated slope with its sea holly, sea bindweed and sand sedge, you will soon find yourself in ground where there is less sand visible and more plants. One group of flowers conspicuous here in early spring are the winter annuals such as common whitlow grass, forget-me-not (*Myosotis ramosissima*) and the grass *Phleum arenarium*. These all have a life cycle completed well before the parched summer conditions arrive, they set seed early and germinate in the damp sand of autumn. The summer brings other plants, like ragwort, colt's-foot or scarlet pimpernel, and the attractive dune pansy with its cheerful blue or yellow flowers. Further inland, sand deposition is less and the marram loses its competitiveness; much of the ground becomes covered with mat-forming mosses, especially the common *Camptothecium lutescens*, and lichens including the various *Cladonia* species and the dog lichens (*Peltigera*) which are dark grey and help give these 'grey dunes' their name.

Many other flowers form part of the fixed-dune community; the more shelly calcareous sands have flowers of chalk

There is a rich assortment of plants along the upper edge of sandy beaches, including sea holly, sea spurge, Portland spurge and sand sedge. One of the most attractive is sea bindweed, with its beautiful striped bells.

grassland (yellow-wort, lady's bedstraw, common mouse-ear and even the orchid autumn lady's tresses) and the turf is often dominated by red fescue. In the older dunes, though, the dune soil becomes more acid as the soluble bases from the shell-fragments in the sand are leached out by the rain. On the most acidic sites heathy communities with ling, bell heather and, in wet depressions, cross-leaved heath can develop. At Winterton in Norfolk (the name reflects its origin as a Saxon winter fishing camp), the heath and acid grassland supports the rare grasses *Ammocalamagrostis baltica* and *Corynephorus canescens,* and there are fern 'meadows' full of broad and narrow buckler-ferns and the very rare *Dryopteris cristata.* Here there is also a natural transition into birchwoods, but elsewhere the dune heathlands have been planted with pines to prevent windblow; Holkham in north Norfolk is an example.

In less acid fixed dunes, a mosaic of rabbit-grazed turf, blackthorn and sea buckthorn scrub can develop. The rabbits have to be kept in balance, though: too many burrows and overgrazed turf can cause blow-outs, but no rabbits at all, as happened during the myxomatosis outbreak some years ago, leads to an explosive development of sea buckthorn scrub.

The great dune systems like Newborough Warren in Anglesey, Ainsdale on the Lancashire coast, and Braunton Burrows in north Devon have a range of wet depressions, where the surface dips below the water table, and there may even be pools or, as at Oxwich, near Swansea, rich calcareous streams winding through the dunes. These depressions are called dune slacks, and they make some of the richest plant communities in Britain. The more saline slacks near the sea may have sea lavender, sea milkwort, sea club-rush and occasionally the enormous sharp rush, with its 3 ft (1 m) stems bearing massive heads of glossy fruits. Away from the sea, marsh or fen communities can be seen. Wet pools with shoreweed and pondweeds, especially *Potamogeton*, are common, whilst lime-rich ground water supports a rich-fen association with many different sedges and marsh pennywort, water mint and lesser spearwort (a small buttercup). These slacks also have more spectacular flowers, like yellow iris or flag, in early summer the marsh helleborine orchid, and later the creamy white Grass of Parnassus, which is not a grass at all!

Creeping willow is an abundant plant of many slacks, humifying the soil and providing suitable conditions for the saprophytic (detritus-digesting) yellow bird's-nest, which lacks chlorophyll. Newborough Warren on Anglesey has large areas dominated by creeping willow and containing rarities like the 'common' butterwort, which supplements its diet with insects, and the round-leaved wintergreen with its spike of white globular bells.

Tentsmuir Point, on the east coast of Scotland, a lime-poor dune system which has grown remarkably over the last 40 years, has a different community of plants. The young dunes are dominated by lyme grass, further inland there is a dwarf shrub heathland, in which the crowberry (*Empetrum nigrum*) is well represented, and rarer plants include abundant purple milk-vetch and baltic rush, and a great deal of the coral root, a pale saprophytic orchid with a spike of small green, yellow and pink flowers.

Scotland has more than 100 dune systems, and each one is slightly different. At St Cyrus in Kincardineshire, for example, a small system has a number of local plants, including the tiny fern moonwort and the maiden pink at about its northern limit. The largest sand dune system in Britain is at Culbin Sands, Morayshire, covering 7,000 acres (2,800 hectares), though much of this has now been afforested. Even so, no less than 450 species of flowering plants occur, 43 of which are at their northern geographical limit. Many northern flowers occur too, such as the mountain everlasting, chickweed wintergreen and the orchids lesser twayblade and creeping lady's tresses.

MACHAIR GRASSLANDS OF THE HEBRIDEAN ISLANDS

Machair (pronounced '*mach*er', emphasising the first syllable) is a special kind of coastal grassland, based on a sand made up of tiny fragments of shells, which in places means that more than half the sand is lime (calcium carbonate). Machair is most extensive on the west side of the Hebridean islands of North and South Uist, Benbecula and Barra; it forms almost the whole of the offshore Monach Isles, and occurs to a limited degree on the Scottish mainland.

The exact way in which machair formed is not really known, but it seems that about 6,000 years ago a series of coastal dunes may have been levelled by strong winds, perhaps down as far as the water table, which was then much higher. Now there is a characteristic series of parallel bands of habitats running up the west coast of the islands; nearest the sea is loose shell-sand beach, then dunes, dry machair, damp machair, nutrient-rich marsh, and calcareous freshwater lochs, such as Loch a Mhachair. To the east can be found the 'blackland', which is acid moor improved with limy shell sand, and nutrient-poor lochs such as Druidibeg.

The fascinating thing about machair is the way the naturally-fertile soils and high rainfall have combined with farming from ancient times to produce the most extraordinary displays of flowers in early summer. The machair is vital to the crofting economy, and the drier areas are ploughed in April and used for cereals, like rye or oats, and potatoes. The land is not cultivated every year; each township has a machair divided into strips allotted to individual crofts. The strips are cultivated on a rotational basis, and the fallow strips, or those left for sheep or cattle grazing, of the dry machair are ablaze with wild flowers in June, especially in the second season after cultivation, just as the woodland flowers of coppice take two seasons to bloom at their best (p. 87).

It is not that the flowers are particularly rare, although more than 220 different sorts have been found on the Monach Isles; the breathtaking glory of the machair grassland is their sheer abundance. As the summer unfolds, the red hues of crane's-bill and stork's-bill, and the yellow of bird's-foot trefoil, give way to the golden yellow of lady's bedstraw, then the blue of harebell and bluish-white of eyebright.

Damper machair is often kept for a hay crop, and here the late cut allows a profuse flowering of hay rattle, ragged robin, red rattle, clovers and several kinds of orchids; early marsh, northern marsh, frog, twayblade and the unique Hebridean form of spotted orchid, with thickly blotched leaves and darker flowers.

Inland, the wetter machair merges gradually into the calcareous fen which surrounds the freshwater lochs. This is an important habitat for waders, many of which, including dunlin and the very rare red-necked phalarope, breed here. In fact the machair is an exceptionally important bird habitat; the corncrake is now virtually restricted to the Hebrides and Orkney, and the dry machair supports about one-sixth of all British breeding ringed plover.

The machair is a delicately-balanced habitat, maintained by traditional farming practices, like so many other rich places described in this book. Today it is threatened both by a decline in traditional farming and paradoxically by improved farming techniques. Once animal manure and seaweed were the only fertilisers used to supplement the lime-rich sands with nitrate and phosphate, but now well-meaning attempts to improve the economy, and inorganic fertilisers from a bag, could threaten the machair with wholesale change.

Machair is coastal dunes of shell sand, often spreading inland as a flat sandy plain, and commonest in the Hebrides, although there are mainland examples near Durness. This example is in Ireland's Aran Isles.

An incredible display of southern marsh orchids and yellow rattle in a dune slack at Saltfleetby on the Lincolnshire coast. Dune slack often supports a particularly rich flora, especially where the sand is rich in calcareous shell fragments, and the water-table remains high through early summer.

Sand dunes are one of the most natural kinds of vegetation in Britain, and are an extremely important habitat for many animals as well as plants. They are often very rich in insects and other invertebrate animals (like snails, wood-lice, pseudoscorpions and spiders), supporting many species which are completely dependent upon this habitat (like the jumping spider *Hyctia nivoyii* at Scolt Head). Winterton has a small population of the declining natterjack toad, whose habits and habitat are so exacting that it is a wonder it ever survived in the past. The largest natterjack population is actively conserved, together with the beautiful sand lizard, at Ainsdale dunes in Lancashire.

The majority of British dune systems seem to have developed their present form during the last thousand years or so; but dunes are inherently unstable and can be destroyed or severely altered almost overnight if there is a freak storm from an unusual quarter. In recent years Culbin Sands have overwhelmed a great deal of farmland.

The main human pressure on dunes today is probably recreational activity, which must be carefully managed to avoid damaging the thin skin of dune vegetation. As dunes are so mobile you will often find the coastline of 100 years ago almost unrecognisable on old maps. The first edition of the 6-inch Ordnance Survey, published about 1858–1878, gives a fascinating insight into the spread or retreat of the coast, and the way in which former natural grasslands on the coast originating as dune pastures (or saltmarshes, see below) became rough grazing.

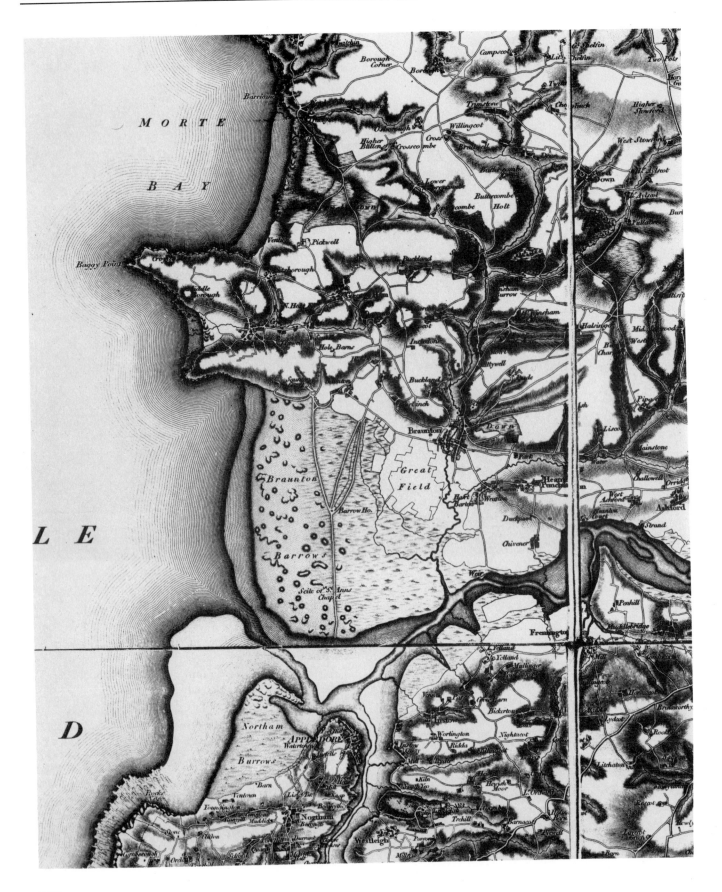

Braunton Burrows, on the north Devon coast, is an ancient feature, graphically shown in this 1810 map. The tall dunes are at the seaward edge, giving way to a sandy plain and finally to the great open field of Braunton, part of which can still be seen. The dunes themselves have an extremely rich flora and insect fauna.

SALTMARSHES AND SILT

Saltmarshes, unlike the dunes above the reach of tides, develop in the intertidal zone, between low and high water-marks, which is a wet, salty and abrasive environment where only truly halophytic plants can survive. These marshes with their glistening mudlands are a watery world of low horizons, vast and magnificent skies and subtle shades of grey green and brown, punctuated by the weed-covered hulks of rotting barges or perhaps the brilliant sails of dinghies.

The saltmarsh proper develops on the wide intertidal mudflats, sheltered places in estuaries or areas protected in the lee of spits or islands, where tidal water movements are so slow that even the finest silt particles drop out of suspension. Our best and biggest marshes lie in great coastal inlets like the Wash, the Thames estuary, the Humber, Morecambe Bay and Solway Firth or the southern harbours of Langstone, Portsmouth and Chichester. There are superb marshes in east Scotland in the Moray and Cromarty Firths, but few in west Scotland where there is little fine sediment.

Saltmarshes differ fundamentally from the relatively unproductive sand-dune systems which support a very wide range of plant species. The saltmarsh contains large quantities of very few species, but these form part of an efficient intertidal 'greenhouse' where the strong coastal sunlight, and the rich soup of plant nutrients which the sea constantly brings, are turned by plants into very large quantities of organic matter. An acre of Essex marsh has been shown to produce 6 tons (dry weight) of organic matter every year. This is achieved by two pathways: first the billions of free-swimming micro-organisms in the coastal waters, the phytoplankton, and secondly the salt-marsh plants themselves. It could well be that Britain's 90,000 acres (36,000 hectares) of saltmarsh are making more than half a million tons of detritus every year, an extremely important resource for fisheries and birds.

SALTMARSH-BUILDING

Mud is the main raw material of the marsh, and each succeeding tide brings more silt from the processes of coastal erosion, or from rivers entering the estuaries. A dramatic example of the quantity of silt involved is given by the drowned valleys of Cornwall's southern rivers, choked with mudlands exposed at low tide.

The muds are a wet desert, and the few plants which can colonise them must be able to survive in a highly abrasive, strongly saline, wind and sun-scorched environment. Because of this, saltmarsh vegetation is strongly zoned according to the ability of each species to withstand chemical or physical stresses.

The pioneer zone

The lowest level of muds, and gravels where exposed, is occupied by the eel grasses. *Zostera marina*, the largest, is killed by as little as half-an-hour of sun, and lives only where it is exposed only briefly at extreme low-water spring tides. *Zostera noltii* and *Zostera angustifolia* are more resistant to drying and can grow from low tide to half-tide.

Around the upper half-tide level other plants grow, like the blue-green algae, which can fix nitrogen; the tasselweed and the limp bright green sea lettuce, which is particularly common where there is organic pollution. The first pioneer plants proper are the various sorts of glassworts, small succulents with swollen stems which were once collected and pickled as 'samphire'. Near mid-tide there is just a scatter, but higher up they carpet the mud, and other plants like sea aster and annual sea blite begin to arrive. Around much of the coast saltmarsh grass or sea manna grass is the commonest grass of the lower marsh, and on sandier north-western sites it may be the pioneer; together with red fescue it is the dominant grass in the famous 'Cumberland sea-washed turf'.

The lower marsh

Above the pioneer zone other plants come in and diversify the marsh. Frequent species are sea purslane (which often dominates mixed marshes in the south-east), sea plantain, sea arrowgrass, and sea lavender, which colours the marshes purple in late summer. Salinity is an important influence on what grows where in the saltmarsh; in the upper estuary where the freshwater influence is more dominant, plants like sea arrowgrass can grow much lower down the intertidal profile, whilst thrift, normally an upper marsh plant, will here grow in the lower marsh community.

The development of the lower marsh gradually flattens the mudland profile, so that the marsh surface drains only slowly, shedding its water when the tide is on the ebb through a complex dendritic (meaning root-like) pattern of drainage creeks. From the air these form beautiful patterns, but out on the marsh they can be a very frustrating habitat

Pioneer plants colonising mudlands in Chichester Harbour. Succulent glasswort (foreground), brown patches of seaweed and the greenish yellow spikes of Spartina *(middle distance) will all gradually trap silt, building up the marsh.*

to try and walk across. The centre of each marsh section is often an unvegetated pool, highly saline; but the outer edges adjoining the creeks are well drained and thickly vegetated with purslane, sea lavender and, in the south, golden samphire with its brilliant yellow flower heads.

The upper marsh

The upper level marsh is rarely covered by the tide, and is much more varied, both because there are more micro-habitats (local changes in salinity and the form of the ground) and because for thousands of years the upper marshes have been grazed, drained or walled off from the sea by man. The ungrazed areas may be quite species-rich, and are often dominated by thrift, sea milkwort, scurvy grass, sea wormwood and sea spurrey. In the rich marshes of Suffolk and Norfolk, you can see the fullest development of the ancient mixed marsh communities, with rarer plants

like the sea heath and two rarer sea lavenders (*Limonium bellidifolia* and *L. binervosum*). The old mixed marshes are rich in flowers and insects, and are probably thousands of years old, though they move about slightly as sea-level changes. In Langstone they seem to have developed no later than Roman times, and are relict features from that interlude when sea-level stopped rising for a time.

The exact composition of the upper marsh is often modified by grazing, which favours grasses over other species. Whilst ungrazed marsh is species-rich with many sedges and flowers, heavy grazing by sheep can transform this community into a thick grassy turf. A study of coastal large-scale maps will soon reveal vast areas where marshes were walled off to prevent flooding by the sea, and turned over to grazing. Some of these reclamations are Roman in origin, as at Farlington (see p. 214). Others were medieval (p. 218) and can be distinguished by their convoluted drainage creeks; a superb example can be seen east of Southminster in the Dengie peninsula, Essex.

Spartina marshes

The classic picture of saltmarsh plants slowly building up the mud levels and forming communities which gradually succeed one another until the diverse upper marsh community is achieved has nowadays to be somewhat modified,

because of the arrival of a plant called *Spartina anglica*. This arose as a result of the accidental crossing of the English cord grass *Spartina maritima* with its introduced American cousin *Spartina alterniflora*. Their first product was infertile, but spread vigorously by rhizomes; later it changed to the fertile form *Spartina anglica* which has devastated the saltmarshes of southern Britain and is still spreading northward. Though the parent *Spartina maritima* is still an innocuous and respectable relict member of the saltmarsh community in Chichester Harbour, its wayward offspring *Spartina anglica* has spread from its birthplace at Southampton to create 12,000 acres (4,800 hectares) of *Spartina* marshland. This new species can colonise bare wet mud well below the reach of glasswort, but also extends up to the highest marsh level, excluding the old mixed-marsh species as it goes. In France it is now known as *le peril vert*. *Spartina* has created a problem. Over the years it has invaded and destroyed a great deal of old mixed marsh, and as it has done so has trapped vast quantities of silt, raising the bare mud level by up to 6 ft (2 m). Since the 1950s, though, the *Spartina* has been dying back, leaving slumping platforms of

Mature mixed saltmarsh, dominated by sea lavender and purslane. In recent decades many of these old saltmarshes have been invaded and destroyed by Spartina grass. Notice the muddy channels through which the marsh drains as the tide ebbs. Many such marshes can be found in the coastal areas of Norfolk and Suffolk, protected by the National Trust and other conservation organisations. National Trust examples include the Blackwater in Essex and marshes at Scolt Head and Blakeney in Norfolk.

bare mud which do not seem to re-colonise with glassworts or other species, and can be seen in estuaries and other marshes along the south coast.

Brackish marshes and reedbeds
At the upper edge of the saltmarsh there is a narrow zone transitional to the inland habitats. Here there is often a fringe of reed, and highly-localised plants like marsh mallow. Beyond may lie woodland or farmland, or rough brackish grazings. The latter are usually places which were once marsh themselves, but where the soil has sweetened, allowing less salt-tolerant species like marsh arrowgrass,

A COASTAL GRAZING MARSH: FARLINGTON

Just a few yards from the M27 motorway at Portsmouth lies the entrance to a peaceful world of marshland, reedbeds and mud-flats, teeming with plants and animals. This is Farlington Marshes in Langstone Harbour, in part ancient grazing marsh and in part the result of eighteenth-century reclamation, and a superb example of the role of man in creating opportunities for nature to colonise around our coast.

Langstone and Chichester Harbours are two vast tidal basins in the coastal plain of Sussex and Hampshire, covering almost 11,000 acres (4,450 hectares). They form a bird reserve of international importance; every winter more than 50,000 wading birds and wildfowl feed here on the rich mud-life and roost on nearby marshes, including Farlington.

Although the harbour has a rich variety of ancient vegetation, *Zostera* beds, ancient mixed saltmarsh with purslane, thrift and sea lavender, and recent *Spartina* marshes, the edge is often narrow or even developed, and there would be little space for high tide roosts if it was not for changes made by man over thousands of years. Stone axes and arrowheads show that man was here even whilst the harbours were forming and the first areas of marsh and mud were walled off from the sea as long ago as Roman times.

Reclamation has been a continual process ever since. An old map show that in 1600 the north shoreline of Langstone Harbour was different from its present shape, with a broad creek up which small craft could ply their coastal trade up to the two villages of Drayton and Farlington, and two large islands offshore. In 1772 the lord of the Manor of Farlington, a man called Taylor, set about re-organising the shoreline, cutting off the creek from the sea and enclosing most of the islands within a new, extended, sea wall. In this way the present extent of Farlington grazing marshes was created and what had been mud and marsh was put to its new use of fattening cattle.

Today Farlington Marshes, a nature reserve run by the Hampshire Naturalists' Trust, is renowned for its rich flora, with over 300 species of plants, including more than 50 wild grasses, a third of the British grass flora. All these flowers are exploiting the slowly changing soil conditions as the marshes slowly stabilise. We can see major differences between three areas: the ancient pre-1600 reclamation; the remains of the old creek, a lagoon known as Shut Lake; and the outer post-1772 marsh. Nearest the entrance are the Roman marshes, dry now and covered in ant mounds, only slightly saline but still showing, in their cattle- and rabbit-browsed turf, the sinuous creeks of the original mudlands. Here there are bent-grasses, meadow grass, buck's-horn plantain, spiny restharrow and the papery red fruits of strawberry clover.

Then, beyond the old pre-1600 sea wall, the soil changes abruptly to the raw silt of an old tidal creek, and the thin turf is dominated by mud rush, saltmarsh grass and samphire and its vivid red autumn shoots. Drier places support sea milkwort and distant and divided sedges, whilst celery-leaved crowfoot fills the ditches. The marsh is dotted with ponds, each with its own particular salinity, and damp hollows have three rare grasses including annual beard-grass.

The undisturbed outer marshes are the essential roosting area for thousands of wintering birds and offer yet another range of conditions: the dry chalky sea bank even supports bee orchids and sea clover, whilst the old cut-off creek of Shut Lake is now a brackish lagoon dominated by a dense reedbed sheltering water birds, reed and sedge warblers, and harvest mice.

The marshes are maintained today by a carefully controlled cattle-grazing regime, which diversifies the conditions for plants and animals, so that Farlington, like many other grazing marshes now managed for nature conservation, shows not just accidental effects of man on the coast, but the deliberate manipulation to provide the plant and animal habitats now largely lost from unprotected areas.

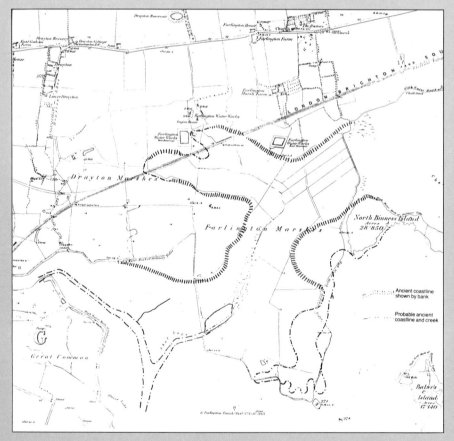

Ancient coastline shown by bank

Probable ancient coastline and creek

In this map the medieval or earlier coast bank has been superimposed on the 6-inch map of 1858 which shows the more planned outline of Farlington Marshes after the eighteenth century, when most of Binness Island became joined to the mainland. Reclamation here actually created the very varied conditions of soil drainage and salinity which enabled hundreds of kinds of plants and insects to colonise.

COASTAL HABITATS OF THE NATIONAL TRUST

The coast occupies a special place in the National Trust's portfolio of landholdings. In 1965 the trust launched 'Enterprise Neptune' to raise funds to acquire and protect 900 miles (14,550 km) of the very best coastline in Britain, as a result of which more than 400 miles (643 km) was actually purchased.

Cornwall and Devon are the National Trust's coastal stronghold; where it owns many miles of superb coast, full of wildlife habitats, including rocky cliffs, sandy coves and dunes, and some estuarine marshes. Amongst the most important sites and areas are:

Cape Cornwall; Chapel Porth (cliff and moor); Crackington Haven (cliffs and sandy habitats); sand dunes at Crantock and Porth Joke; cliffs and moorland in the St Agnes' area; moorland with rich flushes at Bosigran, cliff habitats around Sennen Cove; the great lagoon of the Loe near Helston; the tremendously rich habitats of the Lizard peninsula around Mullion and Kynance; saltmarshes in the Fal estuary; and the very fine coastal headland at the Dodman. Off the north Devon coast lies the Isle of Lundy, whilst the mainland coast offers several fine stretches of cliff and coves.

Dorset and the Isle of Wight share a Jurassic and Cretaceous geology, and many of the National Trust's properties include superb landslips rich in all kinds of wildlife; for example at Black Venn, Lyme Regis; Golden Cap; and on the south coast of the Isle of Wight. Elsewhere there are coastal grasslands adjoining limestone or chalk cliffs around Swanage, and in west Wight – where there is also the superb estuary of Newtown.

In south-east England there are important Trust sites at East Head, Chichester Harbour (sand dunes), and in East Sussex and Kent (chalk cliffs). Northey Island in the Blackwater is a superb Essex saltmarsh, whilst Dunwich Heath is one of the little-known Suffolk coast heaths.

At Horsey in Norfolk, the Broads meet the coast, whilst Blakeney, Brancaster and Scolt Head (p. 198) are sand and shingle wildernesses, interspersed with Trust-owned marshes at Morston and Stiffkey.

The National Trust has a strong presence in North Yorkshire from Scarborough to Whitby, and in Northumberland owns the

A superb example of coast protected by the National Trust, on the Lizard, Cornwall. The display of May flowers includes thrift, kidney vetch and ox-eye daisies.

beautiful sand dunes of Embleton Bay, near Dunstanburgh as well as the Farne Islands with its vast colonies of puffins, razorbills, cormorants and shags, and terns, kitti-wakes and other gulls.

On the west coast, the Trust leases much of the Solway commons in Cumbria, and has recently bought 657 acres (265 hectares) of dunes at Sandscale Haws, and owns several sites in Silverdale and Arn-side. Formby dunes in Merseyside are a sort of west coast parallel to Holkham, with red squirrels and natterjack toads. Anglesey brings the hill-fort of Dinas Gynfor, and the lagoon and beach at Cemlyn, and on mainland Wales in the Lleyn Peninsula the Trust holds several fine stretches of coast. St David's Head, many properties in St Bride's Bay, and the Marloes peninsula, as well as the great dunes at Freshwater and the tremendous range of habitats at Stackpole are also in the Trust's portfolio of protected coast, which is completed in South Wales

by much of the coastline of south and west Gower, including Rhossili and Worms Head, and Whitford Burrows to the north. Northern Ireland is not neglected; apart from the Giant's Causeway and Antrim coast, the Trust owns and manages parts of Belfast and Strangford Loughs, and the heath and dunes of Murlough.

In 1984 Prince Phillip relaunched the Enterprise Neptune Appeal which after twenty years had reached halfway to its 900-mile (1,450-km) target, and it is to be hoped that eventually much more of our coastal heritage will find itself in the Trust's protective custody.

Sheep grazing saltmarsh on Morecambe Bay. Continual sheep grazing produces a fine turf dominated by grass species.

plants; reed dominates everything forming a massive raft of intertwined rhizomes spreading beneath the water. They can be rich in insects, however, and are very important breeding sites for reed and sedge-warblers, and harvest mice.

white clover or tufted hair grass to live. Wild cherry, the tiny white-flowered brookweed, and saltmarsh water-dropwort often grow here.

Brackish marshes are usually grazed by cattle, and they have often been created by man walling-off the upper part of an estuary. The Traeth Mawr embankment across the Glaslyn estuary at Porthmadog in North Wales is a classic example, but there are many others including Titchfield Haven, the former estuary of the Meon in Hampshire, which was reclaimed by the Earls of Southampton around 1611. Here the original saltmarsh creeks can still be picked out as winding depressions in the meadows.

Reedbeds are another important habitat which in many cases owe their origin to human intervention. Some are entirely natural, formed when the sea flung shingle banks across the mouths of small streams, holding back ponds of brackish water ideal for reed growth. Other reedbeds grow in artificial ponds created for tide mills or to provide a causeway across an estuary. Reedbeds are usually poor in

RECLAMATION OF MARSHLANDS

Wherever you live around the larger estuaries of Britain, there will certainly be examples of marshland reclamation. Roman sea-banks have already been mentioned, and reflect the general expansion of agriculture in Roman times (p. 45). The deep silts of the upper marshes have been progressively walled off from the sea and exploited for farmland ever since. Some of the most fascinating places on the coast are those where you can study a succession of reclamations dating from different times as technology or the need (or greed) for farmland has progressed. Farlington marshes in Langstone Harbour (see p. 214) is one example; but the most extensive are on the east coast, where Roman sea-banks along the Lincolnshire coast are now many miles inland. Some of them are aligned along the late Iron-Age coastline where salt-workings have been found; later ones are some 4 miles (6.5 km) further to seaward (p. 219). Salt was an extremely valuable commodity and the evaporation

Reedbeds like these in the Test estuary are excellent habitat for insects and birds. They grow best in brackish conditions, and many of our reedbeds can be found around lagoons or wetlands reclaimed from the sea, so man has helped to create them. If the reeds are not cut regularly, scrub will invade and the habitat will change more or less irreversibly.

of seawater, first in sun-warmed ponds and finally in clay (or later, metal) pans was a major coastal industry which was so lucrative that it attracted a penal rate of tax in the early nineteenth century. Domesday contains many records of saltings all round the south and east coasts. Lymington in Hampshire exported 32,000 bushels of salt in 1341, for example, so it is hardly surprising that many old lanes winding down to small creeks and marshes are known as 'Salt Lane'. Today salterns and saltings are confused on many maps; the latter term often just means saltmarsh. When the salt industry died, from competition from rock-salt mining, vast areas of salt-pans were abandoned and turned into grazing marsh again. Other early industries such as shipbuilding have left few traces, though there are still remains of dammed-off tide-mill ponds in places.

Ancient reclamations in general provided a greater diversity of places for wildlife to live. In Sussex, the Pevensey Levels and Romney Marsh, once coastal marshes, are now lush grazing meadows, but the system of drainage creeks and dykes which dissects them is rich in water plants and contains many rare molluscs and insects, as well as introduced marsh frogs. Today most of these ancient reclamations lie well below the level of the sea, which has risen by several feet since Roman times, so if you walk along the sea wall at high spring tides, you have the odd experience of the sea lapping your boots on one side and cattle grazing many feet lower on the other!

These old sea walls are good places to look for all sorts of plants, both of saltmarshes and mudflats and of coastal grasslands.

Modern reclamation has been much more destructive; thousands of acres of land have been used either to dispose of dredging spoils (mud on mud is no problem, but mud on ancient mixed saltmarsh is not good news for anybody) or actually built up with silt or domestic rubbish (of which we create some 80 million tons every year) to form new land for docks or other developments. The Thames and the Tees estuary have suffered badly; in the latter case the superb natural sandflats have been almost entirely destroyed, leaving just a fraction of the famous Seal Sands. Three thousand acres (1,200 hectares) of Southampton Water and Portsmouth Harbour have been lost since the war.

These modern reclamations are poor places for wildlife, and cut right across the ancient topography; but they are no less a monument to the age which uncaringly created them than are the fascinating, wildlife-rich marshes created in earlier times and recorded in detail on many old maps.

CLIFFS AND LANDSLIPS

Cliffs and landslips form one of the most natural of our plant habitats, largely ignored by cliff-top farmers and cliff-bottom holidaymakers. Cliffs can develop in soft rocks

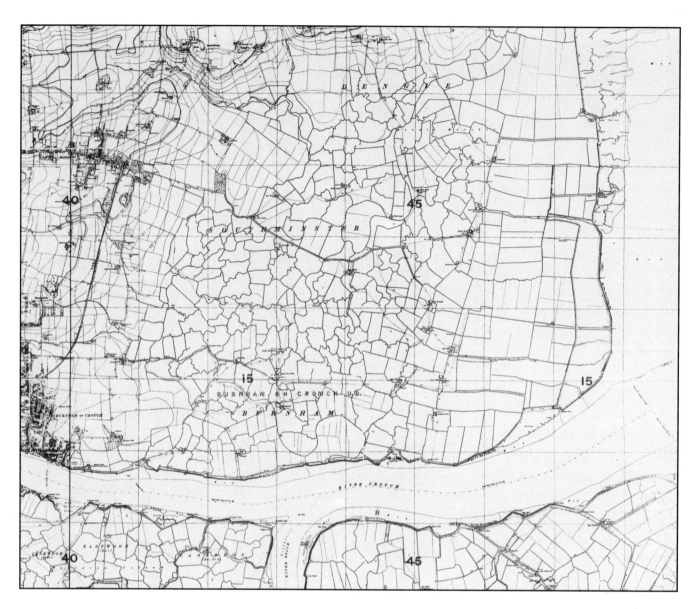

Saltmarsh reclamation, Dengie, Essex. This map shows three kinds of fields: the ancient, possibly Roman, rectangular enclosures on higher ground at left; medieval fields with curving boundaries centre; and at right a narrower zone of more planned reclamation with straight ditches. The sinuous ditches meandering between the medieval fields are derived directly from old saltmarsh creeks. Sea walls and early streams can also be traced. 1939 Edition GSGS 2½-inch Sheet 62/20.

like London clay, as at Sheppey where sharks' teeth and fossil plants are thick in the eroding cliff; or Barton and Bracklesham beds, as at Barton-on-Sea in Hampshire, where the cliffs are retreating so fast that a map of a hundred years ago looks significantly different. Most cliffs occur in hard-rock areas, however, where the sea attacks the rock only slowly, eating its way down and producing a flat wave-cut platform at low-tide level. The base of a cliff is often notched by the breaking waves, leaving a slight overhang. Above it the cliff profile depends very much on the type of rock; softer rocks like chalk generally make vertical cliffs, and harder rocks are likely to be cut back to a slope by erosion by wind and streams.

At the lower cliff level the first plants to colonise form a well-marked group, widely distributed. The lowest are the tiny lichens which cling to the rocks in the splash zone. There are crustose lichens, pressed flat to the rock like the orange *Xanthoria parietina*, the grey-green *Caloplaca marina*, and the black *Verrucaria marina* which is so thin it looks exactly like dried tar; and bushier foliose species, like *Ramalina siliquosa*, the sea ivory.

Sea-level has risen since many marshes were reclaimed. Here the ancient sea wall separates ancient grazing marsh from the tidal basin at right. These old sea walls are excellent places to look for unusual grassland plants.

Above them in a heavy spray zone, where the spray is equivalent to spreading about ¼ in (6 mm) layer of solid salt on the surface each year, lives a group which is halophytic; the rock samphire with its elegant succulent foliage, and others also found in saltmarsh or shingle – sea campion, thrift, rock sea spurrey and buck's-horn plantain, with its stag's-antler leaves. On calcareous cliffs of limestone the rock sea lavender may occur, and perhaps the golden samphire. The wild cabbage (ancestor of our supermarket cabbages) can be found on lime-rich south-western cliffs, and is abundant on the chalk cliffs of the southern Isle of Wight, near the Needles, where there is a very distinctive flora with Danish scurvy grass, kidney vetch and on the narrow undercliff rarities like the Mediterranean white horehound.

One of the fascinating things about cliffs is the way the plant distributions become clearer; in Scotland the southern rock samphire is replaced by another member of the carrot tribe, Scots lovage, which has a northern home, growing with the montane rose-root or alpine mouse-ear at sea level. Growing with either lovage or rock samphire, however, in deeper crevices and overhangs, can be found the rare fern sea spleenwort, which has a western distribution because it cannot tolerate frost – its leaves are killed very quickly by temperatures of −1°C (30°F). The Gulf

At the base of the greensand cliffs in the Isle of Wight is a complex, slumped, undercliff. Almost within reach of salt spray, the plants of the undercliff form a colourful patchwork of pink thyme, the white heads of wild carrot, and the coastal lichens sea ivory (tufts of grey-green) and Xanthoria (orange).

Stream keeps the western shoreline above freezing all the time.

On the upper cliffs, there are communities transitional to grassland; developing where soil accumulates in pockets or on ledges and often dominated by our old friend fescue, a species sensitive to grazing which grows as thick luxuriant turf on inaccessible ledges, but elsewhere is kept short and admits other plants – the ubiquitous thrift, bird's-foot trefoil, sea campion or sea plantain. In south-west England (and one area in south-west Scotland) the attractive blue stars of the little spring squill stud the thick cliff-top turf in May. In the north of Scotland, on the Durness limestone around Cape Wrath the Scottish primrose has a similar habit, but this is a very northern plant indeed. The 'ordinary' primrose is a feature of some shady western cliff grasslands where it may grow in deeper soils with bluebell, showing that its normal woodland habit is in fact an inability to compete with vigorous grasses, which on cliffs are absent.

On the chalk cliffs, where plants like kidney vetch grow, the cliff-top may be a grazed chalk grassland community, like those of the Purbeck chalk around Ballard Down, where the Nottingham catchfly occurs on thin chalk soils, and Durdle Door with deeper soil where tor grass (*Brachypodium pinnatum*) and saw-wort can be seen. Purbeck also has Jurassic limestones and at the cliff edge these support the rare early spider orchid and chalk milkwort. The Carboniferous limestone outcrops along the coast of South Wales, and here there is another type of maritime grassland, where typical limestone flowers like rock-rose and squinancywort share gaps in the red fescue turf with more coastal plants like thrift, sea spurge, bloody crane's-bill and spring squill. A special rarity here at Worms Head is the yellow whitlow grass, but many other western plants are present, including small restharrow, spring cinquefoil, hoary rock-rose and goldilocks aster, and there is an excellent example of calcareous heath, where shallow-rooting bell heather and tormentil grow intermingled with calcicolous (lime-loving) rock-rose and salad burnet.

On cliffs formed of acid rocks, there may be a quite different cliff-top community; maritime heath, which can give spectacular autumn displays of purple bell heather mingled in cushions with brilliant yellow western gorse. In northern cliff-top heaths the crowberry and cross-leaved heath are frequent, whilst southern examples on more fertile soils are often very rich in species, with both dyer's and hairy greenweeds, saw-wort, dropwort and the spiny burnet rose.

LANDSLIPS

Landslips are an integral part of the life and death of many cliffs (perhaps most cliffs) formed in sedimentary rocks. The vast majority are a small and usually unheeded part of the everyday degradation of cliffs by wind, rain and attack by the sea. Quite often slipping is on a massive scale, however, and produces major features of our cliffs with the potential for very rich and diverse habitats. Slipping on this scale is common in the Jurassic and Cretaceous rocks of southern England, and occurs too where they reach the coast in Yorkshire, at Robin Hood's Bay. In many cases solid masses of chalk or greensand beds collapse downwards when the incompetent Gault clay beneath them slips. The mechanism is extremely complex, but saturation of clays by long rainstorms, and the undermining of material at the cliff foot, are both involved to varying degrees. When the collapse comes it can be almost explosive; and usually leaves sections of the cliff-top dropped by 160 ft (50 m) or more, and tilted slightly backwards by a rotational slip.

One of the finest examples is at Folkestone Warren in Kent, where great slipped masses of bare chalk lie alongside areas of fine chalk grassland with one of the richest orchid floras in Britain, including the late and early spider, bee and frog orchids. There are also great ungrazed jungles of scrub and tall herbs, and on the broken chalk masses plants such as carrot and bedstraw broomrapes, wild cabbage, sea heath and rock samphire, and hart's-tongue fern all grow. Similar habitats occur at Chale Bay in the Isle of Wight, with a slightly different flora.

Between Lyme Regis and Axmouth near the Devon border lies one of the most remarkable coastal habitats in the country, a series of landslips formed mainly in Liassic strata, with slipped Cretaceous blocks much in evidence from the enormous slip which took place at Christmas 1839, leaving about 15 acres (6 hectares) of farmland separated from the 'mainland' by up to 330 ft (100 m); the gap is known as the 'Chasm', and the slipped block is called Goat Island. The whole area is very inaccessible and has become a classic site for studying the colonisation and development of ash woodland. The flora and fauna are both very rich, and there is a very distinctive plant community of privet scrub with ivy, hart's-tongue fern and wild madder, with an unusual abundance of gladdon or stinking iris, with its dull purplish flowers and attractive orange fruits.

8 · Conserving the Natural Heritage

HE UNDERLYING theme throughout this book has been the way in which the marvellous range of natural situations and vegetation types have interacted over many thousands of years with the activities of man to produce the rich and fascinating tapestry that makes up the British countryside. Ever since the first Mesolithic people discovered that they could control and concentrate wild game by using fire to create clearings, man has manipulated the environment for his own ends, without particular thought for the fate of habitat or other species, but in so doing has produced a constant succession of rich and varied 'semi-natural' habitats as a by-product.

If this 'artificial' countryside is so wonderful, and so dependent on man's activities, why then should not this same 'man' continue to treat the land as he wishes, for his own ends, and continue to produce a countryside that is the delight of all who visit it? This chapter is devoted to answering this question, but in summary the answer could be likened to the thought that we may, as a race, have survived the First and Second World Wars, but does that mean that we want to embark upon the Third? Just as our

Ancient woodland being cleared for agriculture. The picture shows an ancient woodland, rich in plants and animals, being cleared and bulldozed to provide more agricultural land. The sad part is that such places are irreplaceable and impossible to recreate, so that even if the land should prove unprofitable we could never recover a similar woodland.

means of destroying each other has expanded enormously, so too has our capacity for altering the countryside. Few people who visit the countryside regularly would deny that the countryside is changing rapidly, whether they know much about it or not, and first we should try to quantify the scale of this change and what it means.

THE DECLINE OF THE COUNTRYSIDE

For thousands of years, up until recently, man lived in harmony with nature. To an extent, it was accidental, and to some extent it was deliberate, based on an understanding of the importance of renewable resources, but in either event all of the semi-natural and artificial habitats that it created were rich in wildlife, and their pattern and disposition closely followed the underlying nature of the countryside. The more we discover about the historic management of the countryside, the more we realise how much our predecessors knew of applied ecology, and how wisely they adapted the natural pattern of vegetation; only in times of great social upheaval and population pressure did this fail, as marginal lands were brought into cultivation, only to be abandoned again soon afterwards. If heathland grew best on a site, then the products of that heath were used as pasture, bedding or fodder, rather than altered to make it provide something else; if a site flooded regularly, then its naturally-regenerated fertility was used in pasture or hay meadow, rather than trying to make it suitable for arable land; and so on, with each habitat used to the full.

On an even smaller scale, it was accepted and understood that some underwood species, say, hazel, grew best in some parts of the wood, whereas others, such as alders, grew best in other parts; and there was no unnecessary effort made to make species grow other than where they grew naturally. Whilst much of this came from an inability to do otherwise, the relevant point here is that it ensured that all the habitats except perhaps arable had direct links with the natural habitat that preceded them, and all preserved the wonderful small and large-scale natural variation in site characteristics and vegetation that Britain has. Even the arable land was known to be rich in wildlife, with many different flowers, breeding birds and mammals, and a safe haven for nectar-seeking insects.

All this has changed, however. Beginning in earnest with the drainage and 'reclamation' of the fenlands of East Anglia, and accelerating through the enclosure period and on up to the present day, our capacity for changing the countryside to suit the needs of the moment, *against* the natural pattern variation, has expanded enormously. At the same time, there has been a dramatic shift away from shared community effort and largely self-sufficient communities towards specialisation, giving the opportunity for larger and more monotonous units, laying any 'anomalies' (like heath, bog, or woodland) more open to being removed to give more space. There has also, throughout this period of agricultural change, been a constantly increasing population, increasing the pressure on our limited amount of land.

These early dramatic changes were bad enough, but even so the scale and intensity of change had been limited enough to leave us with a highly attractive and varied countryside, rich in habitats and species, 50 years ago. Most ecologists and conservationists would be more than satisfied if we could regain the extent and pattern of habitats and boundaries that we had 50 years ago. Indeed, despite the changes that had taken place, the major document that laid the foundation for modern nature conservation (*Command 7122: Conservation of Nature in England and Wales*) in 1947, or at least the proposals arising from it, failed to take serious account of the threat that the agricultural industry posed to nature conservation, which is a clear indication of how different things were even then, just 40 years ago. Since then, we have acquired more and 'better' chemicals, larger and more powerful machines, and larger and larger farm units. The patriotic exhortations of the war years translated into a changed financial structure for agriculture, turning it into a highly subsidised industry, yet lacking the controls that are placed on all other industries. The effects of entering the Common Market, with all its agricultural policy absurdities, are by now well-known, but this was only really the last straw, as much had happened before. Our domestic agricultural grant system has taken no account of what is being destroyed by agricultural progress (and it is little better now, except with regard to statutorily protected sites), nor does it consider local requirements.

What this has meant, in practice, is that farmers have had a free hand, with financial assistance, to change the face of the countryside entirely for personal benefit, whatever changes or losses this may have brought about; and until recently there were many methods of destruction of ancient features that were *specifically* grant-aided to help them to take place. All this matters because modern agriculture obliterates almost all that went before it. A rich meadow with 100 or more different plant species becomes a monoculture of one or two grasses, barren of any form of animal life; an ancient woodland, managed for thousands of years, can be levelled in order to grow corn on the land leaving barely a trace that the wood, or its thousands of plant and animal species, ever existed. Similarly, hedges are of little use to the arable farmer and it is estimated from good evidence that approximately 140,000 miles (225,300 km) of hedgerow were removed, mostly for agricultural reasons, in England and Wales between 1947 and 1974.

'Whittlesea mere', Cambridgeshire. Until the mid-nineteenth century, this was one of the largest and richest of lowland lakes, with masses of wildlife. It was drained by pumping in a matter of weeks, and is now the dullest and most sterile of English landscapes.

It is against this background that we are obliged to talk about habitat 'losses'; the land may be still there, and frequently still farmed, but all vestiges of semi-natural habitat may be erased, and thus wholly lost. The figures for these losses make depressing, and even frightening, reading. There is no need to repeat them all here, but a few examples will show how bad the situation is. Most figures show the changes from about 1950 to 1985, a period for which the best information is available, but we also give a few examples dating further back.

Lowland heathlands have declined considerably, through conversion to agricultural land, being built on, or by being planted with conifers. The Suffolk Sandlings have declined by over 90 per cent in 200 years, from 41,000 acres (16,500 hectares) in 1783 to less than 4,000 acres (1,600 hectares) in 1983; whilst Dorset heaths have declined from 100,000 acres (40,000 hectares) in 1750 down to about 14,000 acres (5,600 hectares) in 1983, with losses still continuing in the last few years. In other places, the losses have been less, but in some places it pre-dates accurate records and may be even higher.

For lowland neutral grasslands, such as hay meadows and enclosed pastures (but excluding downland), the figures are not precisely known, since no complete survey has ever been done, and maps and air photographs do not show the vegetation comprehensively, but it is believed that we have lost *at least* 95 per cent since 1949, and possibly distinctly more. For many counties, the only examples of such meadows are a few, almost invariably small, nature reserves set amidst a sea of monoculture. Yet many children's books still portray the countryside as one large flowery pasture or meadow, dotted with contented cows! Perhaps the public outcry has been less than it should have been, simply because public consciousness has failed to catch up with the scale of the loss. Downlands on chalk and limestone have gone the same way, with about 80 per cent lost or badly damaged overall, mainly through agricultural and forestry activities.

Ancient woodlands have fared somewhat better in terms of percentage lost, partly because woods are often much more visible, accessible features than grasslands, or even heathland, but things are still bad enough. Most figures show that between 1949 and about 1980 some 30–50 per cent of ancient broadleaved woodlands were lost, in the sense that they no longer support similar vegetation. These figures are often masked by surveys showing simply the total area of woodland of all types, including single-species plantations (often an old downland or heathland), even though the two types are, as we hope we have shown through this book, worlds apart. This loss rate may be lower than for some other habitats, yet it still leaves us with the fact that almost half our ancient woodland, much of it developed over thousands of years, has been lost in the last 35 years.

The story for all other lowland habitats is the same (and even upland habitats have been changed dramatically through extension of fertilised pastures into rough upland grazings and planting mile upon mile of conifers on upland moors), though enough has been said to indicate the scale of the problem.

The loss of the features that make up the other strand of this book, the underlying historic pattern of the country-side, are less well-documented, perhaps because there is no national organisation to take the task on. Old field patterns are knocked into new shapes without a second thought, ancient commons on which no-one claims any rights are changed from intriguing, convoluted, secret areas into the bland nothingness of square bright green fields; old marlpits are filled in to provide 'more land', Celtic field-systems are ploughed into invisibility, and ancient droveways become no more than a line on the map, with just a wooden sign to indicate the direction across a ploughed field which few dare to cross. Even ancient sacrosanct boundaries like parish boundaries are becoming breached, now, as estates grow ever larger. Everything is becoming more and more similar and homogenised, with all the small-scale varia-bility and beauty being lost; and at the same time all the evidence of our chequered past is going, as one 'living museum' after another is simply bulldozed away.

WHY DOES ALL THIS MATTER?

Almost everything that we are concerned with in this book is the historic product of many generations of men, many changes of climate, and hundreds or thousands of years of evolution. They are, almost without exception, quite un-creatable, and thus totally irreplaceable. It is a salutary thought that, despite much research and considerable effort, we could not even properly re-create one ancient meadow (one of the less complex habitats) within our own lifetime. With a *lot* of effort, we could just about gather together enough seed of the range of higher plants (which could easily be about 150 species or more) that might occur, and could broadcast them vaguely in the parts of the meadow that might suit them best; with a great deal more effort, we could, perhaps simulate the topography of an ancient meadow, perhaps by throwing up some ridge-and-furrow; and then we could manage it in a suitably trad-itional way to see what happened, hoping for the best.

What could we do, however, about the 500-year-old hedges, the undisturbed soil profile, the vast range of insects and other invertebrates that are associated with an old meadow? Or what about the scatter of 150-year-old anthills, the ancient fairy rings, or the fact that many of the plants themselves in an old meadow may have been decades or hundreds of years old? Finally, what secrets would a re-created meadow have to tell us, except for the fact that twentieth-century man had destroyed something ancient and complex, then tried to re-create it?

So, if we can only create a superficial likeness of one example of one of the simpler habitats, with a lot of effort, what hope is there of ever re-creating the incredibly complex, three-dimensional mosaic of an ancient wood-

Limestone pavement damaged by quarrying. Even something as solid and permanent as limestone pavement, with its highly-specialised (and often rare) plants and animals, is vulnerable to loss by man's activities. In this instance, the stone has been quarried mainly for ornamental use in gardens, though the practice has now virtually ceased since it was made illegal.

land, with its 300-year-old pollards, perhaps 500-year-old coppice stools, and thousands of plant and animal species? There is no hope. Each time an ancient habitat is destroyed, and this probably takes place almost every day, to some extent, we lose something beautiful, historic, unre-creatable, and full of plants and animals.

This is bad enough, akin to losing an ancient monument or historic building, but it is worse than that: our semi-natural habitats collectively form a mosaic, an inter-connecting whole, which is richer and more valuable than its constituent parts. We acquired our flora and fauna from the continent after the ice age because each species could move uninterrupted through the tundra, the open scrub, from wetland to wetland, or, later, through continuous woodland. Even by medieval times, despite the great extent of the cleared areas, there was still an effective network of habitats, droveways, hedges, rivers and river-banks, and so on, for species to move through, and this persisted, albeit in reduced form, to the present century, Intervening agricul-tural land may not have been suitable for individual species, but at least it was not positively hostile.

In contrast, today, over much of the lowlands, we are left with 'islands' of habitat in a hostile 'sea' of arable land, with few or no connections and a barrier of toxic sprays or damaging fertilisers. If something goes awry on one of these 'island' sites, like a fire, a flood, a drought, or a mistake in management, then many species will die out, perhaps largely unrecorded; where will they re-colonise from? The answer, sadly, is that they will not, and the inevitable trend is for these habitats to become steadily poorer in species. This happens even where the area is managed as a nature reserve, and there is a famous example of a woodland on the edge of the fenlands losing 60 per cent of its butterfly species despite its status as a nature reserve. No-one knows what other invertebrate species disappeared. What hope is there for sites that are not nature reserves?

WHAT IS BEING DONE ABOUT IT?

Britain is famous for its conservation of the natural and archaeological heritage. There are government organis-ations concerned with the conservation of nature (the Nature Conservancy Council), the conservation of the landscape and general countryside features (the Country-side Commission), and the conservation of archaeological features (e.g. English Heritage); there are voluntary organisations with many thousands of members, like the RSPB, the County Nature Conservation Trusts, the Council for the Protection of Rural England (CPRE), and the National Trust; while many County Councils and formerly Metropolitan Councils have made considerable strides in a

broad spectrum of conservation measures. It is not the place of this book to itemise past successes or failures of the conservation organisations. A great deal has been achieved, and the voice of conservation has grown steadily louder. There are now over 200 National Nature Reserves, over 2,000 non-statutory nature reserves, and countless scheduled ancient monuments; the recent Wildlife and Countryside Act, and subsequent amendments, encom-passes a wide range of countryside protection measures; and there are many less quantified achievements, where motorways have been diverted, development on valued habitats reduced, or farmers persuaded out of removing a hedge or copse.

Yet, clearly, in view of the figures quoted, something is still failing, and with finite unrecreatable habitats, you cannot afford to go on failing for long. The greatest problem, perhaps, is the emphasis on 'key sites'; in other words, the general philosophy of conservation in all its forms, brought on partly by lack of resources but also by lack of under-standing, has been to put most effort into conserving a series of (usually) pre-determined top-grade sites, be they woodlands, mountains or ancient archaeological monu-ments. The Wildlife and Countryside Act has reinforced this by strengthening protection for Sites of Special Scientific Interest (SSSI), but largely ignoring the remainder of the countryside. For those involved in making conservation decisions, there is an undoubted dilemma, for these top sites must be protected, yet that may leave little over for other work, and this may prove increasingly the case as SSSI are now largely protected by financial agreements under which the owner or occupier is compensated annually for the full value of such income as he might have derived from the site had he destroyed it; and as things stand at present this can simply go on in perpetuity, the payments rising with changes in the index of agricultural prices. This will continue to tie up a very large part of both the money and the manpower of the Nature Conservancy Council.

There are, however, at least three problems with this 'key site' approach. First, it leaves all the vast number of 'good wildlife sites' or 'interesting monuments' that just miss reaching key-site status, but which are such an important part of everyone's countryside, unprotected, by and large. Secondly, it does nothing for the steady and inexorable attrition of the ancient boundaries, field patterns, hed-gerows, greenways, old pollard trees, and all the rich tapestry of smaller features that both goes to make up the countryside book, still largely unread, *and* forms the net-work of corridors that keeps our major habitats thriving with wildlife. Without this our 'key sites' will be almost valueless, and the countryside as dull as ditchwater, as you drive between miles of sterile fields searching for a nature reserve where you may rigidly follow a nature trail, with your dog on a lead! Thirdly, it does nothing at all for sites

whose value is as yet unrecorded or unappreciated . . . and there are an immense and surprising number of those.

The recent change in public attitude to agriculture, and the need to reduce surpluses, has provoked two initiatives that may prove to be very significant developments in the long run. Environmentally Sensitive Areas (ESAs) are areas of particular historic landscape or ecological value (or both, as is often the case), precisely defined and mapped. Within these areas, there is the option for all farmers to take various degrees of grant-aid to cease intensive production, and manage their land in a more sensitive or traditional way. The areas are carefully defined to include land where such management agreements are relevant, whilst avoiding areas that are already adequately covered by other forms of protective legislation. The Ministry of Agriculture is the administering authority, though discussion with many organisations is carried out, and the money derives from the European Economic Community. The intention is that the first 12 ESAs will be carefully monitored for the rate of take-up, and success with which they conserve the landscape, before others are considered. The initial 12 areas are; The Brecklands; West Penwith, Cornwall; the South Downs; the Test Valley; the Somerset levels; the LLeyn peninsula; part of the Cambrian mountains; the Shropshire borders; the Norfolk Broads; the Suffolk river valleys; the North Peak, Derbyshire; and the Pennine Dales. Many are areas where there has been previous public conflict

Modern farmland on the Lincolnshire Wolds. This is the ultimate result of a countryside where agriculture is the primary concern. It is virtually devoid of any wildlife or historical interest, and the records of millennia of changes are almost wholly lost. Worse still, the effects of such a landscape are not confined solely to where it occurs, but they spread through polluted watercourses, and by the isolation of patches of unspoilt habitat, much further afield, as is so clearly demonstrated by the demise of the Norfolk Broads as an ecological paradise.

between agriculture and conservation interests, so the ultimate success of these schemes is of interest to many.

'Set aside' is a different idea, under which individual farmers agree to take a proportion of their land (minimum 20 per cent of eligible arable land) out of productive agriculture into some non-intensive, environmentally-sensitive use, with appropriate payments from the Ministry of Agriculture to maintain the farm income. Unlike ESAs, it is not confined to particular geographical areas. Different schemes are available, such as the conversion of arable to fallow or woodland. Although it offers the possibility of enhancing the appearance and ecological value of our landscape, and broadening the base of numbers of plants and animals in the countryside, there are nevertheless a number of problems. For example, when a farmer opts to convert land from arable, he is required to provide a green cover but he may not graze the 'grassland' with anything that might be classed as a farm animal, whereas this is most frequently what is required to produce the optimum sward for nature conservation purposes.

More difficult to resolve is the inherent problem, referred to elsewhere, that what is best in our countryside is ancient and unrecreatable; taking areas of land out of highly-intensive agriculture does not produce more ancient features, nor does it protect any more of those that are remaining. Such schemes are by no means without value, but they require the operation of many other protective and management devices too.

THE ROLE OF THE NATIONAL TRUST IN NATURE CONSERVATION

The National Trust in England, Wales and Northern Ireland, and, to a lesser extent, the National Trust for Scotland, plays a major, and largely unsung, role in nature conservation. It is also a role that increases in value year by year, as the Trust improves its management and knowledge of its own properties, and the acreage of land of ecological and historical interest elsewhere continues to decline where there is no protection.

The figures themselves are remarkable. The requirement to preserve flora and fauna was enshrined in the National Trust's Articles of Association almost 100 years ago, in 1894, and the Trust established its first nature reserve when it acquired part of Wicken Fen in 1899 – an auspicious start, long before most other conservation organisations existed. By 1989, 162,400 acres (65,721 hectares) of National Trust land in England and Wales lay within Sites of Special Scientific Interest (SSSI) – almost 10 per cent of the total SSSI area, and about 30 per cent of the National Trust's landholding in those countries. There is also a huge amount of land of great ecological or historical interest in the National Trust's holding, but which has no statutory recognition.

Ownership by the National Trust confers the benefit of inalienability – a mechanism that is designed to prevent National Trust land from being spoilt – and recent events, such as the pressure from Government on the Nature Conservancy Council to dispose of its National Nature Reserves shows just how fragile some forms of protection can be. However, no amount of land ownership or inalienability is sufficient on its own to conserve the scientific value of the land without appropriate management, for which the necessary prerequisite is survey, to know what you are trying to conserve. In the past, the National Trust has certainly been guilty of failing to conserve aspects of the land which it held, either through lack of knowledge, or through concentration on the conservation of buildings at the expense of the estates that supported them. Now, however, it runs a highly professional central survey and advisory team, the members of which are gradually work-

ing round all rural properties, cataloguing their natural features, and proposing detailed management requirements. The need for survey, management plans and monitoring is fully recognised, and is steadily being put into practice. It is safe to say that the historic natural heritage of Britain would be considerably the poorer without the presence of the National Trust and the National Trust for Scotland.

WHAT ELSE SHOULD BE DONE?

There is much more that could be done to protect and conserve our countryside. This section is not intended as a *critique* of conservation organisations, but more as a collection of pointers to the future and a plea for more resources to find their way into conservation.

Firstly, we still need much more survey work to be done to establish what we have. As long as someone has to make value judgements as to whether a piece of countryside is worth keeping intact, or not, then there will be a continuing need to find out what there is and how interesting it is. It may come as a surprise to some that we do not know this, yet the reality is that there is an immense amount of countryside still not looked at critically and evaluated.

Away from centres of population, and especially into the uplands and border areas, the problem is worst, yet it is marked enough elsewhere, too. In the New Forest, for example, close to the two major conurbations of Southampton and Bournemouth, and awash with conservation organisations, only about 10 per cent of the enclosed agricultural land has been surveyed in detail, even though it is just the sort of situation that might hold much of interest. Every County Naturalists' Trust or County Council which *has* organised a 'field-by-field' survey has discovered many new treasures, frequently totally unexpected ones, yet every year that this work is left undone more of the unknown treasures are destroyed.

Secondly, we must have protection for the less-than-top-grade sites (which may be highly attractive, historic and species-rich, but not quite the best) and the mass of minor countryside features that collectively mean so much. It is reatively easy to find means of protecting the next tier down from the best, and this has been adopted by some County Councils, such as Hampshire County Council, who are notifying and seeking to protect a series of Countryside Heritage Sites and ensure their appropriate management. In the more enlightened counties, these include field-systems, ancient trackways and even old pollard trees, though as yet many counties have no such proposals at all, and they lack the support of national law in any case. Similarly, County Naturalists' Trusts, the Nature Conservancy Council and other bodies have a 'mental list' of lower-grade sites that they seek to protect where and when they can, but again the statutory framework is lacking.

So, this is one approach which can work, but which still needs increased legal support to make it effective. Even so it is bound to leave a mass of minor features totally unprotected, and it will fail on some more significant sites where owners are unwilling to co-operate. Thus, some other wider mechanism is needed, which will make sure that very little of value will fall through the net, which is positive in its approach, in that it encourages active (but correct) management, and which is based on a sound foundation of survey and mapping so that we know exactly what of interest there is left to conserve.

The means of achieving this is the subject of much debate at present, and no clear path through the maze of practical difficulties has emerged. The possibility of extending planning control to the countryside is one option; at present, agriculture is in a peculiarly anomalous position in that it is a profitable industry, using industrial methods, and favoured with much grant aid, yet it is subject to virtually no control. All other industries are subject to planning permission, in even the most depressed areas, yet agriculture has proceeded on its way unchecked. The problems of implementing such a scheme are largely practical, particularly lack of manpower and appropriate knowledge in planning departments, fear in the farming community of delays over routine operations and mounting paperwork, problems of definition of what should be preserved, and the need for an extension of the definition of the law.

Much of this could be solved with a well-thought-out approach that is based on a sound foundation of survey and knowledge; which accepts that a very large part of farming operations *are* purely routine and need no control whatsoever, which carefully defines those operations (such as hedge removal, drainage, or ploughing of permanent pasture) that *do* need control, and which takes on the need for extra staff to achieve this. The advantage of such a system is that, once correctly defined, nothing need fall through the net except if an illegal act is committed, but the disadvantages might be that it is purely protective rather than positive in approach; though this, too, could be solved with the option of management agreements.

An alternative proposal involves the application of Countryside Management Orders, rather like Tree Preservation Orders, that could be applied to an area of land if a threat to it was perceived, and this could be followed up by offer of a management agreement. It would be naive to suppose that this could work if orders were only applied when sites were threatened; a very large number of sites could be (and are) lost before anyone realises it. Thus, this scheme could only operate from the same basis as that of planning control, by being based on thorough survey and evaluation, and prior notification to appropriate owners that they have a thing of value, or an onus on them to check

maps in the planning department before making changes.

In this respect, it will be of particular interest to see how the ESA schemes fare. At present they are very limited in coverage, leaving massive holes in the protection of our countryside heritage, though they are undoubtedly a step in the right direction, with the great advantage of involvement of the agricultural ministry. Even within the designated areas, there are many loopholes, not least the voluntary nature of the agreements, and their complete reversibility, but the 5-year monitoring period may point the way to improving the system.

A problem that pervades every idea of conserving the ancient fabric and vegetation of our countryside is the need for a monitoring scheme to find out what is going on. It may be easy enough to detect major changes in woodlands, or in situations next to villages, but it is virtually impossible to know for certain whether an ancient meadow has been fertilised or sprayed with selective herbicide if it is well away from public scrutiny. There is no foolproof answer to this though it is helped by a sensible system that encourages good management, some provision for monitoring if only selective, and perhaps an acceptance that we will not be 100 per cent successful, though the problem remains that losing sites does not make the remainder any safer.

More thought is needed but, above all, we need early action to prevent the continuing loss of so much of our natural heritage. At the same time as devising a better protective mechanism, we also need better management of places to ensure their survival in their traditional form. Because so much of our countryside has developed through its association with man, it needs continuing management, in a particular traditional way, to maintain the interest. While formal 'management agreements' with financial payments to owners for specified management operations are clearly a good thing, how much better it is to re-discover the value of traditional crops, or ancient ways of doing things. Hazel coppicing has almost died out, and few people remember what it involves; heathland no longer has a place in any agricultural economy in the lowlands, bar a very few, while the old watermeadow structures are levelled by bulldozing to allow maize to be grown. We need more encouragement of ancient crafts, like coppicing, thatching, broom-making and so on, to use local native produce which could be abundant and cheap. It is immensely satisfying to visit somewhere like Bradfield Woods in Suffolk (see p. 86) and see its great productivity after at least 900 years of continuous use with no significant re-stocking; or Bure Marshes in Norfolk where reeds and sedge-beds are regularly harvested commercially, yet they are the home for marsh harriers, swallowtail butterfiles, otters, and so many other species. Surely this all makes more sense than having tiny islands of dwindling habitat set in a sterile sea of arable land producing more crops than anyone needs?

Appendix I: Classification of Woodland Types

I ASH–WYCH ELM WOODLAND
    1A. Calcareous ash–wych elm woods
        a. Southern variant
        b. Northern variant
    1B. Wet ash–wych elm woods
        a. Heavy soil variant
        b. Light soil variant
    1C. Calcareous ash–wych elm woods on dry and/or heavy soils
        a. Eastern variant
        b. Sessile oak variant
    1D. Western valley ash–wych elm woods

2 ASH–MAPLE WOODLAND
    2A. Wet ash–maple woods
        a. Typical wet ash–maple woods
        b. Wet maple woods
    2B. Ash–maple woods on light soils
        a. Variant on poorly-drained soils
        b. Variant on freely-drained soils
    2C. Dry ash–maple woods

3 HAZEL–ASH WOODLAND
    3A. Acid pedunculate oak–hazel–ash woods
        a. Heavy soil form
        b. Light soil form
    3B. Southern calcareous hazel–ash woods
    3C. Northern calcareous hazel–ash woods
    3D. Acid sessile oak–hazel–ash woods

4 ASH–LIME WOODLAND
    4A. Acid birch–ash–lime woods
    4B. Maple–ash–lime woods
        a. Lowland variant
        b. Western variant
    4C. Sessile oak–ash–lime woods

5 OAK–LIME WOODLAND
    5A. Acid pedunculate oak–lime woods
    5B. Acid sessile oak–lime woods

6 BIRCH–OAK WOODLAND
    6A. Upland sessile oakwoods
        b. Upland birch–sessile oakwoods
        c. Upland hazel–sessile oakwoods
    6B. Upland pedunculate oakwoods
        b. Upland birch–pedunculate oakwoods
        c. Upland hazel–pedunculate oakwoods
    6C. Lowland sessile oakwoods
        b. Lowland birch–sessile oakwoods
        c. Lowland hazel–sessile oakwoods
    6D. Lowland pedunculate oakwoods
        b. Lowland birch–pedunculate oakwoods
        c. Lowland hazel–pedunculate oakwoods

7 ALDER WOODLAND
    7A. Valley alderwoods on mineral soils
        a. Acid valley alderwoods
        b. Valley alderwoods on neutral–alkaline soils

7B. Wet valley alderwoods
    a. Sump alderwoods
    b. Base-rich springline alderwoods
    c. Base-poor springline alderwoods
7C. Plateau alderwoods
7D. Slope alderwoods
7E. Bird cherry–alderwoods
    a. Lowland variant
    b. Upland variant

8 BEECH WOODLAND
8A. Acid sessile oak–beechwoods
8B. Acid pedunculate oak–beechwoods
8C. Calcareous pedunculate oak–ash–beechwoods
    a. Dry lime–wych elm variant
    b. Moist wych elm variant
    c. Maple variant
8D. Acid pedunculate oak–ash–beechwoods
8E. Sessile oak–ash–beechwoods
    a. Acid variant
    b. Calcareous variant

9 HORNBEAM WOODLAND
9A. Pedunculate oak–hornbeam woods
    a. Birch–hazel variant
    b. Ash–maple variant
9B. Sessile oak–hornbeam woods
    a. Acid sessile oak–hornbeam woods
    b. Calcareous sessile oak–hornbeam woods

10 SUCKERING ELM WOODLAND
10A. Invasive elm woods
10B. Valley elm woods

11 PINE WOODLAND
11A. Acid birch–pinewoods
11B. Acid oak–pinewoods
11C. Calcareous pinewoods

12 BIRCH WOODLAND
12A. Rowan–birch woods
12B. Hazel–birch woods

(From *Woodland Conservation and Management*, by
G. F. Peterken, 1981, published by Chapman and Hall.)

Appendix II: Plants of Ancient Woodlands

A list of plants which (in southern England) are most likely to indicate an ancient woodland community.

Field maple (*Acer campestre*)
Moschatel (*Adoxa moschatellina*)
Bearded couch grass (*Agropyron caninum*)
Ramsons (*Allium ursinum*)
Wood anemone (*Anemone nemorosa*)
Columbine (*Aquilegia vulgaris*)
Hard fern (*Blechnum spicant*)
Hairy brome grass (*Bromus ramosus*)
Bushgrass (*Calamagrostis epigejos*)
Nettle-leaved bellflower (*Campanula trachelium*)
Large-flowered bitter cress (*Cardamine amara*)
Coral-wort (*Cardamine bulbifera*)
Sedges:
    Carex laevigata
    C. pallescens
    C. pendula
    C. remota
    C. strigosa
    C. sylvatica
Hornbeam (*Carpinus betulus*)
Sword-leaved helleborine (*Cephalanthera longifolia*)
Alternate-leaved golden saxifrage (*Chrysosplenium alternifolium*)
Opposite-leaved golden saxifrage (*Chrysosplenium oppositifolium*)
Autumn crocus (*Colchicum autumnale*)

Lily-of-the-valley (*Convallaria majalis*)
Midland hawthorn (*Crataegus oxycanthoides*)
Spurge laurel (*Daphne laureola*)
Small teasel (*Dipsacus pilosus*)
Narrow buckler fern (*Dryopteris carthusiana*)
Scaly male fern (*Dryopteris pseudomas*)
Broad-leaved helleborine (*Epipactis helleborine*)
Narrow-lipped helleborine (*Epipactis leptochila*)
Purple helleborine (*Epipactis purpurata*)
Wood horsetail (*Equisetum sylvaticum*)
Wood spurge (*Euphorbia amygdaloides*)
Giant fescue (*Festuca gigantea*)
Alder buckthorn (*Frangula alnus*)
Sweet woodruff (*Galium odoratum*)
Water avens (*Geum rivale*)
Wood cudweed (*Gnaphalium sylvaticum*)
Green hellebore (*Helleborus viridis*)
Wood soft grass (*Holcus mollis*)
Wood barley (*Hordelymus europaeus*)
Tutsan (*Hypericum androsaemum*)
Beautiful St John's wort (*Hypericum pulchrum*)
Gladdon (*Iris foetidissima*)
Yellow archangel (*Lamiastrum galeobdolon*)
Toothwort (*Lathraea squamaria*)
Bitter-vetch (*Lathyrus montanus*)
Everlasting pea (*Lathyrus sylvestris*)
Forster's woodrush (*Luzula forsteri*)
Hairy woodrush (*Luzula pilosa*)
Great woodrush (*Luzula sylvatica*)

Yellow pimpernel (*Lysimachia nemorum*)
Crab apple (*Malus sylvestris*)
Wood cow-wheat (*Melampyrum pratense*)
Wood melick (*Melica uniflora*)
Millet (*Milium effusum*)
Wood forget-me-not (*Myosotis sylvatica*)
Wild daffodil (*Narcissus pseudonarcissus*)
Bird's-nest orchid (*Neottia nidus-avis*)
Early purple orchid (*Orchis mascula*)
Bath asparagus (*Ornithogalum pyrenaicum*)
Wood sorrel (*Oxalis acetosella*)
Herb Paris (*Paris quadrifolia*)
Hart's-tongue fern (*Phyllitis scolopendrium*)
Greater butterfly orchid (*Platanthera chlorantha*)
Wood meadow-grass (*Poa nemoralis*)
Common Solomon's seal (*Polygonatum multiflorum*)
Polypody (*Polypodium vulgare*)
Hard shield fern (*Polystichum aculeatum*)
Soft shield fern (*Polystichum setiferum*)
Aspen (*Populus tremula*)
Primrose (*Primula vulgaris*)
Wild cherry (Gean) (*Prunus avium*)
Narrow-leaved lungwort (*Pulmonaria longifolia*)
Sessile oak (*Quercus petraea*)

Goldilocks (*Ranunculus auricomus*)
Redcurrant (*Ribes sylvestre*)
Blackcurrant (*Ribes nigrum*)
Field rose (*Rosa arvensis*)
Butcher's broom (*Ruscus aculeatus*)
Sanicle (*Sanicula europaea*)
Wood club-rush (*Scirpus sylvaticus*)
Orpine (*Sedum telephium*)
Saw-wort (*Serratula tinctoria*)
Golden rod (*Solidago virgaurea*)
Wild service tree (*Sorbus torminalis*)
Betony (*Stachys officinalis*)
Black bryony (*Tamus communis*)
Mountain fern (*Thelypteris oreopteris*)
Small-leaved lime (*Tilia cordata*)
Wych elm (*Ulmus glabra*)
Bilberry (*Vaccinium myrtillus*)
Wood speedwell (*Veronica montana*)
Guelder rose (*Viburnum opulus*)
Bush vetch (*Vicia sepium*)
Wood vetch (*Vicia sylvatica*)
Marsh violet (*Viola palustris*)
Wood dog-violet (*Viola reichenbachiana*)

Bibliography

Anderson, P. and Shimwell, D. (1981), *Wild Flowers and Other Plants of the Peak District*, Moorland Publishing Co., Ashbourne.

Aston, M. (1985), *Interpreting the Landscape*, Batsford, London.

Beresford, M. (1984), *History on the Ground: Six Studies in Maps and Landscapes*, Sutton, Gloucester.

Clapham, A. R. ed. (1978), *Upper Teesdale, The Area and its Natural History*, Collins, London.

Crawford, Peter (1985), *The Living Isles*, BBC, London.

Fowler, P. J. (1983), *The Farming of Prehistoric Britain*, Cambridge University Press, Cambridge.

Godwin, H. (1975), *History of the British Flora*, 2nd edn., Cambridge University Press, Cambridge.

Hall, D. (1982), *Medieval Fields, Shire Archaeology No. 28*, Shire Publications, Princes Risborough.

Hampshire County Council (various authors) (1981 onwards). *Hampshire's Countryside Heritage*:
  1. *Ancient lanes and tracks;*
  2. *Ancient woodland;*
  3. *Rivers and wetlands;*
  4. *Heathland;*
  6. *Chalk grassland;*
  7. *The coast;*
  8. *Man and the landscape;*
  9. *Meadows.*

Harley, J. L. and Lewis, D. H. (eds.) (1985), *The Flora and Vegetation of Britain; Origins and Changes – the Facts and their Interpretation*, Academic Press, London.

Hoskins, W. G. (1982), *Fieldwork in Local History*, Faber & Faber, London.

Hoskins, W. G. (1985), *Making of the English Landscape*, Penguin, Harmondsworth.

Hoskins, W. G. and Millward, R. (eds.), *The Shropshire Landscape*, and others of the County Series, of which 18 are published to date.

Mabey, Richard (1980), *The Flowering of Britain*, Hutchinson, London.

Mabey, Richard and Evans, Tony (1980), *The Common Ground*, Hutchinson in association with NCC, London.

Macmillan (1984), *Macmillan Guide to Britain's Nature Reserves*, London.

Millman, R. N. (1975), *The Making of the Scottish Landscape*, Batsford, London.

Muir, R. (1981), *The Shell Guide to Reading the Landscape*, Michael Joseph, London.

Nature Conservancy Council (1984), *Nature Conservation in Great Britain*, NCC, Peterborough.

Pennington, W. (1974), *The History of British Vegetation*, 2nd edn., English Universities Press, London.

Peterken, G. (1981), *Woodland Conservation and Management*, Chapman and Hall, London.

Rackham, Oliver (1986), *The History of the Countryside*, Dent, London.

Rackham, Oliver (1976), *Trees and Woodlands in the British Landscape*, Dent, London.

Ratcliffe, D. (ed.) (1977), *A Nature Conservation Review*, 2 vols. Cambridge University Press with NCC, Cambridge.

Rose, F. (1981), *The Wildflower Key*, Warne, London.

Steers, J. A. (1969), *The Sea Coast*, New Naturalist series, Collins, London.

Storer, B. (1985), *The Natural History of the Somerset Levels*, Dovecote Press, Wimborne.

Taylor C. (1975), *Fields in the English Landscape*, Dent, London.

Woodell, S. R. J. (1985), *The English Landscape*, Oxford University Press, Oxford.

Index

Illustration Credits

Photographs

All photographs © Phil Colebourn and Bob Gibbons, with the following exceptions: Jane Colebourn page 48; Robin Fletcher 23, 119, 124; Peter Roworth 55; Peter Wilson 158, 171, 220; Museum of English Rural Life, University of Reading 184; Hampshire County Council 102, 192; Cambridge University Committee for Aerial Photography 37, 40, 54, 63 (all), 70, 139, 159, 177, 179, 181, 204; Ministry of Defence, Crown Copyright Reserved, 42, 59; British Museum 88; National Trust for Archaeology 41.

Maps and Diagrams

Bodleian Library page 38 (lower), 44 (right), 46, 56, 61, 91, 93, 101, 160, 174, 183, 196, 205, 210; Hampshire County Council 44 (left), 60, 67, 73, 83, 84, 94; Cambridge University 30; Karen Saxby 12, 20, 38 (top), 48 (top), 69 (lower), 103, 179 (both), 197, 199, 215; Ordnance Survey 141, 143; Oliver Rackham 82; Ministry of Defence, Crown Copyright Reserved 218.